HEREDITY, GENES, AND CHROMOSOMES

HEREDITY, GENES, and CHROMOSOMES

ALEX FRASER *pseud*

Brinton, Henry

Genetics Group
University of California, Davis

Illustrated by Richard Leech

McGRAW-HILL BOOK COMPANY

New York   San Francisco   St. Louis
Toronto   London   Sydney

PREFACE

Students object to a course in which the lecturer closely follows a textbook. They also object to a course in which they need to take extensive notes. This double standard poses a serious problem in the construction of a text such as this, aimed at the introductory course in genetics. My solution has been based on brevity, providing the student with statements on the key points, leaving the lecturer and the student with the need for expansion on points of difficulty or particular interest.

A special point should be made about the multiple-choice questions in the Quick Quizzes. These are not always phrased in the usual format of a single correct alternative. In some, more than one of the alternatives may be correct; in others, all of the alternatives may be correct. The logic behind this deviation from common procedure is to emphasize a situation frequently found in science, where questions may have several correct answers.

Writing this book was a pleasure increased by the generous help of colleagues. Drs. T. Prout and G. Hewitt were especially helpful, as were D. Miller, C. Rundell, and P. Scotti, and it is one of the pleasures of authorship to be able to acknowledge in print the affectionate help and compassionate criticism of my wife, Anne.

Alex Fraser

TABLE OF CONTENTS

INTRODUCTION

The word *elegant* is often used to describe some of the sequences of discovery that have been made in the science of genetics. One of the aims of this text is to emphasize this elegance, without interfering with the primary intention of presenting an introduction to the genetic mode of thought. The main difficulty has been to achieve a balance between the different ways and different intentions of genetic research. J. B. S. Haldane underlined this difficulty in his description of a geneticist:

> Merely to observe differences, without any causal analysis, a geneticist must use many techniques. He must be a morphologist with a keen eye for slight differences. He may have to use biochemical methods, especially if he is investigating economically important characters such as the sugar content of beets or the butter content of cow's milk. If he is investigating human beings, he is likely sooner or later to be concerned with diseases. And he must use every resource of the diagnostician. If he is making a thorough study of any animal or plant, he will have to learn its pathology as well as its anatomy and physiology. The animal breeder will have to deal with problems of behavior. The human geneticist will be concerned with congenital mental defect, and perhaps also with congenital mental superiority. He will have to become something of a psychologist. Further, he will find a number of statements made concerning the innate abilities of different human classes and races. He will not assess these at their correct value unless he has made a study of political science. In his study of human and animal races he will become something of an anthropologist and a taxonomist. In studying genetics in its relations to agriculture and horticulture he will need not only to know the technique of these arts, but their economics. As a final qualification the geneticist may have to become a historian. To sum up, the geneticist must be a jack of all trades, and it is to be feared that he may become a master of none.°

° J. B. S. Haldane, "New Paths in Genetics," Harper & Bros., New York, 1942.

1

Haldane was always a proponent of the genetic mode of thought, using it widely wherever his interests led him. Today, he would have to expand his description. A geneticist now must know of the intricacies of bacteria and viruses. He must be at least aware of the biochemistry and physical structure of the molecules of heredity—the nucleic acids. The electronic computer allows the formidable complexities of systems of genes to be examined; thus geneticists need to know how to use this new tool, too. The list goes on, and will go on expanding, because all of biology is a geneticist's target, and a myriad of techniques can be aimed at the target.

Chapter 1

MENDEL'S LAWS

Genetics is the science of heredity, the science that deals with both the similarities and the differences that occur between relatives. Many of the similarities are so obvious that they are not noticed; we take it for granted that the progeny of rabbits are rabbits, that mice give birth to mice. A farmer planting oats would be somewhat surprised if the grains of oats he had planted grew into oak trees. One of the major problems of heredity is to find an explanation for these similarities. Although the differences that occur between relatives are much less extreme than those that occur between species, they receive a great deal more attention. Minor differences of skin color and nose shape attract more attention than do the constant features of our species, *Homo sapiens,* which differentiate us from the primates. We need to explain these differences.

These two problems are really different aspects of one problem. The similarities that characterize a particular species and the differences that identify individuals are both aspects of heredity. Heredity consists, in its essentials, of the transfer from parent to progeny of a blueprint of the organization of a living thing, and genetics is the science that describes how the blueprint is drawn, how it is transferred, and how a living thing is constructed from it. There are two ways to get information about this pattern. One way is to dissect living things, looking for the physical basis of heredity. The aim is to deduce the nature and function of the hereditary blueprint from its structure. The other way is to analyze the pattern of similarities and differences between relatives. Here the aim is to deduce the nature and structure of the genetic blueprint from its actions on heredity. These two approaches have been given separate names: *cytology* for the direct description of the genetic blueprint, and *genetics* for the indirect analysis

3

of the transmission of the blueprint in heredity. At first we will follow the genetic approach, next the cytologic approach, then we will relate the two approaches into one science.

MENDEL

The first real step forward in our understanding of the transmission of the genetic blueprint was made by an Augustinian monk, Gregor Mendel, in 1864. He introduced an extremely simple method, that of studying characters inherited as simple alternatives. He found several pairs of such characters in garden peas. One was flower color: some plants had red flowers, others had white flowers, but none had both red and white flowers, or pink flowers. (The red flowers were nearer violet-purple in shade, but for simplicity they will be described here as red.) Not all the red flowers were identically red—there were differences in shade—and not all the white flowers were identically white but the difference between red and white flowers was distinct—red and white were clear alternatives. This approach seems too obvious to be worthy of mention, but at that time the scientists studying heredity attempted to experiment with many characters at once, and they did not exclude characters that were not discretely different. We know now that the genetic mechanism is too complicated to be studied as a whole, and it is no wonder that these researchers were unsuccessful. In Mendel's time, the only concept of heredity was one rather vaguely described as a process of mixing and blending.

The starting point of Mendel's experiments was his "pure" lines of garden peas. These were varieties that bred true to type. His red-flowered "pure" line produced only plants with red flowers, and his white-flowered "pure" line produced only plants with white flowers. These pure lines had an unmixed, constant heredity; they bred "true to type." He crossed these pure lines to produce *hybrids,* which is a short way of saying that he used pollen from the flowers of one line to pollinate the flowers of the other line. The seeds from these cross-fertilized flowers grew into plants that produced red flowers not noticeably different from the flowers of the red-flowered pure line. The hybrid plants had an inheritance from both the red-flowered and the white-flowered pure lines, yet only the red-flowered heredity had an effect; the white-flowered heredity seemed to have disappeared. Mendel continued the experiment and showed that the white-flowered heredity was present in these hybrid plants. From the hybrid plants he collected seeds that had been produced by self-fertilization—the flowers had been pollinated by their own pollen. The seeds developed into plants that were either red-flowered or white-flowered; the white-flower character had reappeared and was unaffected by having been mixed with a red-flower heredity. These white flowers were just as white as those of the white-flowered pure line; there was not the slightest suggestion that the heredity of the red versus the white color involved any blending. Although the hybrids had red flowers identical to those of the pure red-flowered line, they contained a white-flower hereditary factor which they could transmit to their progeny unchanged.

Mendel's experiments can easily be extended for many more generations by taking the white-flowered progeny of the hybrids and forming hybrids of them with the red-flowered pure line. These hybrids will be red-flowered but, if they are self-pollinated, will produce some white-flowered progeny which will be no more or less white than the white-flowered pure line. This phenomenon will continue for as long as the experimenter is prepared to go on, showing that there are constant components to heredity which can be transmitted from generation to generation unchanged. Mendel deduced from these experiments that there are factors of heredity that are constant, unchangeable, for long periods of time. We now call these factors genes.

The experiments of Mendel also showed that heredity could have hidden, unexpressed components. The gene for white flowers, for example, could occur in plants without having any effect on the color of the flowers produced by those plants. There were two types of plants with similarly red flowers—in one type the heredity was pure, and these only gave red-flowered progeny when crossed; in the other type the heredity was mixed, and these produced both red-flowered and white-flowered progeny when crossed.

Another of Mendel's innovations was that of counting the frequencies of the alternative types in crosses where both alternatives were produced. This innovation seems just as obvious as that of studying discrete differences, but biologists have always been characterized by a resistance to numerical methods, and this possibly accounts for their failure to recognize the importance of this new idea.

The progeny of hybrid plants may be red-flowered or white-flowered, and Mendel showed that these two types occur in a fairly

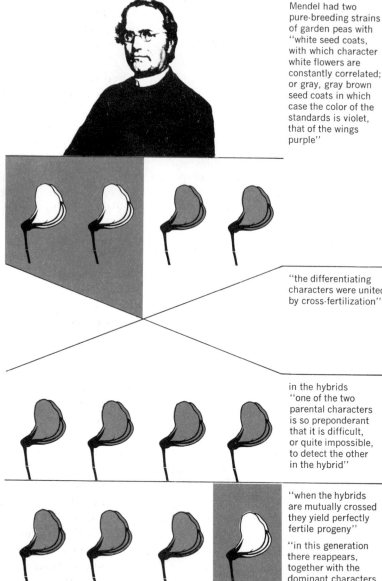

Mendel had two pure-breeding strains of garden peas with "white seed coats, with which character white flowers are constantly correlated; or gray, gray brown seed coats in which case the color of the standards is violet, that of the wings purple"

"the differentiating characters were united by cross-fertilization"

in the hybrids "one of the two parental characters is so preponderant that it is difficult, or quite impossible, to detect the other in the hybrid"

"when the hybrids are mutually crossed they yield perfectly fertile progeny"

"in this generation there reappears, together with the dominant characters, also the recessive ones, with their peculiarities fully developed"

Gregor Mendel "Experiments in plant hybridization" Verhandlungen naturforschender Verein in Brünn, Abhandlungen, 1865

"transitional forms were not observed in any experiment"

simple ratio. On an average, three-quarters of the progeny had red flowers and one-quarter had white flowers. He made some very important deductions from this result:

Heredity is equal from both parents.

It is based on distinct, constant particles or factors.

A hybrid transmits either alternative to its progeny with equal probability.

CROSSES AND BACKCROSSES

Mendel used crosses between pure lines to produce hybrids, and then allowed these hybrids to produce progeny by self-pollination. This is called the F_2 method. The progeny of crosses between pure lines are called F_1 individuals—they are the first filial generation. If F_1 individuals are crossed, their progeny are the second filial generation—the F_2. There is a simpler cross in which the hybrid plants are crossed back to one or the other of the pure lines. If a hybrid between the red-flowered and the white-flowered pure lines is crossed with the red-flowered line then all the progeny are red-flowered, but if the hybrids are crossed back to the white-flowered pure line then the progeny are, on an average, equally often red-flowered or white-flowered. If enough of these progeny are produced, the numbers of plants with red or white flowers will be very close to equal. This is an even simpler result than that found in F_2 progenies, and it can be explained by hybrids that contain both a "red" and a "white" gene, transmitting one or the other equally often. Mendel had no idea of the mechanism that caused this equal transmission of the alternative genes. He studied other characters of the pea plants, e.g. smooth versus wrinkled seed coat, and erect versus prostrate habit of growth. The same principles were true for these characters, showing that his discovery was not something specific to the heredity of flower color. He also experimented with more than one pair of characters at once. He used crosses between hybrids to give an F_2, but we will consider the simpler crosses back to the pure lines.

If a "pure" line with red flowers and smooth seeds is crossed with a "pure" line having white flowers and wrinkled seeds, then the

FIGURE 1.1
Segregation of red and white flowers in crosses of garden peas.

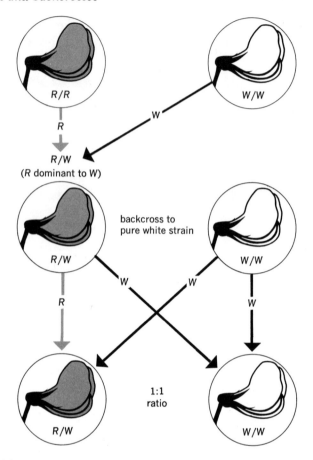

FIGURE 1.2

Segregation of red and white flowers in crosses of garden peas, where the red-flowered hybrids are backcrossed to the pure white strain, giving equal numbers of progeny with red or white flowers.

hybrid progeny will have red flowers and smooth seeds. The gene for white flowers has no effect when paired in a hybrid with the gene for red flowers and, similarly, the gene for wrinkled seeds has no effect when paired in a hybrid with the gene for smooth seeds. These plants are hybrid for both the flower-color and seed-texture characters; they are double hybrids. If these double hybrids are then crossed to the pure line with white flowers and wrinkled seeds, four types of progeny will be produced with equal frequencies.

There will be progeny with:

1. Red flowers and smooth seeds
2. Red flowers and wrinkled seeds
3. White flowers and smooth seeds
4. White flowers and wrinkled seeds

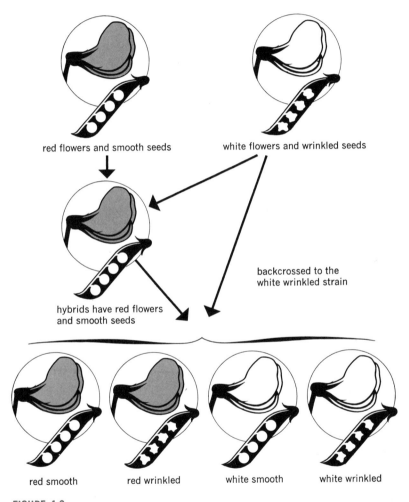

red flowers and smooth seeds　　　white flowers and wrinkled seeds

hybrids have red flowers
and smooth seeds

backcrossed to the
white wrinkled strain

red smooth　　　red wrinkled　　　white smooth　　　white wrinkled

FIGURE 1.3

Simultaneous segregation for two pairs of characters in garden peas, showing their independent transmission. Equal numbers of all four possible combinations are found in progeny of the backcross of the double hybrid to the pure recessive line.

The equal occurrence of these four types means that the transmission of the two pairs of hereditary factors is independent. These results gave Mendel the evidence from which he could deduce that transmission of hereditary factors was not only equal for each alternative of a pair of factors but that this hereditary transmission was a separate, independent process for each pair of factors. The fact that the genes for red flowers and smooth seed coats were inherited by the hybrid from one parent, and that the genes for white flowers and wrinkled seed coats were inherited by the hybrid from the other parent, did not affect the inheritance of these characters by the progeny of the cross of the hybrid to the pure line. The grandparental combinations of red flowers with smooth seed coats, and white flowers with wrinkled seed coats, showed no tendency to stay together in heredity.

BIOLOGICAL COIN TOSSING

Tossing coins can provide an analogy that makes the laws of Mendelian inheritance easier to understand. Suppose that there is a biological coin-tossing machine in which the coins are the pairs of genes, one gene on each face. This machine tosses a coin for each transmission of a gene, with the offspring receiving whichever alternative is on the face-up side of the tossed coin. In pure lines the pairs of genes are both the same; both faces of the coin are the same, so there is no noticeable effect of tossing these coins—the result is the same no matter which face of the coin is up. In hybrids, the pairs of genes are not the same; a hybrid between red-flowered and white-flowered pure lines will have a red gene on one side of the coin and a white gene on the opposite side. If the coin lands red side up then the red-flower gene is transmitted to the progeny, and if the coin lands white side up then the white-flower gene is transmitted to that progeny. The hereditary coin is tossed once for each formation of a reproductive cell, determining which gene is transmitted in that instance.

Heredity in high organisms usually involves two parents (a mother and a father), each transmitting half the heredity of the offspring. Suppose a cross is made between two hybrids for the red-flower gene and the white-flower gene. Then, if we follow the coin-machine analogy, two coins will be tossed for each progeny, one by the male parent, the other by the female parent. There are four possibilities:

1. Both coins will land red side up.
2. The male coin will be red side up and the female coin will be white side up.
3. The male coin will be white side up and the female coin will be red side up.
4. Both coins will be white side up.

Since the white-flower gene has no effect in the presence of a red-flower gene, three of these possibilities will lead to red-flowered plants and only one will lead to white-flowered plants. Mendel found just this result in his experiments—that, on an average, one-quarter of the progeny of crosses between hybrids were white-flowered.

The biological coin-tossing machine is unbiased—each coin of hereditary factors is tossed so that one face is just as likely to turn up as the other. If enough coins are tossed, then the end result is that there will be as many coins facing up one way as there are facing up the other way. This analogy can be extended to different pairs of genes. Suppose, in a double hybrid for the *red* and *white* and the *smooth and wrinkled* alternatives, that the alternatives are on opposite faces of a nickel and a dime respectively, and that the two coins are tossed simultaneously by the coin-tossing machine. There will be four results:

1. The *red* face of the nickel and the *smooth* face of the dime will be face up together.
2. The *red* face of the nickel and the *wrinkled* face of the dime will be face up together.
3. The *white* face of the nickel and the *wrinkled* face of the dime will be face up together.
4. The *white* face of the nickel and the *smooth* face of the dime will be face up together.

If the coin-tossing machine and the coins are unbiased, then these four possibilities will occur equally often, *if* a large number of coins are tossed. Mendel's results show that the alternatives do occur equally often and, therefore, that neither the biological coin-tossing machine nor the hereditary coin is biased.

Mendel, in a few years of research, had shown that an extremely simple mechanism was basic to the phenomena of heredity. He had shown that this mechanism involved hereditary particles that were constant and unchanging, and he had demonstrated the laws whereby these hereditary particles were transmitted from parents to progeny—but no one recognized the importance of his discoveries at the time. Recognition did not come until the turn of the century when three men repeated his experiments independently, arrived at the same conclusions, then freely acknowledged that Mendel deserved the credit for establishing a new science which we now call *genetics*. The aims of this science were to find whether Mendel's laws were generally true, and to discover the physical nature of the biological coin-tossing machine.

PEDIGREES

Genetics in its early phases was noticeable for a marked absence of equipment or complication. It still can be a very unsatisfactory science for people who like a laboratory crowded with complicated equipment, or those who need ostentatiously active scientific status symbols.

A major technique of this new science was the construction of pedigrees. When a pedigree had been drawn for a family, the individuals of that family who showed distinctive features could be identified. At this point, the geneticist relied on his ingenuity to find a rational description of the role played by heredity in determining the specific features being studied. This is easy for fairly simple characters such as *crinkly hair* in man. A number of European families are known in which many individuals have unusually short, crinkly hair. Crinkly hair grows well, but it breaks off at the tip so that the hair length remains short. (Crinkly hair individuals have a congenital crew cut.) This character is very unusual in European stocks, and its occurrence in just a few families is a fairly strong indication that the peculiarity is caused by a gene. Possibly the characteristic is not biologically inherited, being instead an environmental inheritance from a way of life, but there were no indications that these families had a unique way of life. Also, the individuals were widely spread geographically, which is strong support for the supposition that crinkly hair is inherited biologically.

The pedigree of crinky hair families shows two rules for inheritance of crinkly hair:

1. One or both of the parents of a crinkly hair individual have crinkly hair.
2. Not all children of crinkly hair parents have crinkly hair—some of their children have long hair that does not differ from that normal to Europeans.

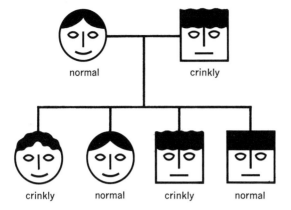

FIGURE 1.4

The cross of a crinkly haired individual with a normal individual has the expectation of equal numbers of normal and crinkly haired progeny.

One of these rules is *definitive*—crinkly hair children definitely have a crinkly hair parent. The other rule is *statistical*—crinkly hair parents may have both normal-hair and crinkly hair children.

A statistical law is one that involves not something's happening, but something's having a chance of happening. The first step in the investigation of such a law is to measure the chance. In one pedigree, 81 children were born to marriages in which one and only one parent had crinkly hair—38 of these had crinkly hair, and 43 had normal hair. This, of course, is close to equality. If all the different families are considered, the percentages are 53% with crinkly hair and 47% with normal hair, from a total of 276 offspring. The second rule of inheritance of crinkly hair can be restated: Crinkly hair parents have an equal chance of having crinkly hair or normal-hair children.

The words *chance* and *probability* have nearly identical meanings, but probability is more acceptable in scientific texts. Both words are used here to denote that a certain type of event may happen with a fixed possibility but with no individual certainty. A crinkly hair parent may transmit either gene equally often, but for any particular transmission (to a particular child) there is no certainty of either alternative being the one transmitted.

Mendel showed how these rules of inheritance could be explained. The heredity of an individual is arranged in pairs, and only one member of a pair is transmitted. Each individual receives one member of a pair of genes from one parent and the other member from the other parent. This mechanism explains why half the children of

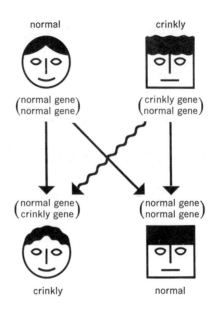

FIGURE 1.5

The character, crinkly hair, is caused by a dominant gene. The mating of a homozygous normal with a heterozygous crinkly hair has the expectation of transmitting the crinkly hair gene to half the progeny.

crinkly hair parents have crinkly hair. Suppose there are two alternative genes that control the type of hair: one causes normal growth, the other causes the hair to curl tightly and to break more readily than normal hair. Further, suppose the gene for crinkly hair is physiologically very active so that its effect dominates over that of the gene for normal hair. If these two suppositions are correct, then an individual who inherits a crinkly hair gene from one parent and a normal-hair gene from the other parent will have crinkly hair, and he or she will pass on either the crinkly hair or the normal-hair gene to the children equally often. On an average, half the progeny of a crinkly hair individual will receive the crinkly hair gene, and half will receive the normal-hair gene. This is a statistical expectation; chances are equal that the progeny will receive one or the other of the pair of genes.

The rules of inheritance of the crinkly hair character can be explained by these suppositions, but that does not mean that the explanation is correct. However, it has the merit of a disarming simplicity, and scientists prefer simple hypotheses. This preference has both an aesthetic and a logical basis: aesthetically, there is

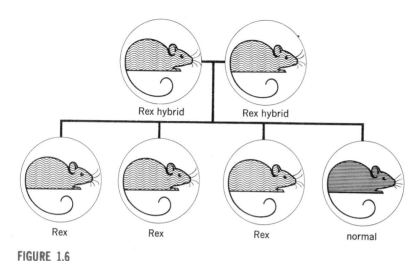

FIGURE 1.6

The Rex character in mice is caused by a dominant gene. Mating two Rex heterozygotes has the expectation of 3/4 of the progeny being Rex and 1/4 being normal.

pleasure in resolving complexity down to simplicity; logically, it is easier to examine the correctness of simple hypotheses since it is easier to make predictions that can be tested by further observation, or by conducting experiments.

The first prediction that can be made is that if two crinkly hair people cooperate in producing progeny, then three out of four of their children, on an average, will have crinkly hair. This expectation comes from a simple multiplication of probabilities. The children with one crinkly hair parent have a 50% chance of inheriting the normal-hair gene, but, if the other parent also has crinkly hair, then, even if an individual escapes inheriting it from one parent, he still has a 50% chance of inheriting it from the other crinkly hair parent. Fifty percent of fifty percent is twenty-five percent, so only one-quarter of the children will miss inheriting the crinkly hair gene from one or the other parent.

Unfortunately, there are very few marriages of this kind on record, and human beings show an understandable reluctance to follow a geneticist's directions in the matter of their mating. However, similar characters have been studied in other organisms which are more amenable to controlled mating. In mice there is a character, *Rex*, that causes the coat to be wavy. Normal mice have sleek, smooth coats. The Rex-type coat is caused by a gene that, like the gene for crinkly hair, is dominant to the normal alternative. If two hybrid Rex mice are mated, the results agree with the prediction. On an average, three-quarters of the progeny have Rex coats, and only one-quarter have normal coats.

DOMINANCE

The crinkly hair and the Rex genes are dominant to their alternatives. The word *dominant* used in this specific genetic sense has a complementary word, *recessive*. A dominant gene is one that shows its effect whether it is inherited from both parents or from one. A recessive gene is one that only shows its effect when it is inherited from both parents. (A recessive gene is a "cowering, timorous beastie" that does not dare assert itself in the presence of any opposition.)

Albinism in human beings is a recessive character. The frequency of albinism in European stocks is about 1 in 20,000. Different races show different proportions, with the San Blas Indians of Panama holding the record at 1 in 132. Pedigrees involving albinism are quite different from those involving the dominant crinkly hair. Albinism is rarely frequent in a family group. Albinos usually are born to normally pigmented parents, whereas crinkly hair children only occur as progeny of a crinkly hair parent. If a large number of pedigrees involving albinism are collected, and the proportion of normal and albino sibs of albinos are counted, then a rule of recessive inheritance becomes apparent—the proportion of normal to albinos is about three to one. This rule differs from the 50 : 50 expectation of the inheritance of crinkly hair, but a little thought will show that this is not a discrepancy. Albino is a recessive gene and, if a marriage produces albino children, both parents must carry the albino gene without showing it (since they have normal coloration). Each parent must have both a normal and an albino gene, and these have a 50% chance of passing the albino gene to their children who, consequently, have a 25% chance of inheriting the albino gene from both parents. This simple hypothesis leads to the prediction that marriages where both parents are albino should produce only albino children. Only a few such marriages have occurred and the offspring are all albino.

Genes are not necessarily dominant or recessive; they may be neither. The genes controlling coat color in shorthorn cattle are neither dominant nor recessive. There are three alternative coat colors—red, roan, or white. Roan is a pink color due to the mixture of red and white hairs. The red and white types are genetically pure. Mating reds produces only red offspring and mating whites produces only white offspring. The roan color is genetically hybrid; mating roans together produces reds, roans, and whites. As can be expected, these three types occur in the ratio 1 : 2 : 1; these results fit the differences of coat color being controlled by a pair of genes, "red" and "white." When an individual inherits a red gene from each parent, the coat color is red. Inheritance of a white gene from each parent produces offspring with a white coat. Individuals who inherit a red gene from one parent and a white gene from the other parent develop the roan color. Roan cattle are hybrid. Genetic analysis is

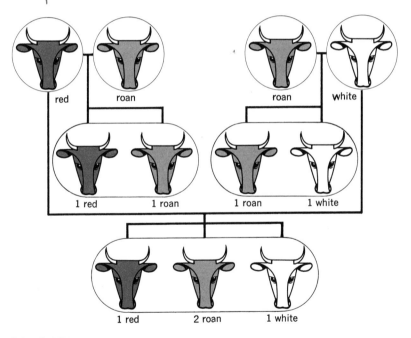

FIGURE 1.7

The crosses between white, roan, and red cattle show that these three characters are hereditary alternatives, with the red character determined by one homozygous state (RR), the white character determined by the other homozygous state (rr), and roan character determined by the heterozygous state (Rr).

much easier for characters that are neither dominant nor recessive because hybrids can be identified by their appearance.

A prediction can be made if the genetic hypothesis explaining the inheritance of coat color is correct. If roans are mated with reds, there should be only two types of offspring produced, reds and roans, which should occur equally often. If roans are mated with whites, there should be only two types of offspring produced, whites and roans, also occurring equally often. These predictions fit the facts, adding very strong support to Mendel's first law of genetics. Hundreds of genetic differences have been shown to be inherited in the same way as crinkly hair or albinism or coat color in cattle. In each example the genes are transmitted unchanged from one generation to the next with some biological equivalent of a coin-tossing machine determining which member of each pair of alternatives is inherited.

Problems

1. Albino mice lack pigment in their fur and eyes. Hybrids between pure colored and pure albino are colored. If colored and albino are Mendelian alternatives, then:

   (*a*) Is the albino or the colored gene dominant?

   (*b*) What frequency of albino progeny is expected from crosses between hybrid colored mice?

   (*c*) What types of progeny are expected if albino mice are mated?

   (*d*) Why can't you make an exact prediction of the types of progeny expected if colored mice are mated?

2. A strain of mice has uniquely short ears and this is inherited as a recessive character.

   (*a*) If an albino, short-ear mouse is mated with a purebred colored, normal-ear mouse, what types of progeny are expected?

   (*b*) If the hybrids from such a cross are mated with albino, short-ear mice, what types are expected in the progeny? What are their expected frequencies?

   (*c*) If the hybrids from such a cross of pure albino, short-ear mice with pure colored, normal-ear mice are backcrossed to normal-colored, normal-ear mice, what types are expected in the progeny?

3. The words *pure* and *hybrid* have been used in the above questions as synonymous with the more descriptive technical terms *heterozygous* and *homozygous*. Can they always be considered as synonymous?

4. Individual human beings may be characterized as having a particular type of blood serology determined by the genes M and N. There are three possible types of blood on the basis of the M/N difference: MM, MN, and N. What types and frequencies of progeny do you expect from the following matings?

(a)   MM × MN

(b)   MM × NN

(c)   MN × MN

5. A woman whose blood is the NN type finds that her children are of the following types:

                 NN,   MN,   NN

What can you say about her husband's type of blood?

If she had ten children, all of the MN type, what could you say about her husband's type of blood?

6. A woman has two children, one by one husband and one by another. The M/N blood types of the two children are:

                 MM   and   NN

What type of blood does the mother have?

7. A strain of mice (W) has a wavy coat which is inherited as a recessive Mendelian alternative to the straight-coat characteristic. Another strain of mice (C) also has a wavy coat which is also inherited as a recessive Mendelian alternative to the straight-coat characteristic. When the W and C strains are crossed they produce progeny with straight coats.

If these hybrids are backcrossed to the W strain, half the progeny have wavy coats, half have straight coats, on an average. The same result occurs when the hybrids are backcrossed to the C strain.

What frequency of mice with wavy coats are expected if the hybrids are crossed?

8. Draw out the pedigree of the following family and determine the type of inheritance of dark versus blue eye color.

Victoria married Jack and produced three children: Elizabeth, Bob, and Carl. Elizabeth married John and produced six children: Alexis, Alan, Andrew, Annette, Aileen, and Alistair. Carl married Mary and produced four children: Don, Dave, Duncan, and Doreen. Victoria, Jack, Bob, Carl, Don, and Dave had dark-colored eyes. The others had blue eyes.

9. (a) If Alexis married Duncan, what would you expect the eye color of their children to be?

(b) If Annette married Dave, what would you expect the eye color of their children to be?

Chapter 2

RULES AND EXCEPTIONS

Mendel's first law is based on the ratio of two hereditary alternatives in the progeny of hybrids from pure lines. Only two ratios are possible in crosses involving a single pair of characters if the heredity obeys Mendel's law—1 : 1 or 3 : 1, depending on whether the cross is a backcross of a hybrid to a pure line, or an intercross between hybrids. If a set of three characters occurs as hereditary alternatives, then a ratio of 1 : 2 : 1 is predicted in the progeny of an intercross. This is the operational definition of Mendel's first law: the occurrence of hereditary alternatives in the offspring of hybrids fits simple ratios. The operational definition of a law usually changes as information about it increases. Exceptions are found that do not obey the operational definition, and it has to be modified to include the exceptions. Thus many operational definitions become so modified that they are left with little practical value, and new definitions must be produced.

Mendel was fortunate, or sensible, in choosing a species of plant (the garden pea) and a series of characters in which there were no complications. His first law had the merit of an extreme simplicity both in its operational definition and in the basic pattern of heredity deduced from it. In the years following the rediscovery of Mendel's laws, many pairs of characteristics were studied that were found to be inherited according to the first law, segregating in simple ratios of 1 : 1 and 3 : 1, but, although many characters agreed with the operational definition, some did not. The word *segregating* used in this sentence has a special meaning to genetecists. If two hereditary alternative types occur in the progeny of a cross in the ratio of 1 : 1 or 3 : 1, then genetic segregation is said to have occurred. The hereditary alternatives have separated equally. A prime rule of science is "treasure the exceptions" because the exceptions show that the rule is not general; they disprove the original operational definition. Another maxim in science is "exceptions can prove the rule"—the important word in this maxim is *can*. Exceptions to the expectations of Mendel's laws show that it is necessary to modify the operational definition, and, if this modification still supports the basic theory that underlies the operational definition, the exception has helped prove the rule.

HUNTINGTON'S CHOREA

Many exceptions to Mendel's first law exemplify these maxims. One character that does not seem to fit the operational definition of Mendel's laws is a form of degeneration of the nervous system in human beings called *Huntington's Chorea*. This disease is inherited; in some families with affected individuals, there is a close agreement with the expectation that half the children from an affected parent will develop the disease. Huntington's Chorea appears to be caused by a gene that is dominant to its normal alternative. If the inheritance of this disease is due to a dominant gene, one of the parents of an affected individual should also show the disease. Many pedigrees of families with affected members do not show this relationship; some children with the disease are produced by unaffected parents. If the pathology of this disease is examined in detail, an explanation can be seen. Huntington's Chorea is not manifested at birth. Most people who inherit it do not show any effects until during or after maturity; in some people there are no effects until late in life. This can explain the exceptional families where neither parent of an affected individual showed symptoms. One of these parents could have carried the gene for Huntington's Chorea and transmitted it to the progeny without having shown any effects of it themselves. If the parent then died of some other cause, there would be no way of knowing whether the gene was present or not.

Huntington's Chorea has some particularly macabre features. Suppose an individual develops symptoms late in life, after he or she has produced a family; on an average, half of the offspring will have inherited the gene. This family will live in fearful uncertainty, wondering whether they have inherited the disease. If they have married young and have had children, they have the additional dread that they may have transmitted the factor to their children.

Mendel's original experiments are based on hereditary factors having definite, diagnosable effects. Where genes are not definite in their effects, varying in the age at which the effect is manifested, the operational definition must be modified to include this variability of the expression of the gene.

BLUE SCLEROTIC

There is a gene in man called *blue sclerotic* that is dominant to its normal alternative. Individuals with this gene have an unusually thin outer wall on the eye which, therefore, has a bluish tinge. This peculiarity has no harmful effects, but the gene often has other effects that are more drastic. There is an otosclerosis that can lead to deafness, and also a marked fragility of the skeletal bones that leads to frequent fractures. Stern[*] quotes a description of one male "blue sclerotic" who turned suddenly in the street to look at the legs of a pretty girl and fractured a leg bone. Another time he took his fiancée on his lap and his thigh bone broke—clearly this is a gene with devastating effects! If only the effect on the fragility of the skeleton is studied, the gene will have a detectable effect only in individuals who put enough strain on their bones to fracture them. In one country only 63% of the individuals who inherited the "blue-sclerotic" gene showed its effects as fractures of the bones. The ratio of normal to affected individuals, judged by their having fragile bones, did not agree with the expectation of equality, being 1.37 : 0.63 instead of 1 : 1. A Japanese family with this particular hereditary defect showed an even more extreme discrepancy—only 29% of the individuals had fractured bones. The ratio of normal to affected individuals is 1.71 : 0.29 in this family, which is such a marked deviation from the expectation of 1 : 1 that it would constitute a disproof of Mendel's law, except that all individuals who received the blue-sclerotic gene could be unequivocally recognized by its effect on their eye color. The ratio of normal to "bluish" eye tone was 1 : 1, in full agreement with the operational definition of Mendel's first law. The effect of the blue-sclerotic gene is definite for eye color, expressed in all individuals who have inherited the gene, but its effect on the fragility of the skeleton is not definite, being expressed only in individuals who put sufficient strain on their bones to break them.

[*]C. Stern, "Principles of Human Genetics," W. H. Freeman and Co., San Francisco, 1960.

TRANSMISSION AND EXPRESSION

The exceptional forms of heredity show how to rephrase our first statement of Mendel's law. It is not that half the offspring of a backcross *show* the effects of a particular dominant gene, or that one-quarter of the progeny of an intercross show the effects of a recessive gene—rather, a hybrid *transmits* the two alternative genes, with equal probability, to the offspring. Whether the offspring receiving one or the other alternative show any effects may depend on factors modifying the expression of these hereditary alternatives. A revised operational definition of Mendel's law, one that includes most of the exceptions where a gene does not always produce a noticeable effect, involves tests of the proportions of inividuals who *inherit* the factor. Mendel himself made this point.

A pair of specific terms can be usefully introduced at this point: *homozygous* and *heterozygous*. An individual is said to be *heterozygous* for a pair of genes when it contains one of each type (a/a^+). An individual is said to be *homozygous* for a pair of genes when it contains only one type (a/a or a^+/a^+). See problem 3, Chapter 1.

PROGENY TESTS

The expression of a particular genotype may vary from one individual to the next. This variation may be so extreme as to obscure a particular genetic difference. This is especially likely for genotypes that result in a visibly different effect in only a small fraction of the individuals of that genotype. Such genotypes are said to have a low penetrance. Conversely, a genotype that is always manifested as a visible difference is said to be completely penetrant. The blue-sclerotic gene is completely penetrant in its effect on the color of the outer wall of the eye, but incompletely penetrant in its effect on fractured bones.

The operational analysis of genes with a low penetrance involves obtaining and testing each individual. If the individual has inherited the gene but has not expressed it, some of its progeny will inherit and express the gene. Experiments involving such genes are possible in organisms having a high reproductive rate, where individuals can produce enough offspring to allow determination of its genotype.

In sheep, rams can be mated to a large number of ewes to verify the incomplete penetrance of a particular gene. The gene N caused lambs to have a coarse birthcoat in a breed of sheep with normally fine birthcoats. The N gene normally is dominant. In the cross of homozygous coarse animals with homozygous fine animals $(N/N \times +^N/+^N)$, a fraction of the resultant lambs had fine birthcoats and the hypothesis could be made that these were $N/+^N$ animals in which the effect of the N gene had not penetrated. Rams with fine coats were mated to a large number of ewes. Approximately half the progeny had coarse birthcoats; the apparent discrepancy from Mendelian expectation was due to incomplete penetrance.

BALDNESS AND SEX

The modification of the expression of genes is particularly evident in the inheritance of baldness in humans. Baldness is inherited, but analyses of pedigrees are puzzling. The sons of bald men frequently develop baldness, yet very few of their daughters are bald. Sometimes sons develop baldness even though their father has a full head of hair. This is all very puzzling, but even Hippocrates knew the answer. He wrote "Eunuchs neither get gout nor grow bald." Aristotle wrote "No boy gets bald, no woman and no castrated man." This shows how the baffling features of the inheritance of baldness can be explained. Suppose there is a gene for baldness that is alternative to a gene for normal hair growth. The evidence suggests that such a baldness gene is dominant in its effects on sexually complete adult males. But suppose that the gene is effective only if individuals possessing it have a normal production of male hormone. If this is so, then it would not cause baldness in males who have no (or very little) male hormone. Men who have been castrated have very little male hormone, so they would not show the effect of a baldness gene even if they had inherited it. Nor do normal females produce much male hormone, so they would not show any effect of a baldness gene. This all fits together fairly well, and the puzzling features of the inheritance of baldness can be explained by females being able to inherit and transmit the baldness gene without showing any of its effects.

A confirmation of this explanation of the inheritance of baldness comes from women who develop tumors of the adrenal gland. These tumors result in the glands forming large amounts of male hormone. Such women show a syndrome of effects called virilism. Their body

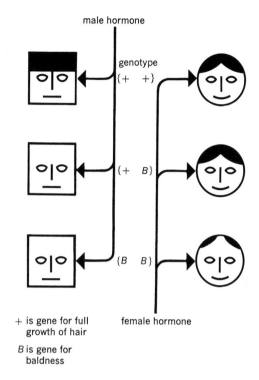

male hormone

genotype

{+   +}

{+   B}

{B   B}

female hormone

+ is gene for full
growth of hair

B is gene for
baldness

FIGURE 2.1

*Baldness is determined by the interaction of the genes for this character
(B and +^{B}) with the hormonal status of the individual. The B gene is
dominant in the presence of the male hormone, recessive in its absence.*

structure and hair growth shift toward the mode normal to males.
Many such women develop baldness. The abnormal production of
male hormone by their malfunctioning adrenal glands allows the
baldness gene to take effect, whereas normally its presence would
have gone without detection. After surgical removal of the tumor
has restored the woman to a normal hormonal balance, hair growth
reverts to normal and baldness disappears. This all makes a great
deal of sense, but it doesn't explain how a small percentage of sexually normal women develop baldness. The answer appears to be
that women may show the effect of the baldness gene if they inherit
it from both parents. Another way of expressing this is to say that
the baldness gene is dominant in males, recessive in females.

Baldness in human beings is only one of many hereditary factors
whose expression is affected by the sex difference. The Romney
breed of sheep is normally hornless, but a gene called the *N* gene

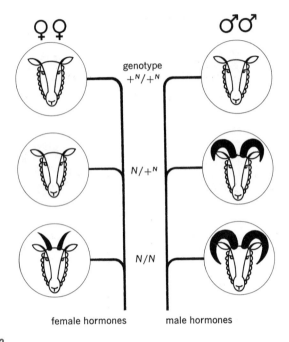

FIGURE 2.2

The N gene causes Romney Marsh sheep to develop horns. It is dominant in males, recessive in females. The effectiveness of this gene is conditioned by the hormonal status of the individual.

has been found in this breed that causes the rams who inherit it to develop impressive horns. Females who inherit this gene show no effect—they are hornless. This applies if they inherit the N gene from only one parent, inheriting the hornless gene ($+^N$) from the other parent. The symbols N and $+^N$ are used for these hereditary alternatives, and such individuals will be represented genetically as $N/+^N$. Such hybrids are said to be heterozygous for the N and $+^N$ *alleles.* (Alleles are alternative genes. The N and $+^N$ genes are inherited as genetic alternatives—they are *allelic.*) If sheep are bred that inherit the N factor from both parents, they are represented as N/N; they are said to be homozygous for the N factor. Rams of this type have extremely impressive horns, and ewes form small but distinctive horns. These facts can be put together to portray the inheritance of horns as dominant in males and recessive in females—the same description that applies to inheritance of baldness in humans.

The difference between rams and ewes in the expression of the N factor is controlled by the male hormone. If heterozygous males are castrated young, before they have been weaned, they do not develop horns. If males homozygous for the N factor are castrated early, they develop horns, but only small ones similar to those formed by females who are homozygous for the N factor.

	Females	*Castrated males*	*Males*
$+^N/+^N$	No horns	No horns	No horns
$N/+^N$	No horns	No horns	Horns
N/N	Small horns	Small horns	Large horns

COAT COLOR AND TEMPERATURE

Another example of how the effect of a gene is not a direct consequence of its presence is afforded by the Himalayan-type coat in rabbits. This type of coat occurs in rabbits that are homozygous for a gene, h^h. Such rabbits are usually white except for their ears, feet, and tips of the nose and tail, which are black. At ordinary temperatures the gene is quite unequivocal in its effects. But if a naked, newborn kid is taken from its dam and exposed to low temperature for a few hours, then returned to its mother, it will develop black hair all over its body. Another experiment shows how the external temperature can modify the effects of the Himalayan gene. If hair is plucked from a normal Himalayan rabbit and an icepack applied to the exposed area, the hair that grows over the plucked area is black. The expression of the gene for Himalayan-type coat is affected by temperature: if temperature is low during development, the hair is black; if it is warm, the hair is white. At normal temperatures the extremities (ears, tail, feet, and tip of nose) are more exposed and colder than the main bulk of the body, and this explains why they produce black hair.

MENDEL'S LAWS

It is important to separate three aspects of Mendel's laws. These are:

1. Heredity units have a considerable constancy.
2. The expression of genes can show considerable complexity.
3. A biological coin-tossing machine acts independently to determine the rules of transmission of hereditary factors.

Genetics has three sets of principles: those governing *constancy*, those governing *expression*, and those governing *transmission*.

Problems

1. The characteristic "yellow" in mice is associated with yellow-colored fur. If yellow mice are mated together they produce two types of progeny: normal and yellow in a ratio of 1 : 2. If yellow mice are mated to normal-colored mice, the progeny are yellow or normal in the ratio of 1 : 1. This characteristic is inherited as a simple alternative to normal coloration, but the ratio of normal to yellow differs from the Mendelian expectation of 1 : 3.

   Is there any way of reconciling this exception to the Mendelian hypothesis?

2. A number of genes have been identified in the house mouse that affect its coat color. The B gene causes the coat to be black, and its recessive allele b causes the coat to be brown. The C gene allows other genes to determine the color of the coat, and its recessive allele c causes the coat to lack all color. White mice are genetically cc.

   What is the appearance of mice with the following genotypes?

   Bb Cc

   BB cc

   bb CC

   bb cc

   What are the frequencies of black, brown, and white progeny in the following crosses?

   Bb Cc × bb cc

   Bb Cc × Bb cc

   Bb Cc × Bb Cc

   The albino gene is said to be *epistatic* to the B/b locus. It is epistatic to all the genes that affect coat color.

3. A pure-breeding white strain of mice is crossed to a pure-breeding brown strain. All the progeny are black. Write the genetic constitutions of the two parents and the F_1 progeny.

Chapter **3**

BIOLOGICAL COIN TOSSING

Mendel showed that heredity involved the biological equivalent of an unbiased coin-tossing machine. The physical basis of this machine was found from the discovery and description that living things, no matter what their size, are formed as collections of minute, living structures called *cells*. Some organisms consist of just one cell and are rarely large enough to be seen without the aid of a microscope. Other organisms, just visible with the unaided eye, are aggregates of a few dozen cells. Large organisms, such as man, are formed of millions of cells.

Each cell is a living entity, and all cells are formed by the division of other cells. The cellular history of each individual cell traces back to a single initial cell which, in higher organisms, is the fertilized egg. The hereditary blueprint of an individual is contained within that single initial cell. In the process of growth, as the initial cell divides and divides again to produce all the cells of the adult body, the hereditary blueprint is copied identically and contained in each cell, apart from a few exceptions.

There are many different types of cells, each tracing back to the same initial cell. They all have specific features reaching high degrees of complexity, but they also all have one feature in common—a small, unimpressive dark sphere called the *nucleus*. It is reasonable to suggest that the hereditary blueprint is located in the nucleus. This suggestion is supported by observations on the process of fertilization. A single sperm joins with the egg to form the fertilized egg; this sperm consists of little more than a nucleus. In many organisms only the nucleus penetrates into the egg during fertilization; the paternal component of the heredity of an individual must, therefore, be contained within that nucleus. If both parents have an equal hereditary contribution to their progeny, the male half has to be contained in the sperm nucleus, and it

29

seems reasonable that the female half is contained in the female nucleus. The joined nucleus then must contain all the hereditary blueprints for the new organism.

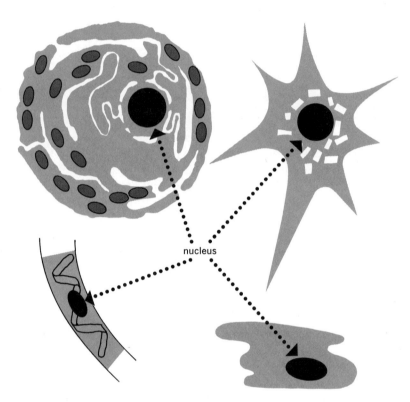

nucleus

FIGURE 3.1

Cells may differ markedly in their form and function but there is a common feature—a small structure called the nucleus.

MITOSIS

A prominent feature of the division of a cell to form two daughter cells is the division of the nucleus to form two daughter nuclei. Cell division is a complicated process, but essentially it has four phases: The chromosomes (1) become visible, then split along their length into daughter chromosomes (chromatids). The chromatids (3) separate to opposite poles of the cell, and a cell wall (4) divides the cell into two daughter cells. The two daughter cells then contain identical copies of each and all the chromosomes present in the initial cell. This process is called a *mitotic cell division.*

One problem that needed to be solved was to find what happened to the chromosomes during the period between cell divisions when the nucleus has an amorphous structure in which the chromosome cannot be identified. It was quite possible that the chromosomes did not exist as integrated structures, being re-formed from the material of the nucleus each time a cell began to divide. Boveri, one of the men who studied the behavior of cells during division, watched the early divisions of fertilized eggs of an intestinal worm of horses, Ascaris. He found that chromosomes appeared in the same positions at the beginning of the second cell division that they had been in when they disappeared at the end of the first division. This finding is very strong evidence that the chromosomes exist as permanent structures within the nucleus. All these researches added up to the conclusion that chromosomes were the hereditary blueprint.

The crude microscopes available in the early days of cytology only allowed the researchers to be sure that such structures as chromosomes existed. As better microscopes were built, it was possible to count the number of chromosomes, and the number was found to be the same for all the body cells of individuals of the same species. The cells of the body of the vinegar fly (*Drosophila melanogaster*) each contain 8 chromosomes, whereas the body cells of corn (*Zea mays*) each have 20 chromosomes. Man has 46 chromosomes in each body cell. Each species of living thing is characterized by a specific number of chromosomes which is the same in most of the body cells of each individual of the species. This was the first step in describing the hereditary blueprint—the number of chromosomes was an important feature.

More and more types of organisms were studied in this way, and some species were found to have very large chromosomes—large enough to distinguish that individual chromosomes differed in size and shape. These differences of size and shape were as constant as the total number of chromosomes. A very interesting feature of these differences between chromosomes was that the chromosomes always occurred in pairs. If there are eight chromosomes in each cell, then there are only four types of chromosomes, two of each type. There are exceptions to this, but it is a valid generalization: chromosomes are individually distinct, with two representatives of each type in each cell. This is worth a great deal of thought when you remember that Mendel's experiments lead to the conclusion that there are two representatives of each genetic factor in each cell of an individual.

mitosis
 chromosomes become visible as separate entities
 chromosomes replicate into identical chromatids
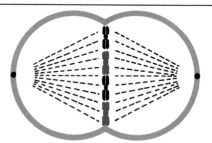
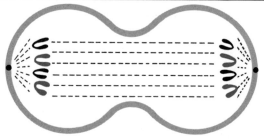 chromatids separate into opposite halves of the dividing cell

An individual receives two sets of chromosomes, one set from each parent, in the sex cells which unite to form the first cell of his identity. This initial cell divides mitotically, so that each body cell of the adult contains an exact copy of the original chromosomes. It is not surprising that there are two representatives of each type of chromosome, one representative inherited from the male parent, the other inherited from the female parent. In human body cells there are 46 individual chromosomes which are separable into 23 types. Each individual inherits 23 chromosomes (one of each type) from a sperm of the male parent, and another 23 chromosomes (also one of each type) from an egg of the female parent. This results in the initial cell, the fertilized egg, containing 23 *pairs* of chromo-

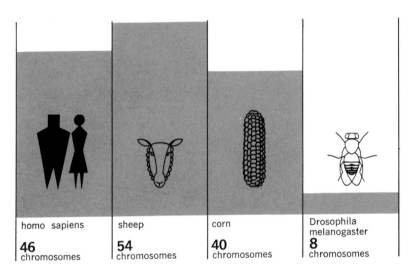

homo sapiens	sheep	corn	Drosophila melanogaster
46 chromosomes	**54** chromosomes	**40** chromosomes	**8** chromosomes

FIGURE 3.3

Each type of organism has a characteristic number of chromosomes, found in all the normal cells of individuals of that type of organism.

FIGURE 3.2

The nucleus loses its identity, separating into a set of thin strands called chromosomes. Each chromosome splits along its entire length into two daughter chromosomes called chromatids. The pairs of daughter chromatids separate, one chromatid of each chromosome going into each half of the dividing cell. The two sets, each identical to the initial set, are each contained in a nucleus. The two daughter cells contain an identical copy of each and all of the chromosomes present in the initial cell.

D.melanogaster   D.willistoni   D.subobscura

FIGURE 3.4

The chromosomes of Drosophila. Each species has a characteristic number of chromosomes with two representatives of each type.

somes. Each pair consists of a paternally and a maternally inherited chromosome. Mitotic divisions in the growth of the body from the fertilized egg then cause each body cell of the individual to have 23 pairs of chromosomes, with each individual chromosome present in all its unique individuality in each and every body cell. Clearly, the sex cells (the eggs and sperms) cannot be produced by mitotic division, or these sex cells would contain 46 chromosomes, and their junction would result in the offspring's having 92 chromosomes.

The division of body cells to form sex cells occurs by a special type of division called *meiosis*. It used to be called the "reduction division" because it reduces the number of chromosomes to half the number characteristic of body cells. Fertilization and meiosis can be regarded as completely complementary: fertilization results in the junction of two sets of chromosomes to give a cell containing two sets; meiosis results in the formation of cells containing only a single set of chromosomes.

MEIOSIS

The essential feature of meiosis, which differentiates it from mitosis, is that the two representatives of each type of chromosomes pair, then separate from each other into opposite halves of the dividing cell. This results in each half-cell's having only one representative of each pair of chromosomes, and each of the two half-cells, therefore, contains just one set of chromosomes. This is the essential feature of meiosis, but it has many other features that are important in understanding heredity.

Individual chromosomes at the beginning of meiosis appear as thin threads; each member of a pair of chromosomes moves toward its partner, and they come to lie parallel to each other through a

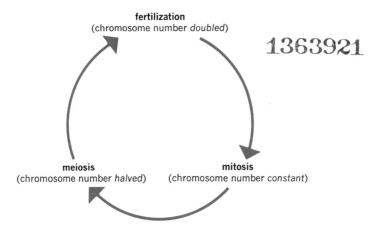

FIGURE 3.5

The basic features of the life cycles of the majority of organisms are the halving of the chromosome number at meiosis, and the doubling of the chromosome number at the junction of gametes (fertilization).

large part of their length. This pairing is highly specific: chromosomes only pair with their partners. Such chromosomes are said to be homologously paired—the two chromosomes are *homologs.* Just before, during, or after this process of pairing, each of the homologous chromosomes divides along its length to form two identical strands held together by a structure called the *centromere,* which does not divide at this stage. A pair of homologous chromosomes now consists of four separate strands, and each chromosome is said to have divided into two *chromatids.* There are now four chromatids lying closely side by side: two of the chromatids will be copies of the initial paternal chromosome, the other two chromatids will be copies of the initial maternal chromosome. In humans there are 23 closely associated pairs of chromosomes, in which each association consists of four chromatids.

At some time early in meiosis, a very important phenomenon occurs that can be described most easily as breaks occurring in opposite chromatids, which then rejoin across the break. This is called a *crossover.* When the paternal and maternal pairs of chromatids separate from each other, they are held together as a consequence of the change of pairing that results from crossing over. The points at which they are held together are called *chiasmata.* Tensions that develop during the later stages of meiosis separate the two chromosomes. Because of crossing over, some of the chromatids will

1

the individual chromosomes are visible as thin threads

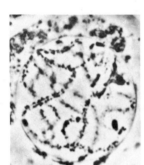

2

the chromosomes move together in pairs and each chromosome splits along its length into identical chromatids

3

the paired chromosomes move away from each other, being held together at the chiasmata, which have resulted from crossing over

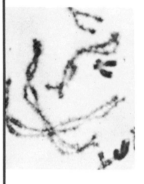

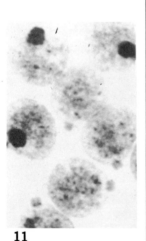

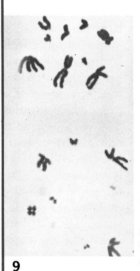

11

the four groups of chromosomes form nuclei in which segregation for presence and absence of the X chromosome can be seen

10

the two groups of chromosomes pass through a second division, first aligning themselves on the spindles, and then separating, resulting in a halving of the number of chromosomes

9

4

5

6

a spindle forms and the pairs of chromosomes move to its equatorial plane

each chromosome is attached to the spindle by its centromere

the X chromosome has no partner

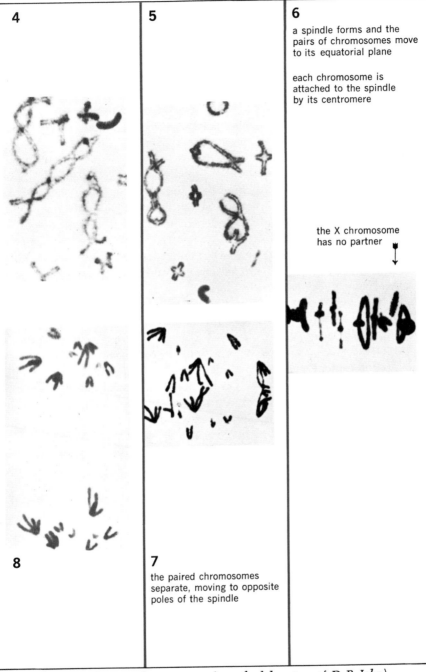

8

7

the paired chromosomes separate, moving to opposite poles of the spindle

Photographs of grasshopper chromosomes, from the laboratory of D. B. John)

consist of sections of both paternal and maternal chromosomes. The originally separate paternal and maternal chromosomes will have been recombined by the process of crossing over into a new sequence. Crossing over leads to recombination between the homologous paternal and maternal chromosomes. (Homologous chromosomes are those that normally pair at meiosis.) After the chromosomes separate, the reduction of the number of chromosomes will be complete, but each chromosome consists of two chromatids, and a second division is necessary to complete the separation. This second division follows the simple mitotic pattern.

Inheritance of chromosomes provides a complete biological basis for the coin-tossing machine that underlies the Mendelian laws of inheritance, *if* the separation of the different pairs of homologous chromosomes is completely independent, and if the genes are located on the chromosome.

Consider an organism that has only two chromosomes in its body cells—one a paternal chromosome, the other a maternal chromosome. Mitotic divisions of cells during growth result in each and every body cell's containing copies of the initial pair of chromosomes, but in the cells that divide to form the sex cells the two chromosomes pair, then separate so that each daughter sex cell contains either a maternal chromosome *or* a paternal chromosome (apart from the effects of crossing over, which can be neglected at this point). Exactly half the sex cells will contain a paternal chromosome and half will contain a maternal chromosome. This exact equality is the basis for Mendel's first law of segregation.

The role of meiosis in heredity can be seen clearly if we reexamine the cross between pure red-flowered and white-flowered strains of garden peas. For simplicity, assume that the body cells of garden peas only have two chromosomes that are homologous, one inherited paternally, the other inherited maternally. The chromosomes of the pure white-flowered parent will be identical as far as the white-flower factor is concerned. Each body cell will have a white-flower

FIGURE 3.7

The cross of homozygous white-flowered and homozygous red-flowered strains of garden peas results in heterozygous red-flowered progeny. Back-crossing these heterozygotes to a homozygous white-flowered strain results in segregation of the "red" and "white" characters. This classical case of Mendelian inheritance is illustrated in terms of the transmission of the chromosomes carrying the "red" and "white" genes.

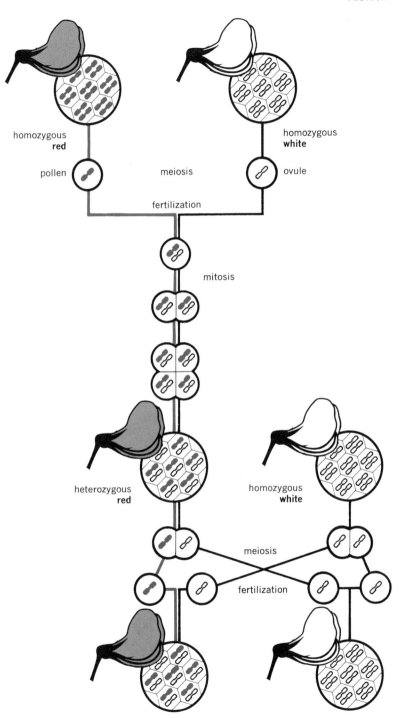

homozygous
red

homozygous
white

pollen   meiosis   ovule

fertilization

mitosis

heterozygous
red

homozygous
white

meiosis

fertilization

gene located on each of its two chromosomes. The sex cells (pollen or ovules) produced by this parent will, therefore, all contain one chromosome carrying a white-flower gene. The same description applies to the pure red-flowered parent, except that the sex cells it produces will all contain one chromosome carrying a red-flower gene. The union of a pollen grain from one parent with an ovule from the other parent will form a cell containing one chromosome with a red factor and one chromosome with a white factor. This cell will divide mitotically to produce two cells, each containing a copy of both chromosomes. This division of cells by mitosis will continue until all cells of the adult are formed, each containing a chromosome carrying a red-flower factor and a chromosome carrying a white-flower factor. The originally inherited pair of chromosomes has been copied through all the body cells of the adult. The meiotic division of any of the body cells to form sex cells (pollen or ovules) results in the chromosome with the red-flower factor pairing with that of the white-flower factor, then separating to give two cells: one will contain the "white" chromosome, the other the "red" chromosome. There will be equal numbers of sex cells carrying either of the two alternative chromosomes. If this pollen is used to pollinate the flowers of a pure white-flowered plant (if the hybrid is backcrossed to the white-flowered parental line), then two types of junction of pollen with ovule can occur, and these will occur with equal probability. All the ovules, since they are produced by a pure white-flowered plant, will contain a "white" chromosome. The junction of pollen containing a "white" chromosome with one of these ovules will result in a cell containing two "white" chromosomes, which will develop into a white-flowered plant. The junction of pollen containing a "red" chromosome with one of the ovules from the pure white-flowered parent will result in a cell containing both a "red" and a "white" chromosome, and this will develop into a red-flowered plant. Since the two types of pollen are equally frequent, the proportions of red-flowered and white-flowered plants will also be equally frequent.

LONG AND SHORT CHROMOSOMES

In some strains of grasshoppers there are visible differences (under the microscope) between homologous chromosomes. One strain may have certain distinctly shorter chromosomes than the other strain. These differences of length between homologous chromosomes are inherited just like any other character, and in hybrids

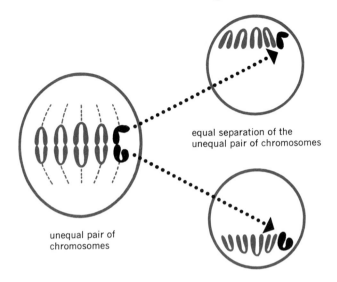

equal separation of the
unequal pair of chromosomes

unequal pair of
chromosomes

FIGURE 3.8

Some organisms have homologous chromosomes that are visibly different in length. Heterozygotes for this difference show that there is no greater tendency for one or the other type of chromosome to be transmitted in the sex cells.

between the two strains, the two chromosomes when they pair are visibly different. In such hybrids the character being transmitted is a visible feature of the chromosome, and a sperm or an egg is just as likely to contain a long or a short chromosome of this type.

Mendel's second law, that of independent assortment, is based on the biological coin-tossing machine treating each pair of alternative factors as if they were independent entities. Meiosis also provides a physical basis for this law *if* different pairs of chromosomes separate at the first division of meiosis without reference to each other. The unequal chromosomes of grasshoppers give a visible demonstration of this. Suppose, first, that the different types of chromosomes in a grasshopper are numbered, and that we have one strain in which the first and second types of chromosomes are each shorter than their homologous first and second types of chromosomes in another strain. Suppose sperm from the "short" chromosome strain fertilizes eggs from the "long" chromosome strain, then the hybrids will have two visibly unequal pairs of chromosomes which will pair at meiosis and separate into daughter cells. If the process of meiosis is examined in such hybrids, it will be found that the two unequal pairs separate independently of each other. Sometimes both the first and the second

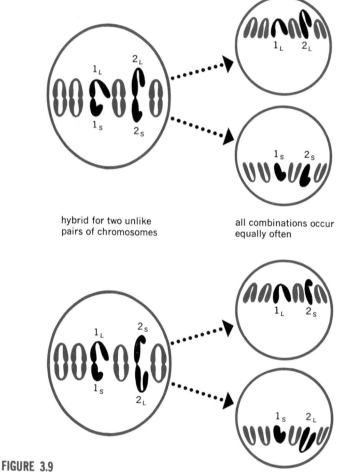

hybrid for two unlike
pairs of chromosomes

all combinations occur
equally often

FIGURE 3.9

Hybrids for two unequal pairs of chromosomes show the independent assortment of chromosomes. If two pairs of genes are located on different pairs of chromosomes, these would also show independent assortment in heredity.

long chromosomes will move together into one daughter cell, with their alternatives, the first and second short chromosomes, going into the other daughter cell. In other cells, a long first chromosome and a short second chromosome will move together into one daughter cell, with their alternatives, a short first chromosome and a long second chromosome, moving into the other daughter cell. These two alternatives occur equally often, showing that there is no tendency for the paternally or the maternally inherited chromosomes to be associated in their behavior during the separation of the paired chromosomes at meiosis. This is exactly the type of behavior of chromosomes that could account for Mendel's second law of independent assortment, if the different pairs of genes were located on different pairs of chromosomes.

This evidence is very strong support for meiosis as the basis of Mendel's laws, with the prediction that the genes postulated by Mendel would be shown to be located on the chromosomes, and nowhere else but on the chromosomes. A further prediction is that some pairs of genes will not be inherited independently. If they are located on the one pair of homologous chromosomes, they will be linked together in heredity.

Problems

1. The terms *haploid* and *diploid* refer to cells containing single and double sets of chromosomes, respectively. Draw the life cycle of a higher animal in terms of meiosis, mitosis, fertilization, haploid, and diploid.

2. Draw the cross of a crinkly hair individual to a normal-hair individual in terms of the crinkly hair gene and its normal allele being located on a homologous pair of chromosomes.

3. Suppose the blue-sclerotic gene is located on the same chromosome as the crinkly hair gene.

   (*a*) If a crinkly hair individual mates with a blue-sclerotic individual, what kinds of progeny could they have?

   (*b*) What would the frequencies of these offspring types be?

Chapter 4

CHROMOSOMES AND SEX

The transmission of genes in heredity has very close analogies with the inheritance of chromosomes. This suggests that the genes are located on the chromosomes, and that the rules of inheritance of genes are simple consequences of the inheritance of chromosomes. Proof of this suggestion depended on showing that the inheritance of specific genes exactly followed the inheritance of specific chromosomes. The first phase of this proof came from the discovery that inheritance of specific chromosomes determined the differences between males and females.

An obvious feature of early studies of chromosomes was that all body cells of all individuals of a species were characterized by a specific number of pairs of chromosomes. This rule, the constancy of chromosome number, is generally valid for most types of living things, but in a number of insects males have one less chromosome per body cell than females.

THE X CHROMOSOME

Just before the turn of this century, Henking found that he could distinguish two types of sperms in certain insects: one type had a darkly stained structure in their nuclei, and the other type lacked this structure. He called this structure the *X body*. Later work showed that the X body was a specific chromosome differing from other chromosomes in its reactions to stains. This very important discovery suggested that a specific chromosome, the X chromosome, was involved in the inheritance of the difference between males and females.

An American scientist, Wilson, showed that in insects of the Protenor genus females had an even number of chromosomes and

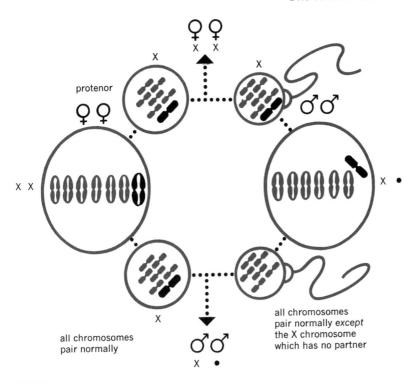

FIGURE 4.1

Sex determination in the Protenor genus is effected by the inheritance of a specific chromosome, the X chromosome. Individuals that inherit an X chromosome from each parent develop into females; those that inherit an X chromosome solely from the female parent develop into males. Males are "heterozygous" for the absence of an X chromosome.

males had an odd number—one less than females. Body cells of females had two X chromosomes, but males had only one X chromosome per body cell. Meiosis in females was normal; each chromosome paired with, and separated from, its normal homolog, thus each egg always contained an X chromosome.

Meiosis in males of insects of this group is normal for all the chromosomes except the X chromosome. The other chromosomes pair and separate normally, but the X chromosome has no homologous partner, and can only separate into one or the other of the daughter cells from the first meiotic division. Half the sperms receive an X chromosome, and half lack this chromosome.

These facts add up to the hypothesis that the X chromosome contains the genes that determine the sex difference—an egg inheriting two X chromosomes develops into a female; an egg inheriting one X chromosome develops into a male. The meiotic separation of the X chromosome in males into one or the other daughter cell results in the X-containing and X-lacking sperm occurring equally frequently; this explains the equal frequencies of males and females.

This mechanism of sex determination is called the *XO mechanism*, since the key feature is whether an egg is fertilzed by a sperm containing an X chromosome (an X sperm) or by a sperm lacking an X chromosome (an O sperm). Both the eggs and the sperms always contain the normal complement of other chromosomes, called *autosomes* to distinguish them from the sex chromosomes. The XO mechanism can explain the determination of the sex difference in organisms where one sex has one less chromosome per body cell than the other sex, but it cannot explain sex determination where both sexes are characterized by the same number of chromosomes.

THE XY SEX CHROMOSOMES

The XO system of sex determination is based on the presence or absence of a complete chromosome. Another system, called the XY system, is based on the presence or absence of parts of chromosomes. Both sexes have the same number of chromosomes; the determination of sex depends not on whether a sperm contains or lacks an X chromosome but, instead, on whether the sperms contains an X or a Y chromosome. Eggs fertilized by an X-containing sperm develop into females, whereas those fertilized by a Y-containing sperm develop into males.

Many organisms have an XY system of sex determination. Three have been studied intensively: Drosophila, mice, and men. The X and Y chromosomes are visually different, Y being longer than X. It has been shown in Drosophila that the X and Y chromosomes each have uniquely different segments, as well as a segment in common.

Sex is determined in the XO system by the difference in *quantity* of the X chromosome material: Inheritance of two X chromosomes switches development in the female direction; inheritance of one X chromosome switches development in the male direction. The XY system could also have a difference in quantity of genetic material as its basis, the difference being the section of the X chromosome that is different from the Y chromosome. This hypothesis does not

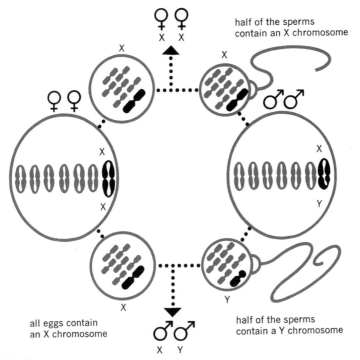

half of the sperms
contain an X chromosome

all eggs contain
an X chromosome

half of the sperms
contain a Y chromosome

FIGURE 4.2

Sex determination by the XY system is effected by the segregation in males of an unequal pair of chromosomes—the X and Y chromosomes. Two kinds of sperm are produced: one type contains an X chromosome, the other type contains a Y chromosome.

consider the Y chromosome as having any major function in the determination of sex—it proposes that it is the amount of the unique X section that determines sex. An alternative hypothesis is that the Y chromosome does have a function in sex determination, carrying male-determining factors that are dominant to the female-determining factors located on the X chromosome. Distinguishing between these two explanations of how the XY system functions required the formation of individuals with abnormal sets of sex chromosomes.

MEIOTIC MIX-UPS

The pairing and separation of chromosomes at meiosis determines an equal separation of the pairs of homologous chromosomes. Occa-

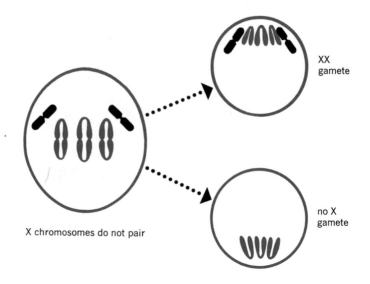

XX
gamete

no X
gamete

X chromosomes do not pair

nondisjunction

FIGURE 4.3

Nondisjunction. If the X chromosomes do not pair correctly during meiosis, the two chromosomes will separate independently of each other, and gametes may be produced that contain two or no X chromosomes. Such mistakes are rare.

sionally this process of pairing and separation fails, resulting in gametes that either lack a particular chromosome, or contain an extra chromosome. This is called *nondisjunction,* a phenomenon that has been a fruitful source of individuals with abnormal chromosomal constitutions.

Drosophila have been identified with a wide range of numbers of X and Y chromosomes. Close study of the sexual structures of these individuals has demonstrated that the amount of X chromosome material is the deciding factor in sex determination, with the Y chromosome playing a minor role.

Chromosomes	*Sex*
X X X	Superfemale
X X	Normal female
X X Y	Normal female
X Y	Normal male
X	Infertile male

The term *super female* is not intended to imply greater sexual effectiveness; such individuals are actually sterile. They have exaggerated female structures, and the term *super* refers to this, not to their effectiveness as females.

The sexual structure of individuals with abnormal numbers of X and Y chromosomes shows that the Y chromosomes does not carry male-determining factors. The difference between males and females appears to be caused by differences in the number of X chromosomes. Both XX and XXY individuals are functional females, showing that the Y chromosome does not affect the determination of femaleness by the two X chromosomes. Both XY and XO individuals are males, showing that the Y chromosome does not affect the determination of maleness by a single X chromosome. Although the Y chromosome has no male-determining factors, it does contain male fertility factors; individuals with only a single X chromosome are male in both external and internal structures, but they are sterile. Recent research indicates that this sterility is caused by the Y chromosome's controlling the length of the sperm tails—males lacking a Y chromosome produce sperms whose tails are short, presumably reducing their effectiveness in fertilization.

In recent years techniques have been developed that allow accurate determination of the number and type of chromosomes in man. These techniques have been used to study many types of sexual abnormalities, and a number of these have been found to be characterized by abnormal sex chromosomes.

Chromosomes	Sex
X X X	Female, with deficient mentality
X X	Normal female
X	Abnormal female
X X Y	Abnormal male
X X Y Y	Abnormal male
X X X Y	Abnormal male
X X X X Y	Abnormal male
X Y	Normal male

In man, the Y chromosome carries male-determining factors. If an individual inherits a Y chromosome, development proceeds in the male direction regardless of the number of X chromosomes, but development is abnormal except in individuals with normal chromosomal constitutions. A similar importance of the Y chromosome has been found in mice, where XXY individuals are males.

The XO system, the Drosophila XY system, and the human XY system are three variations on the chromosomal determination of the sex difference. There are other variations on the same theme: in the ZW system for birds, the male has two Z chromosomes, and the female has a Z and a W chromosome; in some insects, there are two X chromosomes, X_1 and X_2, both of which pair with a single Y chromosome. These facts add up to the inescapable conclusion that hereditary factors are located on the chromosomes, a conclusion that was strongly supported by the discovery of sex-linkage.

SEX-LINKAGE

Mendel's laws are not affected by the sex of the parent. The progeny of a cross between pure lines are the same regardless of which line is the male parent. This does not apply to genes located on specific parts of the X and Y chromosomes. The X and Y chromosomes have a part of their length in common, which ensures that they will pair normally at meiosis. They also have unique sections that do not occur in the other: the X chromosome has a section of its length that has no counterpart in the Y chromosome, and the Y chromosome has a section of its length that has no counterpart in the X chromosome. Genes located in these unique parts of the X and Y chromosomes have unusual patterns of inheritance, in which the sex of the parent has a major effect on the transmission of genes. Such genes are said to be *sex-linked*. These genes may have no role in the determination of the sex difference and yet, because of their location, be affected in their heredity by the sex difference.

The Y chromosome is only transmitted from males to males in organisms where males have the XY pairs of chromosomes, such as Drosophila, mice, and men. A father transmits his Y chromosome to his sons—they are his sons because they inherit his Y chromosome. No definite genes have been shown to be located on the unique part of the Y chromosome. This condition could be due to this part of the Y chromosome's being formed of a special type of material unlike that of the major parts of the other chromosomes.

The X chromosome of a male is only transmitted to female off-spring—they are female because they inherited the father's X chromosome. This means that a male transmits his X chromosome to all his female progeny who then transmit it to half their progeny. A male with a particular gene located on his X chromosome cannot transmit it to his sons, but he will transmit it to half his grandsons through his daughters.

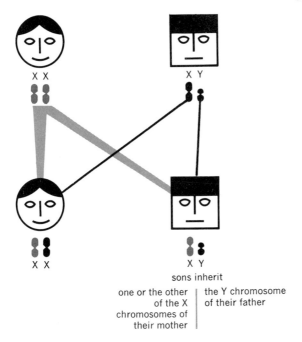

sons inherit

| one or the other of the X chromosomes of their mother | the Y chromosome of their father |

FIGURE 4.4

The inheritance of the X and Y chromosomes differs between males and females. The inheritance of genes located on the unique parts of the X and Y chromosomes follows the same pattern of sex-linked inheritance.

Drosophila have an XY pair of chromosomes in males, and many genes have been shown to have a sex-linked inheritance of the X-linked type. The white-eye gene is an alternative to the red-eye gene, and it has a typical sex-linked inheritance. The symbols w for the white-eye gene and w^+ for the red-eye gene are used to simplify the representation of this difference.

Males have only one X chromosome, and thus there are only two types of males: (1) those with a w gene on their chromosome (these have white eyes), and (2) those with a w^+ gene on their X chromosome (these have red eyes). Females have two X chromosomes, and thus there are three types: (1) those with a w gene on each X—homozygous w/w (these have white eyes); (2) those with a w^+ gene on each X—homozygous w^+/w^+ (these have red eyes); and (3) those with a w gene on one X and a w^+ on the other X—heterozygous w/w^+ (these have red eyes because the w^+ gene is dominant to the w gene).

Males have only one X chromosome which they inherit from their female parent. The eye-color gene on this X chromosome is the only

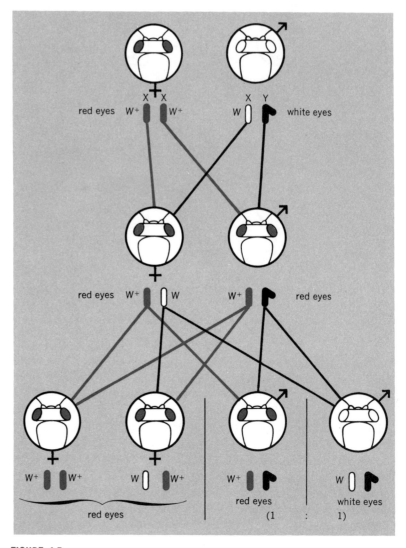

red eyes   W⁺   W⁺   W   white eyes

red eyes   W⁺   W   W⁺   red eyes

W⁺   W⁺   W   W⁺   W⁺   W
red eyes   red eyes   white eyes
red eyes   (1   :   1)

FIGURE 4.5a

one they inherit; therefore the eye color of a male is inherited solely from the female parent.

Females have two X chromosomes, one inherited from each parent. Their eye color is inherited equally from both parents, but the expression of this inheritance is affected by the dominance of the w^+ gene over the w gene. If a female inherits an X chromosome carrying a w gene from only one parent, that female will have red eyes

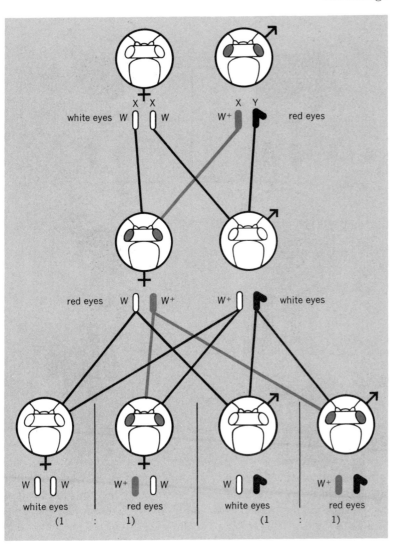

FIGURE 4.5b

The inheritance of red versus white eye color in Drosophila is sex-linked. These two allelic genes are located on the X chromosome, and their inheritance differs according to the direction of the cross. Crosses where the female parent is red-eyed give a result different from crosses where the female parent is white-eyed.

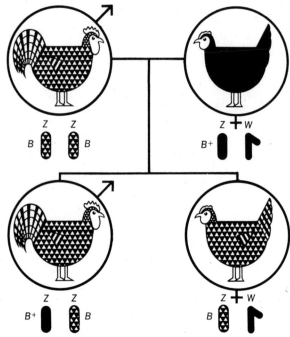

all progeny have barred feathers

FIGURE 4.6a

(such heterozygous individuals are indistinguishable from homozygous red-eyed females).

The complexities of sex-linked inheritance are due to this unequal transmission of the X chromosome. Many of the laws of heredity were found from investigation of sex-linkage in Drosophila; it is worthwhile going over a cross between white-eyed and red-eyed strains in detail. There are two such crosses: white males crossed to red females, and red males crossed to white females.

In the first type of cross, all the progeny are red-eyed, and all female progeny are heterozygous. If these flies are crossed to give a second generation, the white character reappears. The white character reappears in only half the male progeny, and in none of the female progeny. This is quite a different result from that found by Mendel, but the differences are fully explained by the supposition that the red-eye and white-eye genes are located on the unique part of the X chromosome.

If the cross is made in the reciprocal way, with red males crossed to white females, the transmission of the red and white genes is very

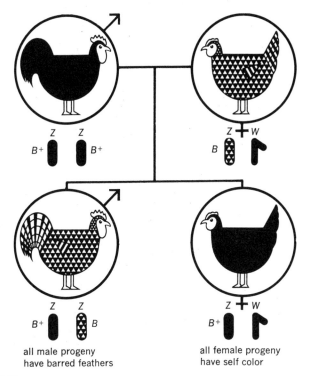

FIGURE 4.6b

Barred versus self feather color in poultry shows a sex-linked inheritance complementary to that found in Drosophila. The explanation is that females have the unequal pair of sex chromosomes (ZW).

different. All the male progeny of this cross are white-eyed, and all the female progeny are red-eyed. Crossing these first-generation progeny will give the second generation, and the occurrence of red-eyed and white-eyed progeny differs from the reciprocal cross. The second-generation progeny of this reciprocal cross segregate for the red and white characters in *both* males and females.

The unusual features of sex-linked inheritance can all be explained if the hereditary factors having this type of inheritance are located on the unique part of the X chromosome that has no homolog on the Y chromosome. If Mendel's laws are restated as the location of discrete hereditary factors on the chromosomes, then sex-linked inheritance is not an exception to the laws, but rather a special case due to one sex having only a single representative of the specific pair of chromosomes containing the factors necessary for sex difference.

SEX-LINKAGE IN BIRDS

Some hereditary differences in birds also show sex-linked inheritance, but in a way exactly complementary to that found in Drosophila. The character *barred* in poultry is expressed as a striped pattern of the feather color. The gene for barred feathers is dominant to its alternative of nonbarred feathers. A cross between a barred male and a nonbarred female results in progeny that are all barred, but the reciprocal cross of a nonbarred male and a barred female results in male barred progeny and female nonbarred progeny.

These results would appear to show that a simple explanation of sex-linkage on the basis of the genes being located on the X chromosome is not valid, *unless* birds differ from Drosophila in males being XX and females XY. This is the explanation. In birds, the female has the unequal pair of sex chromosomes, called the ZW pair, and the male has an equal ZZ pair. Once again an apparent exception helps show that the best explanation of Mendel's laws is that the genes are located on the chromosomes. We can generalize this explanation: specific hereditary factors are always located on specific chromosomes.

Problems

1. The Bar eye gene in Drosophila causes a drastic reduction of eye size. A male with Bar eyes crossed to a female with normal eyes produced progeny in which all females had Bar eyes and all males had normal eyes. Does this cross demonstrate that the Bar gene is located on the X chromosome?

2. A Bar eye male from a homozygous red-eyed stock is mated to a white-eye female from a homozygous normal-eyed stock. What are the eye colors and eye shapes of the progeny?

3. Suppose the progeny from the above cross are mated. What types of progeny will occur?

4. Hemophilia is a sex-linked recessive gene in humans. If a father and son are both hemophiliacs, but the mother is normal, what is the genotype of the mother?

5. In the above family, are any of the daughters expected to be hemophiliac?

QUICK QUIZ *Chapters 1 through 4*

1. When Mendel crossed a pure white-flowered strain of peas with a pure red-flowered strain, the first-generation hybrids had:
   (*a*) white flowers.
   (*b*) red flowers.
   (*c*) some white and some red flowers.
   (*d*) pink flowers.
   (*e*) 3 red flowers to 1 white flower.

2. Hybrids between red-flowered and white-flowered strains were crossed back to the pure red-flowered strain. The progeny of this backcross had:
   (*a*) red flowers.
   (*b*) red flowers on some, white flowers on some.
   (*c*) white flowers.
   (*d*) 1 red flower to 1 white flower.
   (*e*) 3 red flowers to 1 white flower.

3. *Crinkly hair* is a simple dominant character in humans. This means that the parents of a crinkly hair child must:
   (*a*) both be crinkly haired.
   (*b*) both be straight haired.
   (*c*) include at least one crinkly haired individual.

4. Albinism in humans is a simple recessive character. This means that the parents of an albino child must:
   (*a*) both be albino.
   (*b*) both be nonalbino.
   (*c*) include at least one albino.
   (*d*) be human beings.

5. Roan cattle are hybrid for the red and white coat-color genes. The dominant gene is:
   (*a*) the red.   (*b*) the white.   (*c*) neither.

6. Mice normally have straight coats, but mutant strains have been found in which the coat is waved. In each case the waviness was found to be a simple Mendelian character. Does each mutant strain differ from normal:

   (*a*) in the same gene?

   (*b*) in different genes?

   (*c*) There is not enough information to answer this question.

7. Two strains of wavy coated mice differ from normal in a simple recessive way—when they are crossed the offspring have straight coats. Does each mutant strain differ from normal:

   (*a*) in the same gene?

   (*b*) in different genes?

   (*c*) There is not enough information to answer this question.

8. The grandchildren of a person suffering from Huntington's chorea have the following probability of developing the disease:

   (*a*) none.

   (*b*) 50%.

   (*c*) 1 chance in 4.

   (*d*) 1 chance in 8.

   (*e*) 6.25%.

9. How does the character *blue sclerotic* show that a gene may be transmitted without expressing itself?

   (*a*) The characteristic fragility of the bones of blue sclerotics occurs only in individuals homozygous for the gene.

   (*b*) Skeletal fragility may or may not occur, but the effect on the eyes always occurs.

   (*c*) The effect on the eyes occurs in heterozygotes, whereas the effect on the skeleton occurs only in homozygotes.

10. Baldness is a sex-limited character. This means that bald individuals are:

    (*a*) more frequently male than female.

    (*b*) less sexually active than individuals with a full head of hair.

(*c*) homozygous for the bald gene if they are female.

(*d*) heterozygous for the bald gene if they are male.

(*e*) None of these answers is fully correct.

11. The gene "yellow" coat color in mice is a recessive lethal, yet "yellow" mice are viable and reproductive. This means that:

(*a*) the "yellow" mice die early.

(*b*) yellow mice are heterozygotes.

(*c*) homozygous yellow mice die early.

(*d*) the cross of yellow by yellow mice give normal and yellow progeny in the ratio of 1 : 2.

(*e*) . . . the ratio of 1 : 3.

(*f*) . . . the ratio of 1 : 1.

12. Mitosis differs from meiosis in mitotic cell divisions resulting in:

(*a*) two instead of four daughter cells.

(*b*) a halving of the number of chromosomes.

(*c*) the pairing of homologous chromosomes without crossing over.

13. Chromosomes pair during meiosis, break and rejoin in a new sequence, then divide into chromatids.

(*a*) True.   (*b*) False.

14. The chromosomal basis for Mendel's first law of genetics is that:

(*a*) the number of chromosomes is constant.

(*b*) homologous chromosomes pair and separate at meiosis.

(*c*) chromosomes are located at random on the spindle.

15. A red-green colorblind male must, if mutation is excluded, have inherited the gene for this defect:

(*a*) from his father.

(*b*) from his mother.

(*c*) from either father or mother.

(*d*) from both father and mother.

16. The grandsons of a colorblind male have the following probability of being colorblind:

(*a*) zero.   (*b*) 50%.   (*c*) 25%.   (*d*) 12.5%.

Chapter 5

THE THIRD LAW OF GENETICS

Genes are located on chromosomes. Genes located on different chromosomes are inherited independently, but will genes located on the same chromosome be inherited independently? There are far more genes than chromosomes; each chromosome must contain a number of different genes. For example, the vinegar fly, *Drosophila melanogaster,* has only four pairs of chromosomes, yet several hundred different genes have been identified in this organism. The presence of different genes on the same chromosome raises the problem of the inheritance of such genes. Thomas Hunt Morgan discovered the third law of genetics, which deals with the inheritance of alleles of different genes located on the same chromosome.

Morgan's researches led him to conclusions not previously titled as the third law of genetics, but they are as important as Mendel's laws and deserve to be ranked as the third law of genetics. This law has three parts. The first part is that the transmission of separate genes is not necessarily independent; different genes located on the same chromosome can be linked in heredity. The second part of the third law is that this linkage of parental combinations may not be complete; recombinations occur and different pairs of linked genes show different amounts of recombination. Some pairs of genes are extremely tightly linked, with recombinants occurring only rarely. Other pairs of genes may be loosely linked, with recombinants occurring almost as frequently as if the two genes were inherited independently. The last part of the third law will be considered later in this chapter.

COMBINATIONS AND RECOMBINATIONS

Two genes in the mouse are quite different in their effects, yet they are closely related in heredity. The genes are (1) the short-

60

ear gene (*se*) which is recessive to its allele ($+^{se}$), and (2) the coat-color dilution gene (*d*) which is recessive to its allele ($+^{d}$). Crosses between short-eared and dilute-coated mice should produce double heterozygotes, and if these are then crossed the progeny should include all four combinations in the ratio of:

9	3	3	1
normal ears	short ears	normal ears	short ears
normal coat	normal coat	diluted coat	diluted coat

This ratio is the expectation *if* the two genes assorted independently in agreement with Mendel's second law. Instead the ratio was closer to:

2	1	1
normal ears	short ears	normal ears
normal coat	normal coat	diluted coat

The two genes were acting as if they were linked in heredity with *se* linked to $+^{d}$ and $+^{se}$ linked to *d*. In more extensive experiments involving thousands of progeny, a few individuals having the short ear-dilute combination were found. The existence of this combination showed that the linkages of *se* with $+^{d}$ and of $+^{se}$ with *d* were not complete—recombination could occur, but only rarely. Further crosses were made to evaluate the frequency of this recombination:

$$\frac{se \quad d}{+^{se} \quad +^{d}} \times \frac{se \quad d}{se \quad d}$$

This is a backcross to the double recessive stock, and the expectation, in the absence of linkage, is that all four possible combinations should occur equally frequently:

1	1	1	1
normal ears	short ears	normal ears	short ears
normal coat	normal coat	dilute coat	dilute coat

This expectation was not realized. The recombinations of short ears with normal coat and normal ears with dilute coat occurred in only 6 of the 2,899 progeny produced from this cross. Clearly the genes were not assorting independently; they were being inherited as if linked together very tightly. The linkage was not complete but nearly so.

Another example of genes being linked in heredity involves the albino (*c*) and shaker (*sh*) genes in the mouse. Albino is recessive to its normal allele ($+^{c}$) for colored coat, and shaker is recessive to its normal allele ($+^{sh}$) for normal behavior. (The phenotype of sh/sh involves behavior; they have a characteristic upward jerking of the head.)

Mice that are heterozygous for albino and shaker can be produced in two ways: crossing homozygous albino nonshakers with homozygous nonalbino shakers, and crossing homozygous albino shakers with homozygous nonalbino nonshakers. The abnormal characters (albinism and shaking) are said to be *in repulsion* in the first cross, and *in coupling* in the second cross.

Double heterozygote

$$\frac{c \cdot +^{sh}}{c \cdot +^{sh}} \times \frac{+^c \cdot sh}{+^c \cdot sh} \qquad \frac{c \cdot +^{sh}}{+^c \cdot sh} \qquad \text{\textit{Repulsion}}$$

$$\frac{c \cdot sh}{c \cdot sh} \times \frac{+^c \cdot +^{sh}}{+^c \cdot +^{sh}} \qquad \frac{c \cdot sh}{+^c \cdot +^{sh}} \qquad \text{\textit{Coupling}}$$

This distinction has no importance if the genes are not linked. If the genes are linked, it has a marked effect on the frequencies of different types of progeny produced by backcrossing such double heterozygotes to a homozygous double recessive strain.

$$\frac{c \cdot sh}{+^c \cdot +^{sh}} \times \frac{c \cdot sh}{c \cdot sh} \qquad \frac{c \cdot +^{sh}}{+^c \cdot sh} \times \frac{c \cdot sh}{c \cdot sh}$$

An experiment with the above pairs of genes gave the following results.

Grandparental combinations { 46.8% (albino, shaker) 1.3%
48.5% (nonalbino, nonshaker) 1.5% } Recombinations

Recombinations { 2.0% (albino, nonshaker) 47.0%
2.6% (nonalbino, shaker) 50.2% } Grandparental combinations

These results show that the grandparental combinations occur far more frequently than recombinations. The results constitute a clear exception to Mendel's second law, and they show the need for some extension of these laws. This extension becomes apparent if the phenomena of linkage and recombination are related to the location of genes on the chromosomes.

CROSSING OVER

The linkage of genes can easily be understood to be a consequence of the genes' being located on the same chromosomes. The recom-

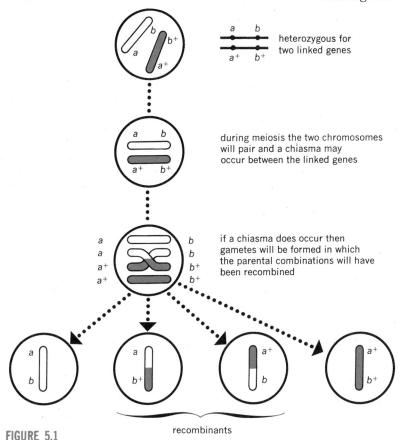

heterozygous for two linked genes

during meiosis the two chromosomes will pair and a chiasma may occur between the linked genes

if a chiasma does occur then gametes will be formed in which the parental combinations will have been recombined

recombinants

FIGURE 5.1

Genes located at different points of the same chromosome will be linked in heredity. This linkage will only be complete if no crossovers occur between the locations of the two genes. The more crossovers that occur, the less tight is the linkage.

bination of such linked genes is not easy to understand unless we refer to the description of meiosis. Homologous chromosomes pair during the first division of meiosis. At the time of this pairing chiasmata are formed which can be described most simply as the breakage and rejoining of opposite chromatids. This phenomenon results in the formation of chromatids that have segments of both the maternal and paternal chromosomes, providing us with a simple explanation of the recombination of two genes located at different parts of the same chromosome. Suppose an individual is heterozygous for two linked genes, with both alleles on one chromosome inherited from one parent, and both alleles on the homolog to that chromosome inherited from the other parent. During meiosis these two chromosomes will pair, and a chiasma may occur between them. If it does, gametes will be formed in which the parental combinations will have recombined.

The phenomena of linkage can be conveniently illustrated from a number of sex-linked genes in Drosophila. Two genes in Drosophila that have a sex-linked pattern of inheritance are the yellow-body (y) and white-eye (w) genes; this demonstrates that both are located on the X chromosome. These two genes are not inherited independently —the parental combinations are transmitted much more frequently than recombinants. The percentage of recombinants is slightly more than 1%. This amount of recombination is a characteristic of the two genes regardless of the type of cross studied.

Some sex-linked genes in Drosophila are extremely tightly linked. Two such genes are the eosin (w^e) and apricot (w^a) genes, both of which affect eye color. They seemed to be hereditary alternatives when they were first discovered and tested. Females that were heterozygous for eosin and apricot produced equal numbers of eosin and apricot male progeny; this is in agreement with their being alternatives. Occasional red-eyed males occurred in these progeny, but these were considered to be wild intruders that got into the cultures by accident. More detailed experiments proved that these red-eyed progeny were recombinants of the eosin and apricot genes. This showed that these are not simple alternatives, but separate genes that are extremely tightly linked, showing only 0.03% of recombination. There is some doubt whether eosin and apricot should be called separate genes, even though they are separable by crossing over. The reason for this doubt will be better understood when the structure of genes is discussed later.

Another sex-linked gene that affects eye color in Drosophila is the garnet gene. Females that are heterozygous for both the eosin and garnet genes produce all four possible types of male progeny almost equally often, but there is a consistently greater proportion of the parental combinations: 57% of the male progeny are one or the other parental type, and 43% are one or the other recombinant type.

Each of these pairs of genes—y and w^e, w^e and w^a, w^e and g—have a characteristic amount of recombination, and this is the second part of the third law of genetics. The amount of recombination found for a pair of linked factors varies from one pair to the next, but is constant for any specific pair of genes. The explanation of this in terms of chromosomes is that the frequency of chiasmata between the locations of two genes has a specific constant value.

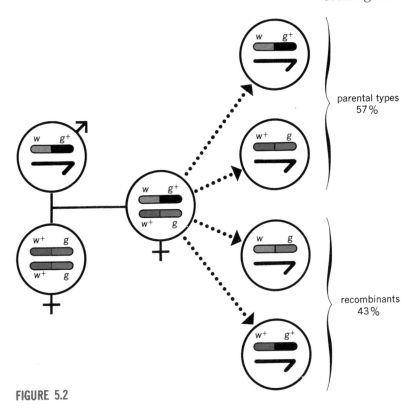

parental types
57%

recombinants
43%

FIGURE 5.2

The third part of the third law is often considered difficult to understand, so we will consider it first for three genes, then widen our consideration to four and to five genes.

Yellow body, (*y*), singed bristles (*sn*), and lozenge (*lz*) are all linked on the X chromosome in Drosophila. They each have characteristic amounts of recombination with each other, and these values can be arranged in a "recombination triangle." Morgan saw that the triangle of recombination between three genes had a simple arithmetic feature: the value of recombination for any side of the triangle was equal to the *sum* or the *difference* of the other two sides. This arithmetic relationship was generally true for any triplet of linked genes.

The simplicity of the arithmetic of recombination was no more than an intriguing fact until Morgan saw that it could be given a simple explanation by postulating that linked genes are arranged

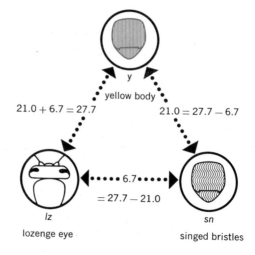

FIGURE 5.3

in line along the chromosome. If y, sn, and lz are arranged in line, the rule of addition or difference of recombination values can be seen to be a simple consequence of the sequence of the three genes. If there is a 21.0% chance of recombination between y and sn and a 6.7% chance of recombination between sn and lz, then if these three genes are arranged in line with y and lz at the ends, the chance of recombination between y and lz would be 27.7%.

A note of warning is needed at this point. The arithmetic of recombination values is simple only when we are considering closely linked genes. If three genes are linked with only a few per cent of recombination among them, the above rules of simple addition and subtraction hold true. But if the genes are linked with greater amounts of recombination, the rules of simple addition and subtraction do not hold exactly because two or more crossovers may occur, and these can result in less than the expected amount of genetic recombination. A recombination produced by one crossover can be recombined back to the parental combination by another crossover of the same strands. This rather abstruse point is important to geneticists constructing linkage maps, but otherwise it can be accepted as only a minor technicality.

The genetic geometry of recombination can be extended by including another sex-linked gene, garnet (g). Garnet can be drawn as the apex of two triangles: one with y and sn, the other with sn and lz. The same law of addition or subtraction holds for the two separate

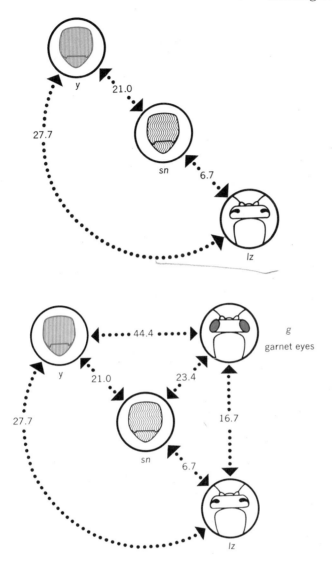

FIGURE 5.5

triangles. If we arrange these four genes into line, all six different values of recombination are simply explained. The four genes can be arranged to form a line in which the amounts of recombination between successive genes add up to the amounts of recombination between the genes at the end of the line.

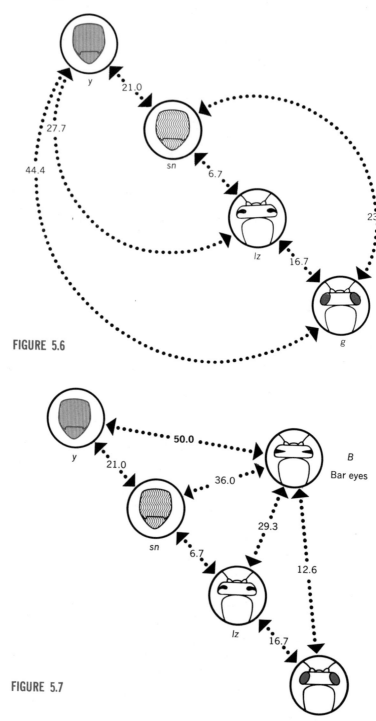

FIGURE 5.6

FIGURE 5.7

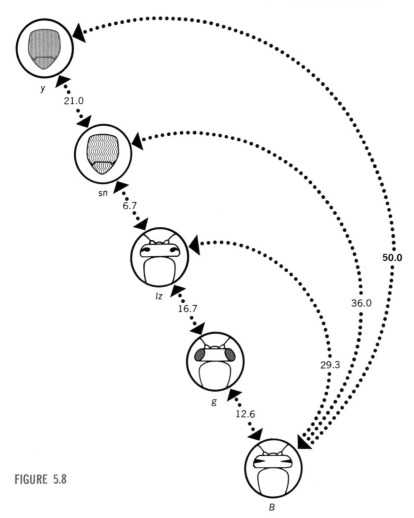

FIGURE 5.8

50% RECOMBINATION

The same arithmetic would be valid for genes spread along the full length of a chromosome, except that *recombination reaches a maximum at 50%*—no genes show more recombination than this maximum. The explanation of this is that crossing over is between chromatids rather than chromosomes. A recombination of 50% occurs if a chiasma always occurs between the location of two genes. Even though this means that a crossover always occurs between the two genes, only two of the four chromatids will be involved in the crossover; the other two chromatids will be unaffected. A recombination of more than 50% could occur only *if* a second chiasma occurred between the locations of the two genes, *and if* the two chromatids involved in this second crossover were different from the two involved in the first crossover. Since recombination has been found to reach a maximum at 50%, it is evident that when two chiasma occur between the location of two genes, the second crossover is quite independent of the first.

Adding another sex-linked gene, Bar eyes (*B*), to our quartet of sex-linked genes, making it into a quintet, shows this restriction in effect. Arranging all these genes in line, with *y* at one end and *B* at the other end, makes sense of the arithmetic of recombination for all but the *y* and *B* genes. These should have a recombination value of 57%, but they have a value of only 50%.

All the different aspects of the third law can be explained if each gene has a specific location on a specific chromosome, and if the probability of recombination is simply proportional to the distance between the locations of the different genes. This can be called the "string-of-beads" hypothesis, in which the chromosome is considered to be a string of genes with each gene occurring only at a specific place; each bead is different and all the beads always occur in the same sequence.

The discovery of the third law led to an exciting period in genetics. Maps of the locations of genes were drawn in Drosophila, corn, mice, and several other organisms. A feature of these maps was the discovery that many chromosomes are so long that genes located on them show no linkage. As more and more genes were identified it was possible to show that many genes that were inherited independently were actually located on the same chromosome. This was accomplished by showing that these independently inherited genes showed linkage with a third gene. In our example from sex-linked genes in Drosophila, *y* and *B* are inherited independently of each other, yet *y* and *lz* have a recombination of 27.7%—they are linked; *lz* and *B* have a recombination of 29.3%—they are linked. Therefore, *y* and *B* must be located on the same chromosome even though they show no linkage in heredity.

FIGURE 5.9

The relationship of crossing over to recombination where the number of crossovers between two loci is 0.5, 1.0, and 2.0. The recombination is 50% for all values of crossing over greater than 1.0, because the second crossovers restore the parental combinations as often as they form recombinants.

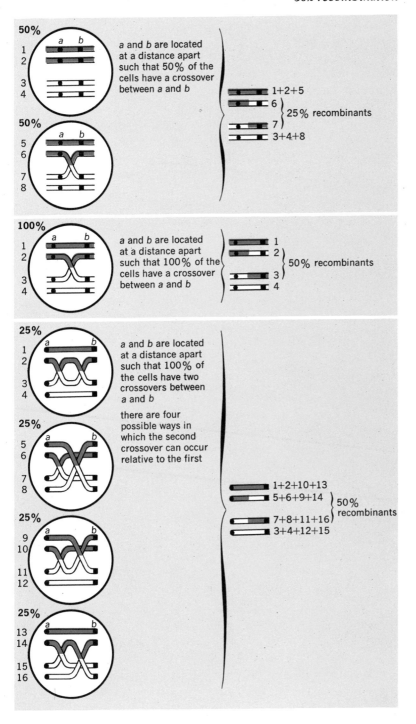

a and b are located at a distance apart such that 50% of the cells have a crossover between a and b

1+2+5
6
7
3+4+8
} 25% recombinants

a and b are located at a distance apart such that 100% of the cells have a crossover between a and b

1
2
3
4
} 50% recombinants

a and b are located at a distance apart such that 100% of the cells have two crossovers between a and b

there are four possible ways in which the second crossover can occur relative to the first

1+2+10+13
5+6+9+14
7+8+11+16
3+4+12+15
} 50% recombinants

Drosophila melanogaster have four pairs of chromosomes called the Ist, IInd, IIIrd, and IVth chromosomes. (The Ist chromosome is the X chromosome, and the IVth chromosome is the very small chromosome characteristic of the species.) Genetic studies of linkage and recombination have shown that there are four linkage groups, equating to the four chromosomes. Ten pairs of chromosomes have been found in corn, and genetic studies of linkage and recombination have shown that there are ten linkage groups equating to the number of pairs of chromosomes.

The discovery and explanation of the complexities of linkage and recombination ended the era of genetics as a minor offshoot of biology. It graduated to being a separate science with the primary aim of identifying the physical structure of the gene.

Problems

1. Morgan's law of linkage and recombination is not restricted to predictions of the types and frequencies of progeny expected from crosses involving two linked genes. It can be extended to three linked genes. What types and frequencies of progeny are expected from the following crosses in Drosophila?

(a) $\dfrac{y \; sn \; lz}{}$ $\times$ $\dfrac{y^+ \; sn^+ \; lz^+}{y \; sn \; lz}$

(b) $\dfrac{y \; sn \; lz}{}$ $\times$ $\dfrac{y \; sn^+ \; lz}{y^+ \; sn \; lz^+}$

2. It is possible to make predictions about crosses involving large numbers of linked genes, but this is unusual in practice. However, crosses involving four loci are often used in a field of genetics called *fine-structure analysis*. What types and frequencies of progeny are expected from the following cross in Drosophila?

$\dfrac{y \; w^a \; w^e \; sn}{}$ $\times$ $\dfrac{y \; w^a \; w^+ \; sn^+}{y^+ \; w^{a+} \; w^e \; sn}$

3. Hemophilia and color blindness are both sex-linked recessive genes in humans. The linkage of these two genes is 12%. The Xg blood-group gene is also sex-linked. It has a linkage of 46% with the hemophilia gene, and a linkage of 34% with the color blindness gene. Draw the linkage map of these three genes.

4. Eight genes, *A* through *H*, had the following set of recombination values. Use these to form a linkage map.

$A \times C = 0.30$ $D \times F = 0.30$

$B \times D = 0.08$ $D \times H = 0.10$

$B \times F = 0.38$ $E \times G = 0.06$ All other values

$B \times H = 0.18$ $F \times H = 0.20$ were 0.50.

$C \times E = 0.26$ $C \times G = 0.20$

Chapter 6

LOCATING THE GENE

Morgan showed how linkage relationships could be used to draw genetic maps in which each gene has a fixed position in a specific linkage group. The obvious conclusion is that each group of linked genes is located on a specific chromosome. The next major step in the advance of genetics was the identification of linkage groups with specific chromosomes. This was accomplished by showing that abnormal patterns of behavior of specific chromosomes were related to abnormal patterns of heredity of specific genes. The exact identification of the chromosomal location of the different linkage groups depended on finding inherited visible abnormalities of the chromosomes, then testing to see which genes had an abnormal pattern of heredity when they were inherited conjointly with the microscopically visible chromosomal abnormality.

EXTRA CHROMOSOMES

The separation of homologous chromosomes to opposite poles during meiosis may fail, resulting in the production of individuals containing one extra or one less chromosome than the normal number. This phenomenon, called *nondisjunction*, has been discussed previously in the analysis of the roles of the X and Y chromosomes in sex determination.

In Drosophila, individuals with an XXY pattern of the sex chromosomes are functional females. A feature of such females is that their transmission of sex-linked genes is abnormal. The white-eye (w) gene is sex-linked and is recessive; the cross of a white-eye female with a red-eyed male normally leads to progeny in which all males are white-eyed and all females are red-eyed. If the white-eyed female is an XXY type, this prediction fails;

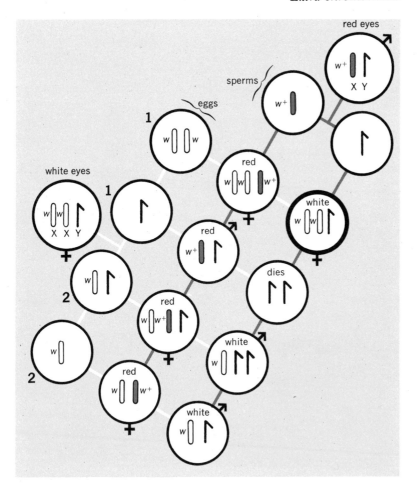

FIGURE 6.1

White-eyed XXY females can produce four types of eggs. One of these contains two X chromosomes, and the fertilization of such an egg by a Y-bearing sperm will result in a white-eyed female. This is an example of how an abnormality of the chromosome constitution can result in an abnormal pattern of heredity.

about 4% of the female progeny are white-eyed. This is because the XXY triplet of chromosomes does not separate normally at meiosis, and a proportion of the eggs inherit two X chromosomes from their female parent. Half of these abnormal eggs will be fertilized by a sperm carrying a Y chromosome; this results in XXY individuals that have inherited both their X chromosomes from their female parent. Since the female parent was homozygous for the white-eye gene, the XXY progeny will inherit two white-eye genes and will be white-eyed.

The correlations of an abnormal inheritance of the white-eye gene with the abnormal transmission of the X and Y chromosomes illustrates how genes can be identified with specific chromosomes.

The haploid set of chromosomes in Drosophila has four members: the Ist, IInd, IIIrd and IVth chromosomes. (The X chromosome is the Ist chromosome.)

The eyeless (*ey*) gene in Drosophila is located on the IVth chromosome. This was demonstrated by crosses involving strains with an extra IVth chromosome. Wild type individuals with three IVth chromosomes carry three normal alleles to the eyeless gene; they can be shown as $+/+/+$. Crossing such individuals with *ey/ey* produces progeny that are $+/+/ey$ or $+/ey$. The latter, crossed to *ey/ey*, gives the normal 50% eyeless progeny, but $+/+/ey$ crossed to *ey/ey* gives only one-sixth eyeless progeny. This is the expectation if the eyeless gene is located on the IVth chromosome.

ALTERED CHROMOSOMES

Showing that a group of genes is located on a specific chromosome did not resolve the problem of the location of individual genes. This depended on the discovery that some strains of Drosophila were characterized by abnormal chromosomes. These strains had the normal number of chromosomes, but one or more of these chromosomes differed from normal in the number or sequence of its parts. Four types of abnormality were discovered: parts were missing (called *deficiencies*); parts were duplicated (called *duplications*); a part was inverted to have the opposite sequence (called an *inversion*); nonhomologous chromosomes had parts exchanged (called *translocations*). Many such abnormal chromosomes have been identified both cytologically by direct microscopic examination, and genetically from their effects on the inheritance of genes located in the abnormal segments.

The genetic effect of translocations is that the linkage relations of the genes located in the interchanged segments will be transferred from one linkage group to another. The gene for vestigial wings (*vg*) in Drosophila is located in the second linkage group, segregating independently of genes in other linkage groups. However, if the segregation of *vg* is examined in crosses involving a translocation of the segment containing the *vg* gene, it is found to have changed

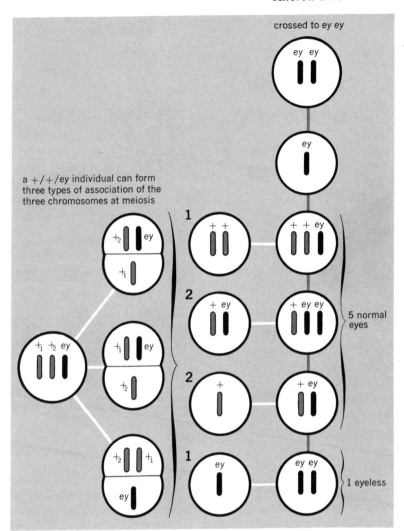

FIGURE 6.2

The eyeless gene shows an abnormal pattern of heredity in crosses involving individuals with an extra IVth chromosome. This shows that the eyeless gene is located on the IVth chromosome.

its linkage relations, being linked with genes of another linkage group.

One such translocation was first detected by an alteration of the linkage relations of the third and fourth linkage groups. Some genes of the third linkage group were found to be linked with genes of the

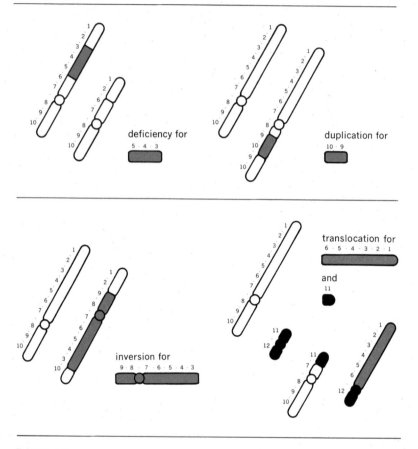

FIGURE 6.3

The chromosomal constitution of individuals can differ in the "quality" of their chromosomes, as well as in their number. Chromosomes may have sections missing, sections duplicated; sections may be inverted, or trans-located between nonhomologs.

fourth linkage group. A detailed study of this abnormality showed that the segment of interchanged chromosome contained the loci of genes from near the location of the curved wing gene to the location of the minute gene. Cytological studies of the chromosomes were made, and it was found that a large section of the IIIrd chromosome had been interchanged with a small section of the IVth chromosome. These two sets of results showed that the third linkage group of genes was located on the IIIrd chromosome; it also demonstrated that the genes from curved wing to minute were located in the part of the IIIrd chromosome that had been replaced.

Although cytogenetic studies showed that specific genes were located in specific parts of the chromosomes, it was not possible to see enough detail along the length of the Drosophila chromosomes to make out the structure of the individual genes. These chromosomes could be usefully studied only when they had contracted into relatively featureless rods.

Other organisms had chromosomes in which a great deal more detail could be discerned because they could be studied at early stages of cell division before the process of contraction had begun. Belling showed that the chromosomes of a species of Lilium consisted of a long chain of different-sized granules which were called *chromomeres*. These granules vary in size, but the differences are constant, and it is possible to find that the sequence of chromomeres along a chromosome does not differ from that along its homologous partner. This was a cytological extension of the string-of-beads hypothesis. The suggestion was made that each chromomere was a gene.

It seemed for some time that the researches toward identifying the physical structure of the gene had reached a cul-de-sac. The work with Drosophila had led to an extremely precise description of its genetic mechanism, but its chromosomes had proved too small and too difficult for any detailed investigations. The work of cytologists on other organisms, whose genetics was not easily described, had shown that it was possible to describe chromosomes precisely, and there must have been a certain amount of frustration at the inadequacy of Drosophila in this respect. This frustration was removed by an exciting discovery.

SALIVARY-GLAND CHROMOSOMES

The salivary glands of Drosophila were found to consist of very large cells containing extremely large nuclei in which "giant" chromosomes could be seen in a tangled coil. Clearly such large chromosomes would allow extremely detailed correlations between genetic and cytological maps, but these cells did not divide; hence it was not possible to study the giant chromosomes except as a tangled mass inside the nuclei. Painter saw that if the chromosomes would not come out of the nuclei, some way was needed to get them out. He found that if the salivary glands were dissected out of the larvae

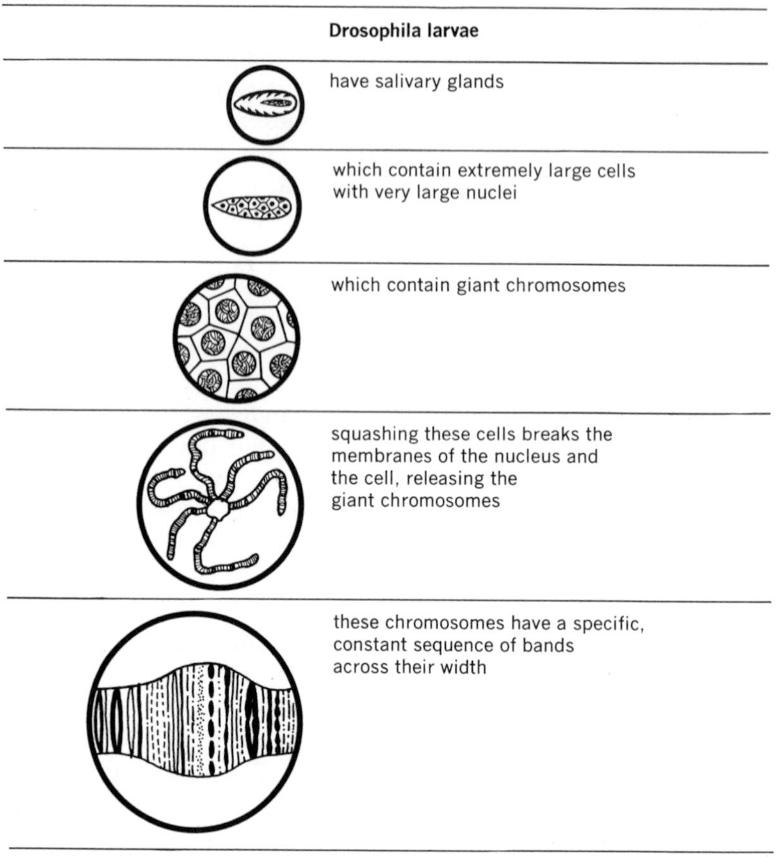

Drosophila larvae	
	have salivary glands
	which contain extremely large cells with very large nuclei
	which contain giant chromosomes
	squashing these cells breaks the membranes of the nucleus and the cell, releasing the giant chromosomes
	these chromosomes have a specific, constant sequence of bands across their width

FIGURE 6.4

Salivary-gland "chromosomes." Each chromosome consists of many separate chromatids lying side by side.

and squashed on a miscroscopic slide, the membranes of the cells and nuclei broke, and the chromosomes spread out. This technique is still one of the most dramatic in genetics. The salivary gland chromosomes spread out to their full length, which is many times longer than that of any other chromosome.

The salivary-gland chromosomes are not just longer than other chromosomes, they also have a sequence of different-shaped bands across their width. Each chromosome has a different sequence of bands that is normally constant for that chromosome. It is possible to identify very small sections of chromosomes from their sequence of bands.

The explanation of the size of the salivary-gland chromosomes is that they consist of dozens of identical chromosomes paired section by section along their length. It appears that, although the salivary-gland cells do not divide, their chromosomes divide repeatedly, until they consist of an aggregate of several hundred separate chromosomes. The bands are analogous to the chromomeres, each band consisting of a set of identical chromomeres lying side by side across all the strands. The length of the chromosomes is due to their lack of contraction or coiling.

A precise description of the salivary-gland chromosomes was completed in a few years of intensive work. The stage had been set for the exact identification of the physical locations of individual genes. This was accomplished by the use of overlapping deficiencies.

DEFICIENCIES

A series of separate mutations in Drosophila, all of which cause a notch in the wings, are characterized by deficiencies of the X chromosome. This means that Notch flies are hemizygous for the deficient section.

A hemizygote is an individual containing only one of a pair of genes. Males are usually hemizygous for sex-linked genes because these are located on the section of the X chromosome that does not have a homologous section in its partner chromosome, the Y chromosome.

The Notch deficiencies had a peculiar effect on some but not on all sex-linked genes. If a Notch female with red eyes is mated to a white-eyed male, all the female Notch progeny have white eyes, which contrasts with all the non-Notch females having red eyes. The Notch deficiency seems to have the function of transforming the white-eye gene from a recessive into a dominant gene. The same phenomenon occurred for other genes located near the white-eye locus. Notch deficiencies appeared to transform all the genes in a section of the X chromosome from recessives into dominants. The explanation is that Notch females are hemizygous for the deficient section of the X chromosome; thus any recessive genes located in that section would be fully expressed. The deficiency that causes the Notch effect must also involve the location of the white-eye gene.

Notch deficiencies that affect the expression of the white-eye gene do not necessarily involve the loss of identical sections of the X chromosome, but they all have in common the loss of one particular

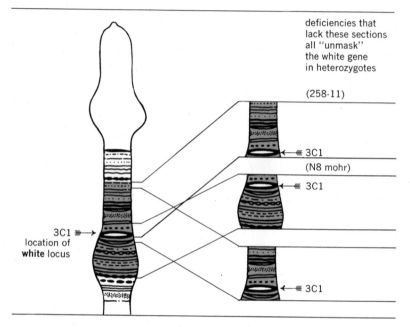

deficiencies that
lack these sections
all "unmask"
the white gene
in heterozygotes

(258-11)

3C1

(N8 mohr)

3C1

3C1 ⟫→
location of
white locus

3C1

FIGURE 6.5

Localization of genes by the method of "overlapping deficiencies." The expression of the white gene is similarly affected in individuals heterozygous for all three deficiencies, which have only one section in common— the lack .of the 3C1 band. Deficiencies that do not include this band do not affect the expression of the white gene. This shows that the white gene is located in, or in close proximity to, this particular band of the chromosome.

band—the 3C1 band. The white-eye gene must be located in or near this particular band.

The search for the physical location of the gene was now centered within the individual bands of the salivary-gland chromosomes. The simplest possibility was that each band represented the location of a separate gene. There are between five and six thousand separate bands; this would set the total number of genes at the same value, *if* each separate band were a separate gene.

The X chromosome in normal metaphase chromosomes has a volume of about 1/12th cu μ. The fully extended length of the X chromosome in salivary-gland chromosomes is about 200 μ. The width of the uncontracted chromosome calculated from these measurements is about 20 mμ. Muller and Prokofyeva have concluded that breaks to form inversions and deletions can only occur between genes, and they have calculated that the intervals between genes is about 125 mμ. If all these assumptions and approximations are correct, the maximum size of a gene is about 125 × 25 mμ. This is very small in terms of visible structures, but it is very large in terms of chemical structures. (The hemoglobin molecule is 2.8 × 0.6 mμ in size; a mμ is one millionth of a millimeter or 10 Å.)

The idea that each band of the salivary-gland chromosomes is a gene or the location of a gene was shown to be too simple an answer by the work of Muller and Prokofyeva. They found a minute deficiency of part of a band at the end of the X chromosome which included both the yellow-body and the achaete-bristle genes. The search for the gene was not finished. The individual bands of the salivary-gland chromosomes are small, but since more than one gene can be located in a single band, the size of the gene must be smaller than the estimate of Muller and Prokofyeva (125 × 25 mμ).

Problems

1. Genes *A, B, C,* and *D* have the following recombination values in a particular stock:

    $A \times C =$ 5% $B \times C =$ 22% $A \times D =$ 17%
    $B \times D =$ 10% $C \times D =$ 12%

    and these values in a different stock:

    $A \times C =$ 24% $B \times C =$ 22% $A \times B =$ 2%
    $B \times D =$ 10% $C \times D =$ 12%

    Can you explain this difference of the patterns of recombination in the two stocks? Justify your explanation.

2. Figure 6.6 shows three drawings of X chromosomes in strains of Drosophila. What differences can you detect among these?

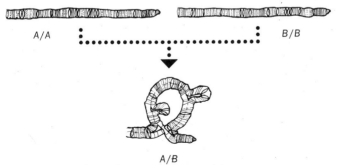

A/B

FIGURE 6.6

Salivary-gland chromosomes from three individuals. A/A is from homozygote normal, B/B is from homozygote mutant, A/B is from heterozygote between these.

Chapter 7

THE SUBSTANCE OF THE GENE

The discovery that genes are located in minute sections of chromosomes ended the first phase of genetics, but it was the beginning of the second phase: describing the structure of the gene. A biochemist, Miescher, had already made the first step of the second phase with his isolation and description of a particular chemical substance which he extracted from the nuclei of animal cells. He called this substance *nuclein;* it is now called *nucleic acid.* At the time not much importance was given to this discovery. Biochemists were isolating and identifying dozens of different chemical substances from the cells of living things, and nucleic acid was just another substance in a long list until geneticists started to identify the chemical structure of the hereditary material.

The first methods were very crude, consisting of staining cells with different dyes, and finding which colors were adsorbed by the chromosomes. The dyes used were not specific in their effects and thus the results were not very convincing. Dyes were needed that would color only specific chemical substances. Feulgen discovered just such a dye, one that colored only nucleic acid. It was not only specific to nucleic acid but affected just one type of nucleic acid. There are two kinds of nucleic acid: deoxyribonucleic acid, and ribonucleic acid, called DNA and RNA for the obvious advantage of brevity. The Feulgen method stains only DNA. Its use showed that DNA occurs as part of the chromosomes and, apart from minor exceptions, nowhere else but the chromosomes. This did not prove that DNA was the material of heredity; it was possible that the chromosomes also contained other substances, and that these rather than DNA were the material of heredity.

Body cells have twice as many chromosomes as gametic cells, and measurements have been made of the amounts of DNA in these two types of cells. The results were not unequivocal but, in general, twice as much DNA was found in body cells as was found in gametes. This was strong support for the idea that DNA is the material of heredity.

More support came from the same kind of measurements made on cells of the salivary glands of Drosophila larvae. The salivary chromosomes are longer and thicker than any other chromosomes, not because they contain more material, but because each chromosome consists of a whole set of chromosomes that lie exactly side by side, paired so closely that together they seem to be a single giant chromosome. The cells of the salivary glands start with just two sets of chromosomes but, as the cells grow larger, these chromosomes double and keep on doubling until each "chromosome," in some species, consists of over 1,000 individual chromosomes. The measurements of the amount of DNA in these special cells followed the same sequence: as cells developed, the amount of DNA doubled and kept on doubling until the amount corresponded with the cells containing over 1,000 sets of chromosomes.

This suggested that DNA is an inseparable component of the chromosomes, but none of this evidence is completely definite. The identification of the material of heredity must involve its extraction, purification, and insertion into living cells in such a way that it becomes part of their heredity. This kind of experiment seemed an impossibility in the 1920s, but a bacteriologist, Griffith, showed that crosses could be made between strains of pneumococcus in which one parent was dead.

BACTERIAL TRANSFORMATION

Strains of pneumococcus were known that differed in shape: one strain had a rough outline, another strain had a smooth outline because each cell was enclosed in a capsule. These two strains, the smooth and rough strains, bred true: cultures of smooth pneumococci divided to form smooth daughter cells, and cultures of rough pneumococci divided to form rough daughter cells.

Griffith performed an experiment in which he injected live rough and dead smooth pneumococci into mice. The mice developed pneumonia and from them he extracted cultures of bacteria containing both rough and smooth types. Somehow, the hereditary factor for having a capsule around each cell was transferred from the dead smooth bacteria into the live rough bacteria, resulting in live smooth

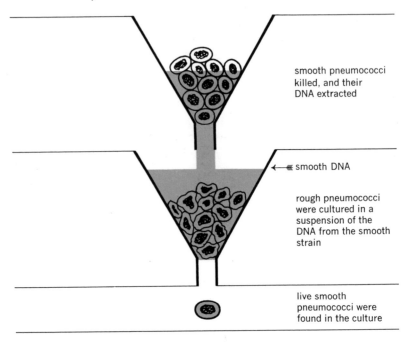

smooth pneumococci
killed, and their
DNA extracted

◀◀◀ smooth DNA

rough pneumococci
were cultured in a
suspension of the
DNA from the smooth
strain

live smooth
pneumococci were
found in the culture

FIGURE 7.1

Transformation of rough pneumococci into a smooth type by the action of an extract of DNA from a smooth strain. This phenomenon also occurs for other characteristics: drug resistance, serological specificity.

cultures. This experiment showed that it was possible for hereditary material to be transferred from dead cells into live cells.

Avery, MacLeod, and McCarty followed Griffith's lead to perform one of the really important experiments of biology. They analyzed bacteria into different chemical parts, finding that the only constituent of the dead pneumococci that could effect a modification of the heredity of living cells was nucleic acid. If they cultured rough pneumococci in a strong suspension of nucleic acid (DNA) from smooth pneumococci, some of the rough cells were transformed into the smooth type, and the transformation was constant in heredity. The DNA from the smooth cells had, in some way, been inserted into the rough cells, changing their heredity into a smooth type. Similar transformations were shown for other characters and in other bacteria, demonstrating that this phenomenon of transformation was not just a peculiarity of the smooth-capsule trait in pneumococcus.

Bacteria are small organisms visible only with a microscope. There are even smaller living things, viruses, which are too small to be seen with an ordinary microscope; they can only be seen with the electron microscope. Viruses are extremely simple forms of life that appear to be really alive only when they have entered a living cell. It appears that they are not complete living things and must use the processes of life in cells of higher organisms to effect their own reproduction. Many diseases of higher organisms are caused by viral infections, in which viruses enter human or animal cells and multiply, destroying their host cells in the process. There are also viruses that infect bacteria, which are called *bacteriophages* (phages for short). A large part of modern genetic research is concerned with bacteriophages.

BACTERIOPHAGES

Electron microscope studies show that phages have a head, tail, and a foot that attaches to the bacterial cell during the process of infection. All or part of the virus then enters the bacterial cell, where it multiplies. Eventually the host cell is killed and all particles of phage are released to exist in a free state until they become attached to other bacterial cells.

Phages consist of only nucleic acid and protein, and the infection of a bacterial cell by a phage particle can involve three possibilities:

1. The protein part of the phage may enter, being all that is needed to reproduce an entire phage particle within the host cell.
2. The nucleic acid part of the phage may be the only part that enters.
3. The complete phage may enter.

If infection occurs in the first way, the heredity of the phage is contained in the *protein* component. In the second way, the heredity of the phage is contained in the *nucleic acid* component. If the entire phage enters, it is not possible to decide whether heredity is contained in one or the other or both components of the phage.

A famous experiment by Hershey and Chase showed which of these three possibilities actually occurred. The experiment involved two artificial radioisotopes (elements that have been transmuted into a radioactive form by immersion in an atomic pile). The two elements were radioactive phosphorus (P^*) and radioactive sulfur (S^*). These two elements were chosen because each occurs in only

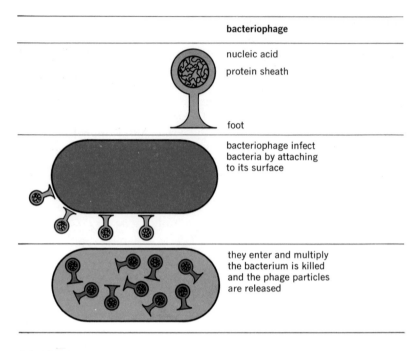

bacteriophage

nucleic acid

protein sheath

foot

bacteriophage infect bacteria by attaching to its surface

they enter and multiply the bacterium is killed and the phage particles are released

FIGURE 7.2

Bacteriophages have an extremely simple structure, and they can only reproduce within a bacterial host.

one of the two components of the phage particles: phosphorus occurs only in the nucleic acid, and sulfur occurs only in the protein. Phages can be produced that contain either radioactive P* in their nucleic acid, or radioactive S* in their protein, by culturing them on bacteria grown in the presence of one or other of these elements. Phages containing radioactive P* were allowed to infect bacteria, then tests were made to see whether the P* had entered the bacteria or had been left outside. These tests showed that there was radioactivity inside the bacteria. The P* of the virus had entered the bacteria during the process of infection—*the nucleic acid of the phage enters the bacteria.* The other part of this experiment, where phages containing S* were allowed to infect bacteria, did not give the same result. No S* was found in the bacteria, showing that *the protein part of the virus does not enter the bacteria.*

This experiment proved that only the nucleic acid part of the phage is needed for its multiplication; the hereditary information necessary to determine all features of the phage is in some way

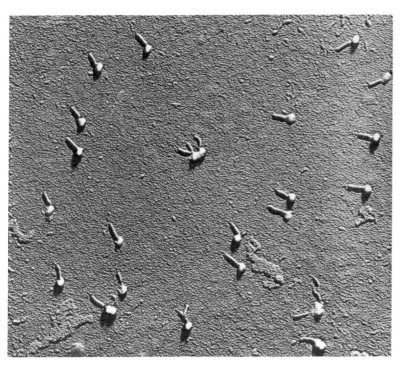

FIGURE 7.3

An electron-microscope photograph of Pseudomonas bacteriophage at a magnification of 46,000X showing the typical structure of a head and a tail. The phage particles attach themselves to the host bacterium by the tail. (Photograph courtesy of N. Baigent and J. Pangborn, University of California, Davis.)

contained in the structure of DNA. The search for the chemical basis of the gene had finally centered on just one substance: DNA. The next phase was to fully dissect this substance.

NUCLEOTIDES

By the time the geneticists and bacteriologists had shown the central importance of DNA, the biochemists had established many facts about its structure. It was made of two types of building blocks; each could occur in two forms. These building blocks consist of a molecule of sugar, a molecule of phosphoric acid, and either a purine or pyrimidine molecule, joined into one chemical unit: *a nucleotide*.

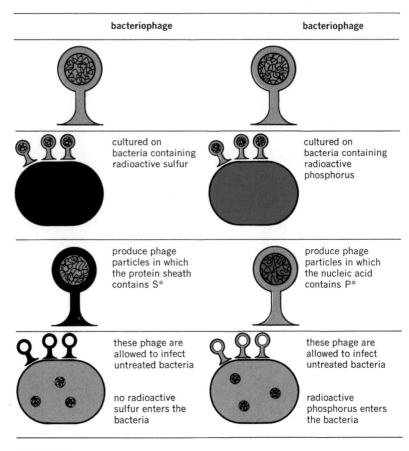

FIGURE 7.4

The Hershey-Chase experiment showed that only the nucleic acid component of bacteriophage enters the bacterial host.

All the nucleotides of DNA have the same sugar, deoxyribose, and the same phosphoric acid. They differ in whether they have a purine or a pyrimidine molecule. This chemical description of DNA did not offer much potential for its acting as a genetic blueprint; it seemed too simple to be capable of existing in all the different forms necessary for the genetic blueprint. There are thousands of different genes and, if DNA is the chemical substance of the gene, there must be thousands of uniquely different forms of DNA. This is difficult to imagine for a substance containing only two types of building blocks (purines and pyrimidines), particularly since a feature of the chemical dissection of DNA was that it contained equal amounts of purines and pyrimidines.

More detailed chemical analyses showed that there are two types of purines and two types of pyrimidines in DNA.

Purines	*Pyrimidines*
Adenine	Cytosine
Guanine	Thymine

This gives a bit more scope for DNA's existing in a variety of forms, which was strongly supported by the discovery that, although DNA contained equal amounts of purines and pyrimidines, it could vary widely in the proportion of adenine and guanine, and cytosine and thymine.

THE DOUBLE HELIX

The case for DNA was confirmed completely by the work of two scientists, Watson and Crick, at Cambridge in 1953. They studied the structure of DNA, using the method of X-ray diffraction, which is a way of finding how the chemical building blocks are linked together to form a supermolecule. If a beam of X rays is directed through a sample of nucleic acid, some of the rays are bent away from a straight line. The amount they are bent and the direction of bending can be analyzed to give a picture of the structure of DNA. Watson and Crick found that DNA had a unique structure: it did not consist of one long chain of nucleotides, but consisted of two chains coiled around each other to form a double helix. This was interesting enough, but they also showed that this double helix was held together by a purine in one chain linked to a pyrimidine in the other chain. This pairing was very specific: an adenine purine had to be linked only to a thymine pyrimidine, and a guanine purine had to be linked only to a cytosine pyrimidine.

Purine linked to *Pyrimidine*

Adenine ===== Thymine
Guanine ===== Cytosine

This complicated analysis led to a very simple and extremely important conclusion about DNA: the two long chains spiraled about each other were exact complements. If one chain consisted of a specific sequence of purines and pyrimidines, its sister chain must be exactly complementary since an adenine in one chain can only be matched

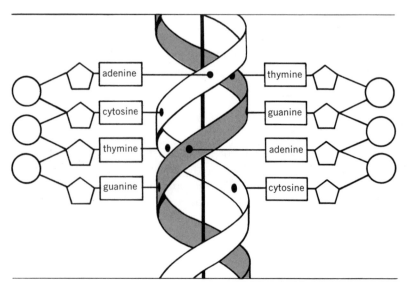

FIGURE 7.5

The basic structure of DNA is a double helix, in which the nucleotides of the two strands are linked by hydrogen bonds. There is a restriction that only adenine can pair with thymine, and only guanine can pair with cytosine. The two strands must therefore be complementary in their sequence of nucleotides.

with a thymine in the other chain, and a guanine in one chain can only be matched to a cytosine in the other chain.

Suppose that the sequence of nucleotides in one chain is

A T G C C C T T A A A G C

then the other chain must be

T A C G G G A A T T T C G

These two chains will normally be coiled around each other.

This unique chemical structure clearly is just what is required of a molecule that must be capable of duplicating its own structure exactly. A major feature of genes is that they duplicate themselves exactly, without change, over and over again. The structure of DNA can easily be imagined to fit this requirement. Suppose a double helix of DNA could be separated into its two sister strands—suppose it could be "unzipped" into its two complementary chains. Each of these two chains could then act as a template on which sister strands could be constructed, resulting in two daughter helices that would be identical.

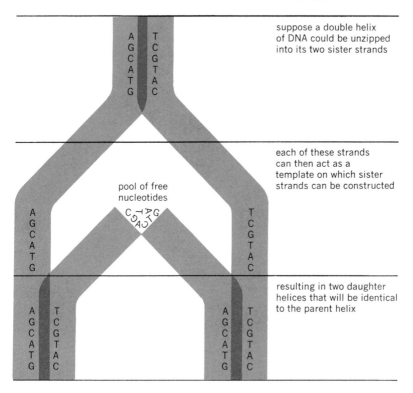

FIGURE 7.6

The two strands of DNA are complementary to each other. Separating the double helix into its separate strands, and constructing new molecules of DNA on each strand, will result in exact replication of the original molecule.

This picture of the structure and replication of DNA has an elegant simplicity. It would seem that the search for the gene begun by Mendel less than a century before had now reached its end, but one more experiment was needed—to show that the two sister strands do separate and act as templates for the formation of new strands.

MESELSON AND STAHL

Meselson and Stahl devised a way to identify individual strands of DNA by using a radioactive form of nitrogen (N^{15}) which is slightly heavier than normal nitrogen (N^{14}). Each nucleotide of DNA contains several atoms of nitrogen, and DNA containing N^{15} will be

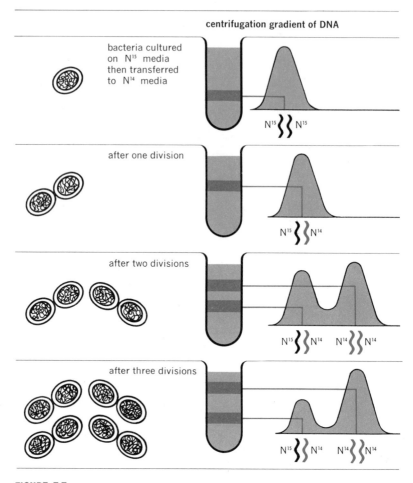

FIGURE 7.7

The Meselson-Stahl experiment supported the idea that the replication of DNA is semi-conservative, based on the separate strands of the double helix.

slightly denser than DNA containing N^{14}. This difference of density is very slight, but it is enough to be detected with special techniques. A substance that normally floats on a liquid can be made to sink into the liquid by spinning the mixture at high speed. Meselson and Stahl used this method to separate DNA containing different amounts of N^{15} and N^{14}. They put the DNA into tubes containing salt solutions and spun these at very high speed in the ultracentrifuge, with the result that the DNA containing N^{15} sank farther down the tube than the DNA containing N^{14}.

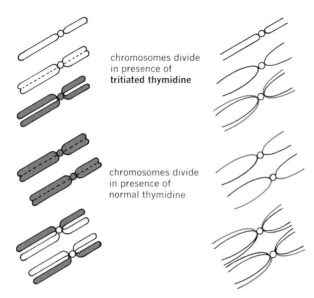

FIGURE 7.8

Taylor showed that the division of chromosomes can be understood most easily if each chromosome consists of a double strand of DNA, with each strand acting as the matrix for formation of a new chromosome.

They cultured bacteria on media containing N^{15} for a long time, until the DNA of the bacteria contained effectively only N^{15}. These bacteria were transferred to media containing only normal nitrogen (N^{14}). If the model of replication of DNA by the two strands acting as separate templates were correct, then after the first division the DNA would all be "hybrid," with one strand containing only N^{15}, and the other containing N^{14}.

The next division of these bacteria should give two different types of DNA: a hybrid type and an N^{14} type.

The proportion of hybrid DNA should halve each time the bacteria divided, and this could be traced by measuring the densities of the DNA produced with the ultracentrifuge. The results were exactly what was expected if DNA replicated in this way.

The Meselson and Stahl experiment was followed by another that was equally elegant, the Taylor experiment. This was based on the cells of beans (Vicia) that have large, easily studied chromosomes. It is possible to spread these chromosomes out on microscope slides. This was an important part of the experiment—it allowed Taylor to place photographic film on top of the chromosomes so they could "take their own photographs." Normal chromosomes will not affect

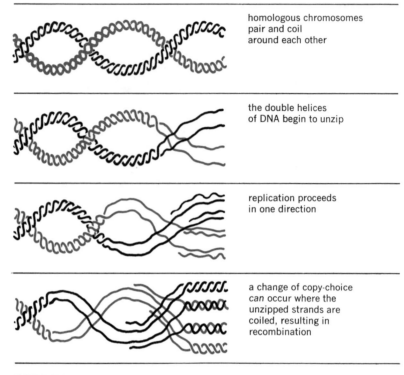

homologous chromosomes
pair and coil
around each other

the double helices
of DNA begin to unzip

replication proceeds
in one direction

a change of copy-choice
can occur where the
unzipped strands are
coiled, resulting in
recombination

FIGURE 7.9

Copy-choice model for recombination. Crossing over can be envisaged to result from the replication of the DNA helices during meiosis, with the daughter strands copying one parental strand at one point and another parental strand at another point. This model cannot explain many genetic phenomena.

photographic film, but chromosomes that contain tritium give off "soft" radiation that exposes the film. (Tritium is a radioactive form of hydrogen that gives off soft radiation.) Cells will incorporate tritium into their newly formed chromosomes if they are cultured on a medium containing "tritiated thymidine." Thymidine is used in the formation of DNA and, if that thymidine contains tritium, the new chromosomes will contain tritium.

Taylor cultured plants on media containing tritiated thymidine for just one cell division and found that all the chromosomes were radioactive. He then transferred the plants to a medium containing only normal hydrogen, in which cell division occurred. Only one or the other of the resulting chromatids was radioactive. This is exactly what is expected if the chromatids each consists of a strand of DNA, and if the formation of daughter chromosomes results from the unzipping of the double strand of DNA, with each strand acting as the matrix for a new chromosome.

The exact method of replication of DNA may not be by the "zipper" method, but there is no doubt that the search downward into the cell for the physical basis of heredity is effectively over. Heredity has, as its basis, the transmission from parents to progeny of specific sequences of nucleotides in the form of nucleic acid.

Problems

1. If the sequence of nucleotides of one strand of a DNA helix is

    A T C G C A T T A

   what is the sequence of nucleotides of the other strand?

2. DNA can be analyzed into separate nucleotides. There will be four types: adenine, guanine, cytosine, and thymine. Can you say anything about their proportions?

3. There is a type of virus in which the DNA is single stranded; it is not in the normal form of a double helix. If such DNA is analyzed into its four nucleotides, what can you say about their proportions?

Chapter 8

CHEMICAL ASSEMBLY LINES

Genes are known that cause almost every imaginable effect on the form and function of living things. Genes have been shown to be minute lengths of DNA located on the chromosomes. One of the major questions of genetics is: how do these lengths of DNA cause the wide variety of effects from which their existence is diagnosed?

Although most genes are described by some main effect, it is normal for genes to have effects on many separate parts of the individual. This phenomenon is called *pleiotropy*. At first this was thought to be a rare exception, but it is now realized that manifold effects of genes are more the rule than the exception. Most genes are pleiotropic.

PLEIOTROPY

The manifold effects of genes may be caused by a number of separate actions, or by a single action complicated by the intricacies of development into a number of apparently separate effects. A distinction can be made between *true* and *spurious* pleiotropy. In true pleiotropy, a gene has a number of different actions, each causing a distinct effect. In spurious pleiotropy, an initial gene action results in manifold effects because of the complexity of development.

The recessive dwarf gene (*dw*) in the house mouse causes a marked reduction of body size, and the occurrence of this gene is diagnosed from this effect. It has other effects: dwarf mice are sterile, with little if any development of the secondary sex characters, and these mice have underdeveloped thyroid glands. There are other effects, but these sufficiently illustrate how the manifold effects of the *dw* gene are caused by a simple initial action.

true pleiotropy   spurious pleiotropy

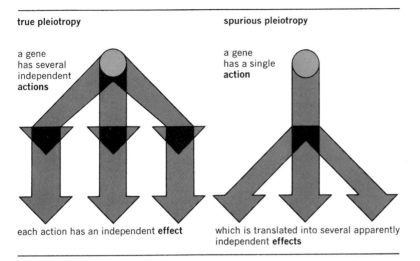

a gene has several independent actions

a gene has a single action

each action has an independent **effect**

which is translated into several apparently independent **effects**

FIGURE 8.1

Genes may cause several effects. This multiplicity of effect may be due to a similarly multiple set of initial actions (true pleiotropy), or to a single initial action that has different effects in different phases of development (spurious pleiotropy).

It is necessary to understand how the production of hormones by the endocrine glands is controlled, because this is the basis of the complexity of effects of the *dw* gene.

The pituitary gland is the master gland producing a number of separate hormones that affect the functions of the other glands. For example, the pituitary gland normally produces the gonadotrophic hormones that act on the sex glands, stimulating them to produce the sex hormones. It also produces the thyrotrophic hormone that stimulates the thyroid gland to produce thyroxin. It produces a third hormone, the growth hormone, which is necessary for normal growth. The pituitary gland's function is to stimulate the other glands to produce their individual hormones.

The pituitary glands of dwarf mice are apparently normal, but a detailed study of their internal structure showed that they lacked a particular type of cell: the eosinophil cells. The hypothesis to explain the pleiotropy of the *dw* gene was based on its having an initial action on the cellular structure of the pituitary gland that caused the gland to be defective in its production of hormones. This hypothesis was tested by transplanting pituitaries from normal mice into young

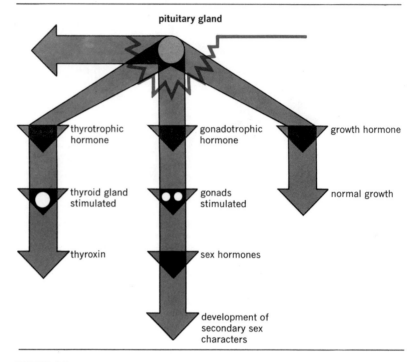

FIGURE 8.2a

The pituitary produces a set of hormones that stimulate the secondary endocrine glands. The recessive dwarf gene has a primary action on this function of the pituitary, resulting in a wide range of effects due to the lack of stimulation of the secondary endocrine glands.

dwarf mice. If these transplanted pituitaries function, they should produce the hormones necessary to stimulate the gonads and thyroids of dwarfs into normal production of the sex hormones and thyroxin. The "growth hormone" from these transplanted pituitaries should cause the young dwarf mice to grow to full size. The transplanted pituitaries produced the expected type of response and showed that the *dw* gene acts only on the pituitary gland. Its effects on the other glands are secondary consequences of loss of the normal controlling function of the pituitary gland.

An interesting extension of this picture of the effects of the *dw* gene is that the development of the secondary sex structures depends on production of sex hormones by the gonads. Secondary sex structures

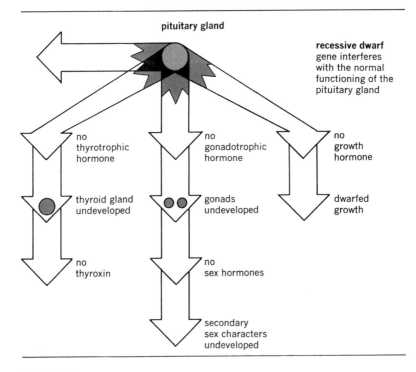

FIGURE 8.2b

do not develop in dwarf mice because the pituitary gland is defective in producing the gonadotrophic hormone. This results in the gonads not producing the sex hormones with the consequence that the secondary sex structures do not develop.

COMPETITION BETWEEN HAIR FOLLICLES

Similar investigations on many genes with manifold effects showed them to be spuriously pleiotropic. The *N* gene in sheep has an extremely complex set of effects which can be explained by the gene's having an initially simple effect on the development of hair

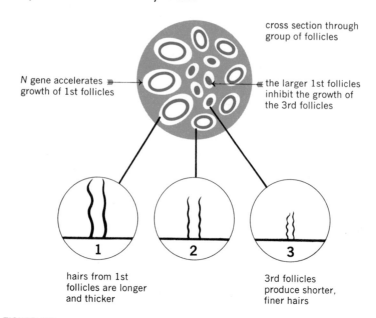

cross section through
group of follicles

N gene accelerates ⟶
growth of 1st follicles

the larger 1st follicles
inhibit the growth of
the 3rd follicles

1   2   3

hairs from 1st
follicles are longer
and thicker

3rd follicles
produce shorter,
finer hairs

FIGURE 8.3

The N gene causes an increase in the rate at which the first follicles produce their fibers, which results in an increased competitive pressure on the third follicles. These then produce their fibers at a slower rate.

follicles in the skin. The main diagnostic effect of this gene is that it causes some of the skin follicles to produce much longer, thicker hairs; these follicles extrude hairs at two to three times the normal rate. Another effect of the gene is that other skin follicles produce shorter, narrower hairs than normal; these follicles extrude hairs more slowly than normal. The N gene had opposite effects: it accelerated the growth of hair by one type of skin follicle, and slowed the growth of hair by another type of skin follicle.

The explanation of these effects of the N gene was that adjacent follicles compete with each other; large follicles inhibit the growth of smaller follicles located alongside them. Three main types of follicles develop alongside each other in discrete groups: the first follicles to develop form one side of a group, the second follicles develop to form another side of the group, and the third follicles develop in the center of the group. The N gene acts to increase the size of the first follicles; this causes them to crowd in and inhibit the growth of the third follicles which are, consequently, smaller than normal. The pleiotropy of the *N* gene is spurious; there is no need to postulate that the *N* gene has two actions, one on the first follicles and an opposite action on the third follicles.

It is possible that some genes may have manifold actions, but enough examples of genes with manifold effects have been shown to be due to initially simple actions to lead to the conclusion that genes have simple actions. The complex effects of genes are the consequence of complex development.

EYE-COLOR "HORMONES"

Normally the meal moth, Ephestia, has black eyes. A recessive gene, *a*, causes them to have red eyes. Testes from black-eyed (a^+/a^+) larvae were transplanted into red-eyed (a/a) larvae. These developed black eyes, showing that the testis from a^+/a^+ larvae produce a substance, a "hormone," that diffuses through the a/a larvae and causes them to develop the normal black color.

These experiments showed that the eye-color of these insects is not determined by the genetic constitution of the cells that form the eyes, but by the genetic constitution of the tissues that produce the *color-determining hormone.*

An opposite conclusion was drawn from the occurrence of Drosophila with bicolored eyes. These mosaic individuals consisted of two genetically different types of tissues with each type of tissue determining a different eye color.

GENETIC MOSAICS

Mosaic Drosophila are usually females in which a mistake occurred during one of the early cell divisions; as a result, one of the daughter cells received only a single X chromosome. As development proceeds it would be based on two genetically different types of cells: those having two X chromosomes, and those having one X chromosome. Varying proportions and parts of the adult fly would be derived from the two types of cells, depending on where and when the original mistake occurred. Flies have been found ranging from one side being XX and the other X •, to almost all the body being XX with just a small patch of X • tissue. Genetic mosaics that involve the loss of an X chromosome are called *gyandromorphs* because the XX

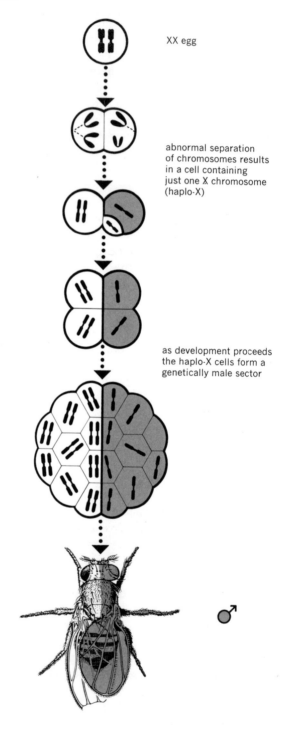

XX egg

abnormal separation
of chromosomes results
in a cell containing
just one X chromosome
(haplo-X)

as development proceeds
the haplo-X cells form a
genetically male sector

tissue develops along the female path, and the X • tissue develops along the male path. Such individuals are mixtures of male and female parts.

Suppose the original cell in which mitosis went wrong was heterozygous for the white eye-color gene: w^+/w. Then the loss of the X chromosome carrying the w^+ gene would result in a genetic mosaic in which some of the body would be formed by w^+/w cells—this part of the body would be female and genetically red-eyed. The rest of the body would be formed by $w/$• cells—this would be male and genetically white-eyed. In such mosaics, where parts of the eyes are formed of $w/$• cells, these parts are white; this shows that the effect of the white gene is *autonomous*, contrasting with the *nonautonomous* effect of the a gene in the meal moth.

(A gene's effect is autonomous if it is not affected by genetically different neighboring tissues.)

Mosaics were found for many eye-color genes in Drosophila; it appeared that Drosophila differed from Ephestia in having an autonomous determination of eye color. However, a mosaic was found involving the vermilion gene in which the determination of eye color appeared to be nonautonomous. This was confirmed by an ingenious use of the linkage of vermilion with another eye-color gene, garnet. The effect of the garnet gene is autonomous—mosaics for the garnet gene have eye sectors that are dull pink. Vermilion-garnet flies have yellowish red eyes, so mosaics for vermilion and garnet should have yellowish red sectors, if vermilion is autonomous in its effects. If vermilion is nonautonomous, these mosaics should only show the effect of the garnet gene—they would have dull pink sectors. Vermilion-garnet mosaics in fact have dull pink sectors, showing that the effect of the vermilion gene is not manifested in sectors that are $v \cdot g/$•. Some diffusible substance from the neighboring $v^+g^+/v \cdot g$ tissue must act on the $v \cdot g/$• eye cells, causing them to produce normal pigment (normal as far as the v^+ gene is concerned).

The nonautonomy of the vermilion gene was proved by taking eye buds from vermilion larvae and implanting them into the body cavities of wild type hosts. The eye buds develop reasonably well

FIGURE 8.4

Production of gyandromorphs in Drosophila, in which part of the body consists of XX cells, and part consists of X • cells. The XX tissue develops in a normal female manner, and the X • tissue develops in a male manner.

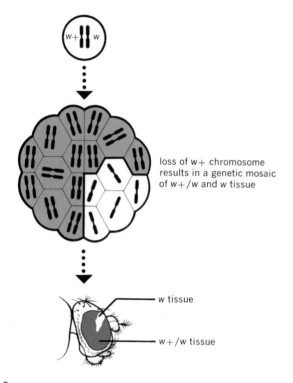

loss of w+ chromosome
results in a genetic mosaic
of w+/w and w tissue

w tissue

w+/w tissue

FIGURE 8.5

A w⁺/w individual in which the w⁺-carrying chromosome was lost early in development can have tissue that is w/ •. If this tissue involves part of the eye, that part will lack pigment.

in their transplanted location, but they develop the wild type color. The v^+ gene causes the formation of a substance, the *vermilion substance,* necessary for the development of the wild type eye color. The v gene cannot produce this vermilion substance.

Another eye-color gene, cinnabar, was also shown to be nonautonomous. Transplantation of cinnabar eye buds into wild type hosts gave the same results as for vermilion; the cinnabar eye buds developed the wild type eye color. The cn^+ gene causes the formation of a substance, the *cinnabar substance,* necessary for the development of the wild type eye color.

When these results were obtained a further problem was apparent: are the vermilion and cinnabar substances different, or are they one and the same substance? This question was answered by transplant-

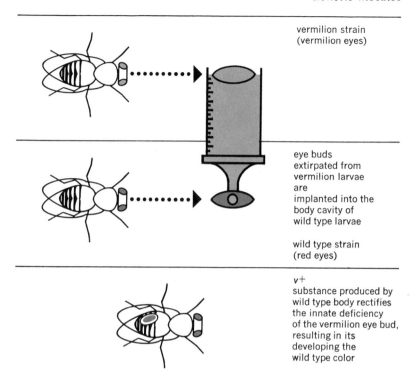

vermilion strain
(vermilion eyes)

eye buds
extirpated from
vermilion larvae
are
implanted into the
body cavity of
wild type larvae

wild type strain
(red eyes)

$v+$
substance produced by
wild type body rectifies
the innate deficiency
of the vermilion eye bud,
resulting in its
developing the
wild type color

FIGURE 8.6

An eye bud from a "vermilion" larvae implanted into a wild type larvae develops the wild type color. The vermilion color is caused by the absence of a substance (the v^+ substance) that is present in wild type individuals.

ing eye buds from vermilion larvae into cinnabar hosts, and vice versa.

Eye buds from *vermilion* larvae transplanted into *cinnabar* hosts develop *wild type* color.

A vermilion eye bud develops the full wild type eye color when it has been transplanted into a cinnabar host. This shows that the cinnabar host produces the vermilion substance that acts on the vermilion eye bud and causes it to develop the wild type pigment. The experiment shows that the cinnabar substance is not the same as the vermilion substance, and that the cinnabar gene does not affect the vermilion substance—cinnabar flies produce the vermilion substance.

The reciprocal experiment gave quite different results.

Eye buds from *cinnabar* larvae transplanted into *vermilion* hosts develop *cinnabar* color.

The experiment shows that the vermilion hosts do not produce the cinnabar substance. The simplest view of these complicated experiments is that two substances are needed for development of the wild type eye color. The cinnabar gene cannot produce one of the substances, the cinnabar substance, but it can produce the other, the vermilion substance. The vermilion gene cannot produce either substance. This makes sense if it is considered that the development of pigment proceeds along a genetic assembly line, with each gene performing some specific change of the pigment substance. This gives a new concept of genes, in which each gene acts as a specific chemical engineer, taking a chemical substance and changing it into some new substance.

GENETIC ASSEMBLY LINES

The substances involved in the effects of the vermilion and cinnabar genes have been identified. The chemical assembly line begins with a substance, *tryptophan*. This is changed into another substance, *kynurenine*, by the v^+ gene. This is then changed into *hydroxy-kynurenine* by the cn^+ gene. The v and cn genes cannot accomplish these changes.

Genes act by causing a specific chemical change—this is a pleasantly simple view of how genes act. The basis of every genetic difference is some simple change of one substance into another.

FIGURE 8.7

The nutritional requirements of mutant strains of Neurospora can be determined by culturing the strain on a series of test media and specific media. The majority of mutants will grow successfully with the addition of a single substance to the minimal media. Very few mutants have a multiple requirement, though many will grow successfully with addition of one or the other of several substances.

| wild type neurospora grows well on **minimal media** (inorganic salts, sugar, biotin) | nutritional mutants do not survive on minimal media | the mutant strains will grow well on **complete media** (wide range of vitamins, amino acids, etc.) |

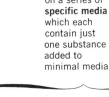

a particular mutant strain is cultured on a series of **test media** which each contain a family of substances added to minimal media

amino acids   vitamins

etc.

the strain is then cultured on a series of **specific media** which each contain just one substance added to minimal media

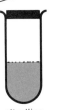    

citrulline   ornithine   arginine   serine   tryptophan

the mutant   etc.
strain cannot
synthesize
arginine

a substance E, which is necessary for growth, is synthesised
from a substance A, through a series of intermediates: B, C, D.

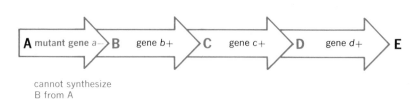

cannot synthesize
B from A

if B is added to the media, then the synthesis of E occurs

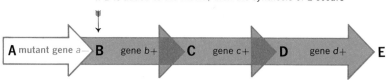

if C is added to the media,
then the synthesis of E occurs

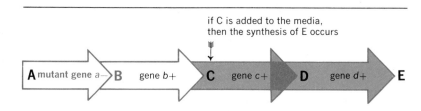

if D is added, then the
synthesis of E occurs

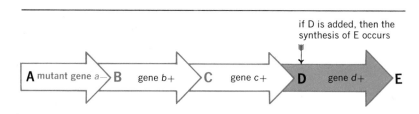

This concept was not new; in 1909, a physician, Garrod, put forward this view of how genes act. But, like Mendel and Miescher, he was ahead of his time, and the importance of this concept of gene action was not fully realized for nearly thirty years.

As attention became focused on the chemistry of gene action, geneticists investigated new organisms that were better suited than Drosophila for these new types of experiments. The first of these new organisms was Neurospora, a mold that could be grown in test tubes on a very simple medium containing only sugar, some inorganic salts, and a vitamin (biotin). This is called the *minimal* medium; Neurospora can form the whole range of substances necessary for its existence from these simple ingredients. Mutant strains were found that could not survive on the minimal medium; they had to be cultured on a *complete* medium rich in a variety of vitamins, amino acids, etc.

Genetically inadequate strains of Neurospora could not grow on the minimal medium because they could not synthesize some substance or substances needed for their growth. The specific inadequacy of each mutant was identified by culturing the strain on a series of *test* media. Each of these contained a family of substances added to the minimal medium. One contained just amino acids, another contained just vitamins, and so on. A mutant strain cultured on these test media would grow on only one of them, showing the type of substance needed. The specific need of the strain could then be identified by growing the strain on another set of *specific* media. Each of these media contained just one substance added to the minimal medium. The growth of the strain in these cultures then identified the specific inadequacy of the mutant strain. The great majority of the mutant strains needed only the addition of a single substance to the minimal medium for complete growth; very few needed the addition of more than one substance.

FIGURE 8.8

Suppose a substance E is synthesized from a substance A and that the genes a, b, c, and d each modify a part of A toward E; then, if the first gene mutates, the whole assembly line will come to a halt. The effect of this mutation will be lethal, unless the substances B or C or D or E are added. Any one will do because genes b, c. or d are normal, and they can act to keep the assembly line (biosynthesis) going.

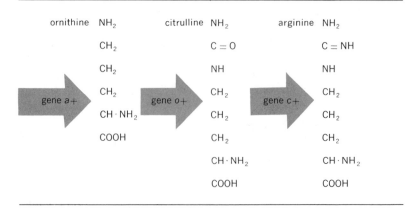

FIGURE 8.9

The synthesis of arginine proceeds from ornithine via citrulline, with a specific locus mediating each step.

A number of the strains could develop fully on media that had been supplemented with one or another of a whole series of substances; this is what is expected if the synthesis of substances by Neurospora is on the assembly-line principle.

A much-quoted example of this kind of biochemical assembly line is the synthesis of the amino acid, arginine, in Neurospora. Three genetically different strains were found that could all grow if they were cultured on media containing arginine. They were all arginine-requiring. Two of the strains could also grow on media containing another amino acid, citrulline, and one could grow on a medium containing a third amino acid, ornithine.

These results make sense if three normal genes (o^+, c^+, and a^+) are concerned in the synthesis of arginine, which is accomplished by first synthesizing ornithine (gene o^+ does this). Ornithine is then transformed into citrulline by gene c^+, and citrulline is transformed into arginine by gene a^+.

A strain in which a^+ has mutated to an inadequate form will not be able to synthesize arginine from citrulline. Adding ornithine or citrulline to this strain will have no effect because it is not deficient except at the final stage of the assembly line. Only the addition of arginine will allow it to grow.

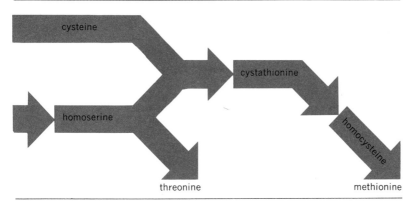

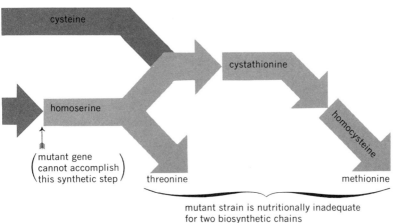

FIGURE 8.10

The substance homoserine is a precursor to the synthesis of both cysta-thionine and threonine. A mutation that results in a block of the synthesis of homoserine will result in both the cystathionine and threonine pathways being blocked. Such mutant strains will have a double nutritional need in the absence of homoserine.

In a strain in which c^+ has mutated to an inadequate form, the assembly line has been interrupted at the transformation of ornithine into citrulline. Adding ornithine will not help, but the addition of either citrulline *or* arginine will result in full growth.

These researches led to the hypothesis that each gene was concerned in the synthesis of a specific single substance. However, several examples were discovered where the mutation of a single gene caused a block in several apparently independent biosyntheses. These seemed to show that the mutation of one gene resulted in the loss of ability to synthesize more than a single specific substance. A mutant strain of Neurospora was found that could only survive if both threonine and methionine were added to the minimal medium. The mutant gene seemed to have blocked two different biosyntheses: one leading to methionine, the other leading to threonine. A more detailed analysis of this strain showed that it could survive with the addition of just one substance: homoserine. This substance is involved in the biosynthesis of both methionine and threonine, so the mutant strain's inability to produce homeserine results in the blockage of two apparently independent biosyntheses.

The identification of genes that all affect the same biosynthetic assembly line allows scientists to determine the sequence of changes involved in the synthesis of the final substance. It became evident as this work proceeded that the genes affecting different steps of a biosynthesis were genetically independent—they were not alleles. This led to the hypothesis that each gene acts to cause just one specific substance to change into another. Growth could be regarded as a process of chemical cookery, with each gene acting as a chef directing one particular aspect of the cooking. The next question is: how do they effect this? How do genes control specific biosynthetic steps?

Problems

1. The mutation from o^+ to o in Neurospora results in a nutritional requirement that can be satisfied by supplements of ornithine, citrulline, or arginine. The o gene has a series of effects; does this show the gene to be truly pleiotropic or spuriously pleiotropic?

2. A number of independent mutant strains of Neurospora will not grow on minimal media, but they will grow on test media containing supplements of substances A, B, C, D, E, or F as shown in the following matrix. (A plus sign shows that growth occurred, a minus sign shows that no growth occurred.) What can be deduced about the biosynthesis of these substances from these data?

		Supplement				
		A	B	C	D	E	F
	1	+	+	−	−	−	+
	2	−	+	−	−	−	+
Mutant strain	3	+	+	+	−	+	+
	4	+	+	+	+	+	+
	5	+	+	−	−	+	+
	6	−	+	−	−	−	−

Chapter 9

ENZYMES, PROTEINS, AND GENES

Biochemists have found that living things control the chemical processes of living by producing substances called *enzymes*. Each specific type of enzyme controls a particular chemical reaction. This can be illustrated from the processes of digestion. The food of most animals consists of large chemical substances—proteins, fats, and carbohydrates—which must be reduced to smaller units before they can be used. Proteins consist of long chains of amino acids, and two enzymes of digestion, pepsin and trypsin, act to reduce the long chains into shorter chains, and finally into individual amino acids. Carbohydrates consist of groups of sugar molecules, and an enzyme, maltase, acts to cut carbohydrates down into complex sugars which are then broken down into simple sugars by other enzymes. Many enzymes have been isolated and purified, and chemical analyses have shown them to be proteins.

Enzymes are not restricted to a destructive role. Many enzymes are known that catalyze the construction of complex substances from simple ones. The amino acid, tryptophan, is formed by the junction of two simpler substances, indole and serine. An enzyme, tryptophan synthetase, catalyzes this reaction.

Genes have been shown to cause their effects by controlling specific chemical reactions; enzymes catalyze specific chemical reactions. Beadle put these two facts together into one hypothesis: the one gene—one enzyme hypothesis. This hypothesis was stated, in its simplest form, as: each gene, and only that gene, controls the production of a single specific enzyme.

ONE GENE–ONE ENZYME

Metabolism must involve the destruction and excretion of unwanted substances. If this process does not function correctly, malfunction may occur because waste products accumulate. A substance, homogentisic acid, is a waste product that is normally

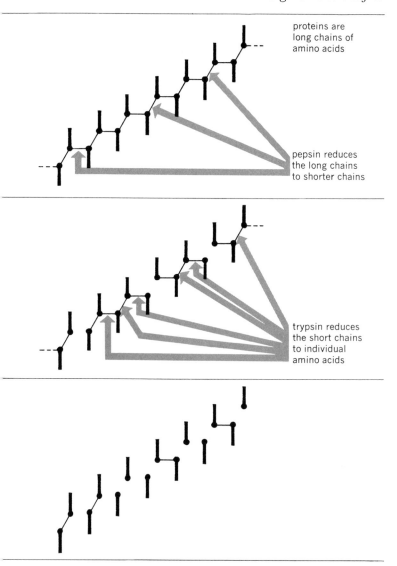

proteins are
long chains of
amino acids

pepsin reduces
the long chains
to shorter chains

trypsin reduces
the short chains
to individual
amino acids

FIGURE 9.1

The digestion of protein involves different enzymes that break various chemical links, eventually reducing the proteins to their individual constituents—amino acids.

broken down into maleylacetoacetic acid by an enzyme, homogen- isic acid oxidase. A hereditary disease of humans, *alcaptonuria*, is caused by the inheritance of a mutant gene that cannot accomplish this particular reaction. This biochemical inadequacy results in the

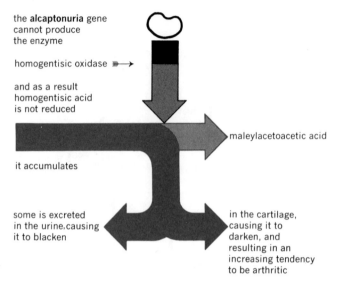

the **alcaptonuria** gene cannot produce the enzyme

homogentisic oxidase ➤➤→

and as a result homogentisic acid is not reduced

maleylacetoacetic acid

it accumulates

some is excreted in the urine,causing it to blacken

in the cartilage, causing it to darken, and resulting in an increasing tendency to be arthritic

FIGURE 9.2

The human disease, alcaptonuria, is caused by a recessive gene that is incapable of producing an enzyme, homogentisic oxidase.

body's containing an excess of homogentisic acid; some of this is excreted in the urine which consequently blackens on exposure to the air. The rest accumulates in cartilage, causing it also to darken, and resulting in an increased tendency to become arthritic. Studies of the enzymatic content of alcaptonurics showed that these were quite normal except for the absence of one particular enzyme, *homogentisic oxidase*. The obvious deduction from these facts is that the mutant gene cannot produce this particular enzyme, and lack of this enzyme causes the biochemical inadequacy.

Many such examples have been discovered, and the one gene—one enzyme hypothesis can be considered to have been given a firm foundation in fact. This did not mean that the hypothesis had been proved; it only meant that the hypothesis could be accepted as a plausible theory.

Exceptions were discovered in which more than one gene was found to be concerned with the occurrence of a particular enzyme. Mutation at three separate genetic loci was shown to result in modification of the effectiveness of the tyrosinase enzyme in Neurospora. These three genes, *T*, *ty*-1, and *ty*-2, seemed to be jointly concerned in the production of the one enzyme. This appeared to disprove the

one gene—one enzyme hypothesis, but som.   ·searches
showed that it is only the *T* gene that can pr.   enzyme; *ty*-1
and *ty*-2 have the function of determining wl.   .r the *T* gene acts
to produce the enzyme. In effect, only one gene determines the
structure of tyrosinase. The other two genes act as controllers of
whether the *T* gene shall be active or quiescent.

The genetic control of the production of the enzyme, tryptophan
synthetase, has been studied very intensively in both Neurospora
and bacteria. The results of these researches have shown how mutation of a gene can affect its production of a specific enzyme.

TRYPTOPHAN SYNTHETASE

Many separate mutations have been found in Neurospora that cause
the strains carrying them to need tryptophan. These strains can only
be kept alive if tryptophan is added to their cultural media. Genetic
analyses showed that all these mutant genes were alleles, demonstrating that the synthesis of tryptophan is controlled by only one
gene.

Extracts of normal strains were found to have the ability to synthesize tryptophan. These extracts were concentrated and purified,
resulting in a preparation that had a very high tryptophan-
synthesizing ability. The substance in these extracts was protein,
showing that normal Neurospora produces a protein that can catalyze
the synthesis of tryptophan. This enzyme was called *tryptophan
synthetase* (T'ase for short). No trace of T'ase could be found in
extracts from mutant strains, which could mean that these could
not form T'ase, but it could also mean that they produce an inactive
form of T'ase.

Some method was needed to identify the presence of T'ase that
did not involve its role in the synthesis of tryptophan. This was
accomplished by serological methods. If a particular protein is
injected into a rabbit, the rabbit will produce antibodies in its blood.
These antibodies react specifically with the protein and only with
that protein or extremely similar proteins. This phenomenon can
be used to identify a particular protein. First, if the protein is
injected into a test animal, it will cause the formation of specific
antibodies. If a mixture of proteins is then tested against serum
containing the antibodies, a reaction will occur if the mixture contains the original protein. The antibodies, in some way, lock onto
the protein, inactivating it.

The injection of an extract of T'ase from normal Neurospora into a rabbit will cause it to form T'ase antibodies. If serum containing these antibodies is mixed with an extract of T'ase, it loses its ability to synthesize tryptophan because the T'ase antibodies in the serum lock onto the T'ase, inactivating it. This method has been used to determine whether mutant strains contain inactive forms of T'ase.

Serum containing T'ase antibodies will normally inactivate an extract of T'ase, but if the serum is first mixed with an extract from a mutant strain, it may lose the ability to inactivate T'ase. This will happen if the mutant extract contains an inactive form of the T'ase enzyme. Most of the mutant extracts react with the T'ase antibodies, showing that although the mutant strains do not produce T'ase, they do produce a protein closely similar to it. Some mutant strains do not react with T'ase antibodies, showing that their Tryptophan gene is either completely inactive or produces a protein that is not similar enough to T'ase to react with T'ase antibodies.

These complicated results lead to an important modification of the one gene—one enzyme hypothesis which can be restated as one gene—one protein. Mutation of a gene can result in a change of the type of protein it produces. The next step in the search toward an understanding of how genes act was the description of exactly how mutation affects the type of protein produced by a gene. The main advance came from the study of the structure of hemoglobin in humans.

SICKLE-CELL ANEMIA

Many U.S. Negro families have pedigrees of an inherited hemolytic anemia, a condition that usually results in death in early childhood. It is called *sickle-cell* anemia because if blood from these anemics is kept at a low oxygen level, a peculiar defect of the red blood cells becomes apparent. They distort from a normal regularity of roundness into collapsed shapes reminiscent of a sickle. Not all individuals with the sickle-cell character develop the anemia. It was shown that individuals who only develop the sickle-cell trait are heterozygous for a gene (Hb^s) that also causes the hemolytic anemia in homozygotes (Hb^s/Hb^s).

The Hb^s gene primarily affects the hemoglobin in the red blood cells. Pauling and his research team showed that the Hb^s gene affects the structure of the hemoglobin. They took blood from the

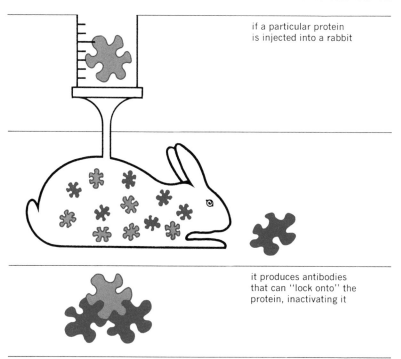

if a particular protein
is injected into a rabbit

it produces antibodies
that can "lock onto" the
protein, inactivating it

FIGURE 9.3

Rabbits will produce specific antibodies to foreign proteins that have been injected into their blood stream. Such antibodies can be used to demonstrate the presence of the original protein because the protein and the antibody form a complex, in which the protein is inactive. If the protein is an enzyme, it loses its enzymatic feature when combined with an antibody.

three genotypes, Hb^A/Hb^A, Hb^A/Hb^S, and Hb^S/Hb^S, and extracted the hemoglobin from each type. Each of these extracts of hemoglobin was tested for the speed at which it moved during electrophoresis. The hemoglobin from normal people (Hb^A/Hb^A) moved at one range of speeds, whereas that from sickle-cell anemics (Hb^S/Hb^S) moved at a different range of speeds. The hemoglobin from heterozygotes (Hb^A/Hb^S) was a mixture: some of it moved at the speeds characteristic of normals, and some moved at the speeds characteristic of sickle-cell anemics. This is what is expected if each of the two Hb genes acts independently, one producing A type hemoglobin, the other producing S type.

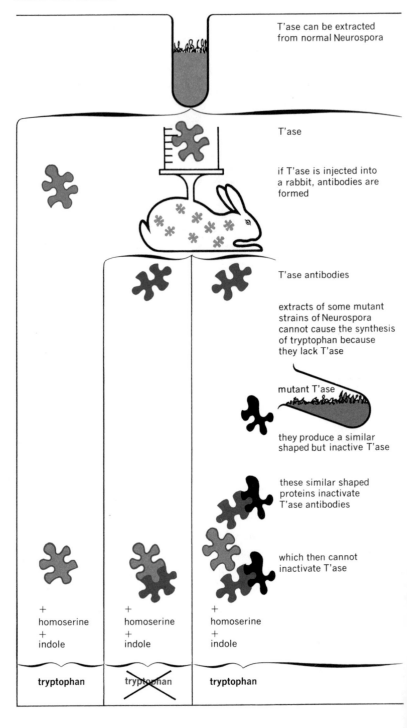

T'ase can be extracted from normal Neurospora

T'ase

if T'ase is injected into a rabbit, antibodies are formed

T'ase antibodies

extracts of some mutant strains of Neurospora cannot cause the synthesis of tryptophan because they lack T'ase

mutant T'ase

they produce a similar shaped but inactive T'ase

these similar shaped proteins inactivate T'ase antibodies

which then cannot inactivate T'ase

+
homoserine
+
indole

+
homoserine
+
indole

+
homoserine
+
indole

tryptophan

tryptophan

tryptophan

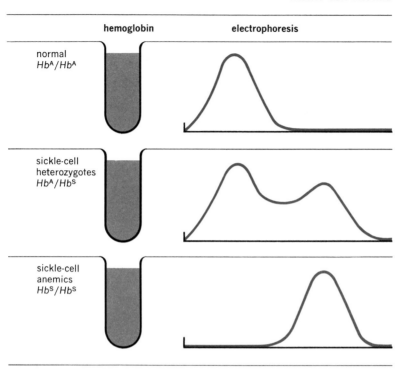

hemoglobin   **electrophoresis**

normal
*Hb*ᴬ/*Hb*ᴬ

sickle-cell
heterozygotes
*Hb*ᴬ/*Hb*ˢ

sickle-cell
anemics
*Hb*ˢ/*Hb*ˢ

FIGURE 9.5

The hemoglobins produced by normal, sickle-cell heterozygotes and sickle-cell anemics differ in their rates of movement in an electrophoretic field.

The speed at which a substance moves in an electrophoretic field depends on its electrical charge. Since the A and S hemoglobins move at different speeds, it follows that they must differ in their electrical charge. This takes us a bit closer to understanding how genes act. The change from the *Hb*ᴬ to the *Hb*ˢ gene causes a change

FIGURE 9.4

Tryptophan synthetase (T'ase) is an enzyme that catalyzes the synthesis of Tryptophan from homoserine and indole. Antibodies to T'ase will inactivate it so that it cannot catalyze the synthesis. If antibodies to T'ase are first treated with extracts from a mutant strain that cannot produce T'ase, the antibodies lose their ability to inactivate T'ase. This shows that the mutant strains produce a protein very similar to T'ase.

of the electrical structure of the protein produced by this locus. There are two ways in which this could happen. The chain of amino acids that constitutes the molecules of hemoglobin could be folded in a different way to mask or expose electrically charged groups, *or* the actual chain of amino acids may be changed. The Hb^A gene could form a protein with one sequence of amino acids, with the Hb^S gene forming a protein with a different sequence.

Distinguishing between these two possibilities involved some outstanding biochemical work by Ingram, who analyzed the sequence of amino acids in the A and S hemoglobins, using the "fingerprinting" technique.

CHEMICAL FINGERPRINTS

The chemical fingerprint technique combines electrophoresis with paper chromatography. If a mixture of amino acids is soaked up in a corner of a sheet of filter paper, and a solvent (some organic liquid) is allowed to diffuse through the spot down one side of the paper, then the different substances will move in the direction of absorption of the solvent. This can result in a separation along the length of the sheet of paper. The next step is to take the paper out and place it in an electrophoretic field at right angles. This results in the different substances being spread in a pattern across the sheet of paper, producing a chemical fingerprint with each particular type of substance located in a different place. The technique was applied to the A and S hemoglobins, which were first chemically broken into a number of fragments. The fingerprints were remarkably similar except in one fragment. Ingram extracted and analyzed this particular fragment into its amino acids, and found that hemoglobin A differed from hemoglobin S in only one amino acid.

Hemoglobin A . . . .   Pro   Glu   Glu   Lys

Hemoglobin S . . . .   Pro   Val   Glu   Lys

Pro = Proline

Glu = Glutamine

Val = Valine

Lys = Lysine

They differed in having either a glutamic acid or valine at one specific location. There were no other differences. The difference

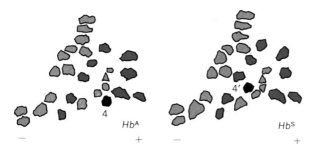

FIGURE 9.6

Chemical fingerprints.

between A and S hemoglobins, one having glutamic acid and the other having valine at a particular position in the amino acid chain, can explain the difference of the electrical charge: glutamic acid has a negative charge, whereas valine is electrically neutral.

Our picture of the action of genes now reduces to the production of specific sequences of amino acids joined to form particular proteins. The next question is how does the DNA of a gene achieve this?

QUICK QUIZ *Chapters 5 through 9*

1. *Drosophila melanogaster* have eight chromosomes in each body cell. How many linkage groups will there be?
   (*a*) 1
   (*b*) 2
   (*c*) 8
   (*d*) 4
   (*e*) 3

2. A white-eyed XXY female is mated to a red-eyed XY male. The female progeny will be:
   (*a*) all red-eyed.
   (*b*) all white-eyed.
   (*c*) mainly red-eyed, with a few white-eyed.

3. *Poly* means "many"; *tene* means "thread." Salivary-gland chromosomes are termed *polytene* because:
   (*a*) each salivary-gland cell has more than eight chromosomes.
   (*b*) salivary-gland chromosomes consist of many homologous chromosomes lying side by side.
   (*c*) salivary-gland chromosomes have many bands of dark staining material.

4. The transformation of rough pneumococci by DNA extracted from smooth pneumococci was shown by:
   (*a*) Mendel.
   (*b*) Morgan.
   (*c*) Griffith.
   (*d*) Avery, MacLeod, and McCarty.

5. DNA consists of chains of nucleotides. Nucleotides are:
   (*a*) purines.
   (*b*) pyrimidines.
   (*c*) complex sugars.
   (*d*) molecules of sugar, phosphoric acid, and either a purine or pyrimidine.

6. DNA normally contains equal amounts of purines and pyrimidines. If A, G, C, T are the four nucleotides of DNA, then:

(*a*) A + G = C + T

(*b*) A + C = G + T

(*c*) A + T = G + C

(*d*) All DNAs are different and nothing can be said about their constitution.

7. DNA consists of two complementary chains of nucleotides. If the sequence of nucleotides in one chain is A G C T T C G A, then the sequence in the other chain is:

(*a*) T A G C A T A T

(*b*) G A T C C T A G

(*c*) T C G A A G C T

8. In Neurospora the synthesis of arginine proceeds from ornithine to citrulline to arginine. A mutant gene blocks the synthesis of citrulline. Strains with this mutant can grow only if the medium contains:

(*a*) ornithine.

(*b*) arginine and citrulline.

(*c*) citrulline and ornithine.

(*d*) arginine or citrulline.

9. Tryptophan synthetase is:

(*a*) artificially synthesized tryptophan.

(*b*) a protein.

(*c*) an enzyme.

(*d*) a protein that acts as a catalyst of the synthesis of tryptophan.

10. Sickle-cell anemia has this name because:

(*a*) the red blood cells of sickle-cell anemics are sickle-shaped.

(*b*) the red blood cells of sickle-cell heterozygotes are sickle-shaped.

(*c*) the red blood cells of heterozygotes become distorted into collapsed shapes when the oxygen tension is low.

Chapter 10

RIBONUCLEIC ACID, RIBOSOMES, AND PROTEINS

Genes cause specific sequences of amino acids to be joined together to form particular proteins. The next question that needed to be answered was whether the genes control protein synthesis directly, or whether a chain of intermediary steps is involved. There is ample evidence that synthesis of proteins occurs in the cytoplasm. This shows that there must be intermediate steps between the synthesis of proteins in the cytoplasm and the genes located in the nucleus. Some system of messengers must operate between the genes and the cytoplasm. These messengers must be able to copy the information contained in the genes, move out from the nucleus into the cytoplasm, then use their contained information to effect the synthesis of specific proteins.

Caspersson, in 1940, suggested that the messengers were molecules of ribonucleic acid (RNA). This was a very nice idea; it elevated RNA from some unknown role to being a major partner with DNA. There was evidence that RNA played a major role in the synthesis of proteins—cells that are actively synthesizing protein are rich in RNA—but this could not be taken as conclusive. Cells without nuclei provide stronger support for the idea that RNA effects the synthesis of proteins. The techniques of micro-surgery on cells have advanced to a level where it is possible to remove nuclei from cells. These enucleated cells usually survive for some time, and they often synthesize proteins, but they lose this ability if they are treated with the enzyme *ribonuclease*. This enzyme has a specific destructive effect on RNA, and the experiment shows that, although the synthesis of proteins can go on in the absence of a nucleus, it cannot proceed in the absence of RNA.

RNA VIRUSES

Some viruses do not contain any DNA. They consist solely of RNA inside a coat of protein, yet they effect their reproduction

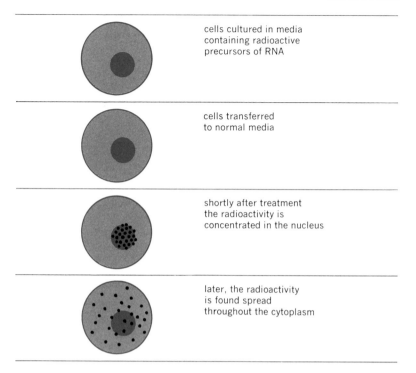

cells cultured in media
containing radioactive
precursors of RNA

cells transferred
to normal media

shortly after treatment
the radioactivity is
concentrated in the nucleus

later, the radioactivity
is found spread
throughout the cytoplasm

FIGURE 10.1

Bacteria cultured on media containing radioactive precursors of RNA will incorporate these into any RNA that they synthesize. Such RNA will be radioactive; in these experiments at first only the nuclear RNA is radioactive. Later both the nuclear and the cytoplasmic RNA is radioactive. The primary RNA is synthesized first, in the nucleus, then moves into the cytoplasm.

inside a host cell. The virus responsible for the tobacco mosaic disease is of this type, and some very important experiments by Fraenkel-Conrat showed that an extract of the RNA of this virus could produce an infection. Somehow the RNA entered the tobacco cells and there multiplied into a number of complete virus particles consisting of both RNA and protein. The RNA contained all the genetic information necessary for the formation of both the RNA and the protein that constitute the complete TMV particles.

These experiments and many others conclusively demonstrated that RNA is concerned in the synthesis of proteins, but some experimental way was needed to demonstrate that RNA formed by the DNA of the nucleus moves out into the cytoplasm.

RIBOSOMES

The RNA of a cell is not a homogenous quantity. There is a soluble form called *soluble* RNA. Another form of RNA occurs bound to very small granules called ribosomes; this is called *ribosomal* RNA. There is a third type of RNA bound to even smaller fragments. This third type has not been named, but it will make our discussion clearer if we give it a name: *primary* RNA.

A very neat series of experiments were performed; these showed that the main synthesis of RNA occurs in the nucleus, and it is primary RNA that is synthesized. This primary RNA then moves out from the nucleus and becomes incorporated into the ribosomes. The main experiment involved culturing bacteria in media containing radioactive precursors of RNA, then extracting the radioactive RNA from these bacteria and finding whether it was soluble RNA, ribosomal RNA, or primary RNA. The experiment involved close timing. If the bacteria were cultured in the radioactive medium for two minutes, most of the radioactive precursor was incorporated into the primary RNA. A longer exposure of ten minutes resulted in the radioactive precursor's being incorporated into both the primary and the ribosomal RNA. The simplest explanation of these results, and the one most generally accepted, is that RNA is synthesized as primary RNA which then becomes incorporated in the ribosomes. The problem now becomes one of locating the site of synthesis of the primary RNA.

SALIVARY CHROMOSOME PUFFS

The salivary-gland chromosomes of Drosophila have a characteristic pattern of crossbands that is normally constant for any species. This description is essentially true, but the shape of particular bands changes during development, presumably due to differences in the activity of the gene or genes in the particular bands. However, the sequence of bands does not change; the differences that occur are of the shape of bands that may be compact at one stage of development, and diffuse (puffed) at another stage. It is thought that these differences during development reflect differences of activity. The compact bands are thought to be less active than the diffuse (puffed) bands.

The general idea we are examining is that the DNA of the genes synthesizes RNA, which moves out into the cytoplasm where it is central in the formation of proteins. This general idea was related to the "puffing" of the salivary chromosomes. If puffing does represent the activity of a particular gene, and if genetic activity involves the synthesis of RNA, then the puffed bands of salivary chromosomes should represent regions of active synthesis of RNA. The truth of these suppositions was demonstrated by using *tritiated uridine* and *actinomycin D*. Uridine is a component of RNA, and actinomycin D is an antibiotic that inhibits the synthesis of RNA.

Tritiated uridine is uridine in which the hydrogen atoms have been replaced by the radioactive isotope of hydrogen, tritium. This form of uridine is radioactive, and its presence in any particular part of a cell can be detected because the radioactivity will cause exposed grains on a thin photographic film laid across the cell. This technique can be used to locate where uridine is being incorporated into RNA. Larvae are first cultured on a medium containing tritiated uridine, then the salivary-gland cells are dissected out and flattened. A photographic film is laid across these flattened cells. The locations of active incorporation of uridine into RNA will be marked by the parts of the film where there are heavy clusters of exposed grains. The actual experiment showed such clusters around the puffed bands. This appeared to be conclusive proof that the puffed bands synthesize RNA, and a further experiment confirmed this. Larvae were cultured on media containing both tritiated uridine *and* actinomycin D. No clusters of exposed grains were found around the puffed bands because the actinomycin had inhibited the synthesis of RNA.

This experiment provided the last link relating DNA to RNA. The DNA of the gene *somehow* causes the synthesis of RNA, which *somehow* moves out into the cytoplasm, where it *somehow* becomes bonded to the ribosomes, where it *somehow* directs the synthesis of specific proteins. An elegant series of experiments had added a new concept to the theories of genetics—but, as usual, they had also raised a new crop of questions.

Another type of evidence came from the infection of bacteria by bacteriophages. The DNA of bacteriophage enters the bacteria and in some way modifies the living processes of the bacteria. This modification results in the synthesis of bacteriophage protein and the replication of bacteriophage DNA. The end point is the formation of many complete bacteriophage particles with a core of DNA surrounded by a shell of protein.

If the synthesis of protein requires the formation of RNA by DNA, then, when the DNA of bacteriophage enters bacteria, the first result should be the synthesis of a new type of RNA, which could direct the synthesis of bacteriophage protein. The problem was how to identify this bacteriophage RNA. A beginning was made by comparing the chemical constitution of the bacteriophage DNA with that of RNA from infected bacteria. There were close similarities; this supported the idea that the first step in the formation of protein by DNA is the formation of RNA, which is chemically similar to the DNA.

DNA–RNA HYBRIDS

Spiegelman introduced a new approach to the problem by separating DNA into its complementary strands, then mixing this "single-strand" DNA with RNA. Sometimes the single-strand DNA paired with the RNA to form DNA–RNA hybrid molecules. The coupling occurred only if the DNA and the RNA had a common origin, as when DNA from bacteriophage is mixed with RNA from infected bacteria. The simplest explanation for the coupling of DNA with RNA is that the sequence of nucleotides along an RNA chain can match with that along a DNA chain in very much the same way as the two complementary strands of a DNA molecule match, and are then linked by hydrogen bonds to form a complete double helix. This is the simplest explanation, and it is now accepted as a basic part of the modern "dogma" of molecular genetics—DNA at some stage and under some regulating control separates into its complementary strands. One or both of these then act as a template from which an exact replica is formed in the RNA mode of nucleic acid.

The next steps came from experiments in which cells were broken up into their parts. These parts were separated and used for test-tube experiments to determine which parts of cells were concerned in the synthesis of proteins. The dividing lines between the subjects of genetics, biochemistry, and physiology have become very diffuse in this phase of biology.

SYNTHETIC PROTEINS

Extracts of cells can be made that will synthesize proteins. The amounts synthesized are very small—too small to be detected by normal chemical methods—but it is possible to detect the synthesis of even a minute trace of protein by using radioactive amino acids. These are added to a cell extract, and after a time the protein is separated from the extract. If this protein contains any radioactivity, then some of the radioactive amino acids must have joined to form protein. Normally there would be so little of this that it could not be detected, but the radioactivity is a sure signal of its occurrence.

This technique was used to discover which parts of cells were essential for the synthesis of proteins. Some parts were left out of the extracts, and it was found that the synthesis of proteins occurred at the same rate as when they were present. Other parts could not be left out; they were essential. The two dominant components are the mitochondria and the ribosomes. The role of the mitochondria is to supply chemical energy in the form of adenine triphosphate (ATP for short). The ribosomes have a more complicated role that is not completely understood. Other components that are needed are soluble RNA (the small RNA); some primary RNA and, of course, some amino acids. This is a fairly complicated recipe, but the general picture of how it works has been established, and the detail should all be filled in over the next few years.

The soluble RNA joins the amino acids to form amino acid–RNA compounds. Each type of amino acid joins the appropriate type of RNA. The name given to this type of RNA is *transfer* RNA because its role is to couple with the amino acids and transfer them to the ribosomes where they join.

The primary RNA has a different role: it carries the genetic information from the DNA to the ribosomes. It has the appropriate name of *messenger* RNA. The necessary message to direct the linking of the amino acids into a chain is contained in the form of the sequence of its nucleotides.

One of the present ideas on how these parts fit together is that the messenger RNA moves out to the ribosomes, connecting in some way to their ribosomal RNA. The transfer RNA molecules with their connected amino acids move into place along the messenger RNA. The sequence of amino acids are then joined to form a protein.

There are many gaps, but the most significant was filled by the work of Nirenberg and his group. They used a technique for producing synthetic RNA based on a bacterial enzyme that can link nucleotides together to form RNA. If this enzyme is added to only one type of nucleotide, a synthetic RNA is produced containing only that nucleotide. If the enzyme is added to uridine nucleotides, a long chain of uridylic acids is formed. A synthetic polyuridylic acid is formed.

Nirenberg and his group took cell extracts that had everything necessary for the synthesis of protein except messenger RNA, and

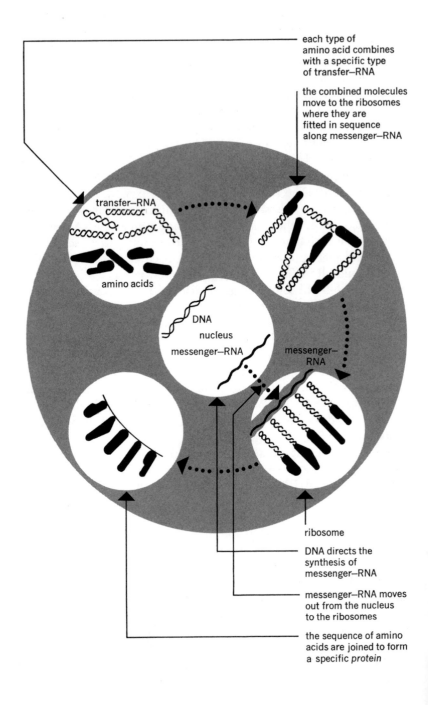

each type of
amino acid combines
with a specific type
of transfer—RNA

the combined molecules
move to the ribosomes
where they are
fitted in sequence
along messenger—RNA

transfer—RNA

amino acids

DNA

nucleus

messenger—RNA

messenger—
RNA

ribosome

DNA directs the
synthesis of
messenger—RNA

messenger—RNA moves
out from the nucleus
to the ribosomes

the sequence of amino
acids are joined to form
a specific *protein*

they added the synthetic RNAs to these extracts. They found that polyuridylic acid caused only the incorporation of phenylalanine into protein. They went on to more and more complicated variations of this experimental theme, gradually producing a picture of the significance of the sequence of nucleotides in RNA. Thus they began to establish the language of the genetic code.

THE GENETIC CODE

The basic letters of the genetic code are:

A Adenine

T Thymine

C Cytosine

G Guanine

These are the nucleotides of DNA, and their sequence along a molecule of DNA determines the specific role of that sequence—it determines the exact sequence of the messenger RNA. The basic letters of the messenger code are not identical with those of the genetic code. Uracil takes the place of thymine.

A Adenine

U Uracil

C Cytosine

G Guanine

This difference between RNA and DNA could be significant in allowing recognition of whether strands of nucleic acid are RNA or DNA. At present the difference is simply an interesting fact.

The sequence of nucleotides in some way contains the information necessary to fit together a sequence of amino acids, which can then

FIGURE 10.2

The DNA–RNA dogma. This represents the present view of the way in which the DNA of the genes directs the synthesis of specific proteins. The molecules of transfer-RNA are shown bent back and coiled; this may be their structure—it is not certain. The alignment of transfer RNA and messenger RNA is shown at the interface between two ribosomes—this is not certain. The whole dogma should only be accepted as a basis for more work. This phase of genetics is by no means completed.

be joined to form a protein. There are 20 different types of amino acids and there must be specific combinations of the basic nucleotide letters that identify each of these 20 types of amino acids. Clearly there are not enough single nucleotide letters, so the code must involve sequences of letters. A great deal of effort and thousands of words were used trying to find the basic grammar of the code. Two letters at a time do not provide enough alternatives, and three at a time provide too many. It is not absolutely established, but several independent researches point to the nucleotide letters being grouped as three-letter words. This is the famous *triplet code.*

THE TRIPLET CODE

The main evidence pointing toward the genetic code's being based on triplets of nucleotides comes from the work of Crick and his colleagues on the *r*II "gene" of T4 bacteriophage. This extremely simple organism can be bred and manipulated to give remarkable precision to genetic analysis, which is particularly useful in the study of recombination between mutations. Colonies of millions of phage particles can be raised from single initial infections of a bacterial cell. This makes it possible to measure rates of recombination between mutations at different points *within* a "gene," which are so close together that "crossovers" are extremely rare. It has become increasingly difficult to be sure just what we mean by "gene"—the initial view that genes are units that can be separated by crossing over has been discarded.

Crick and his group treated T4 phage with proflavine. This substance (proflavine) is mutagenic—it increases the mutation rate in a specific way. Proflavine interferes with the replication of DNA in some way that results in either the loss or addition of nucleotides. The mutations of the *r*II gene studied by the Crick group affected the ability of the phage to infect a particular strain of bacteria. The researchers collected a number of strains of the virus containing different proflavine-induced mutations of the *r*II gene, none of which could infect the special strain of bacteria.

Many of the mutations were recombined in pairs to produce strains with two separate mutations located in separate parts of the *r*II gene. A very interesting difference between the mutations emerged. They could be classed into two groups. Combinations of two different mutations of the same group resulted in a defective phage that could not infect the resistant bacteria, whereas combinations of one mutation from each group resulted in a phage that functioned as well as if it contained no mutations at all. Combining the two mutations had "repaired" the phage (returned it to normal).

The answer to the question suggested by this set of facts appears to be that one set of mutations involves the loss of a nucleotide from the DNA sequence, whereas the other set of mutations involves the gain of a nucleotide. Thus, if a DNA molecule is formed with a loss in one part and a gain in another part, it *can* function as effectively as an unmutated DNA molecule. This immediately raises the question: why should the combination of the loss of a nucleotide in one part and the addition of a nucleotide in another part result in regaining the normal function? The answer to this question appears to be that the information contained in the sequence of nucleotides consists of a set of words, each containing the same number of nucleotide "letters," and that these words are read from one end.

The Crick group made some other pertinent discoveries. They combined *three* deletions and found that the resultant strain functioned normally. The same result was found when they combined *three* additions. They went farther and combined sets of four deletions or four additions, but these did not function normally. All this makes sense if the nucleotides are read in groups of three. The basic unit of the gene is not the individual nucleotide, but a set of three nucleotides.

Suppose a strand of DNA has the following sequence of nucleotides, which is "read" from left to right, with relatively unimportant information at the left and crucial information at the right.

CAT · TAG · CAT · TAG · CAT · AAA · TTT · GGG · CCC
     ↑
A *deleted*   All *the original sense lost*

CAT · TGC · ATT · AGC · ATA · AAT · TTG · GGC · CC . . .

C *added*   *The original sense restored*
↑
CAC · TTG · CAT · TAG · CAT · AAA · TTT · GGG · CCC

The sequence is to a large extent returned to its original form. If the information at the left is unimportant, with the crucial information at the right, then the doubly mutated DNA will function normally; it will have the necessary sequence of information.

If three deletions are combined into the same initial strand, the sequence is similarly returned to its original form.

CAT · TAG · CAT · TAG · CAT · AAA · TTT · GGG · CCC

↑
Deletion   *Original sense lost*

CTT · AGC · ATT · AGC · ATA · AAT · TTG · GGC · CC...

↑
Deletion   *Original sense lost*

CTA · GCA · TTA · GCA · TAA · ATT · TGC · GCC · C...

↑
Deletion   *Original sense restored*

CTA · CAT · TAG · CAT · AAA · TTT · GGG · CCC...

The combination of three deletions results in a sequence in which the crucial right-hand information is unchanged.

This triplet-code view of the structure of DNA has some "ifs and buts" involved, but there is increasing evidence supporting the concept of the triplet code. A number of research teams are focusing their work on fully describing the code, determining which triplets of the nucleotide alphabet correspond to each of the 20 amino acids.

DECODING THE CODE

The first step toward finding the exact relationship between nucleotide triplets and amino acid incorporation into proteins has already been mentioned—Nirenberg and his group produced synthetic RNA molecules containing just one type of nucleotide. They formed polyuridylic acid, which is a long chain of uracil nucleotides:

U U U U U U U U U U U U

This synthetic RNA was added to a mixture of amino acids with all the ancillary substances necessary for incorporating amino acids into protein. Only one type of amino acid was incorporated, phenylalanine, although all 20 types of amino acids were present. This established the identity of one particular nucleotide triplet with incorporation of a specific amino acid.

– U U U –   Phenylalanine

The next step was to form different synthetic RNAs and determine which amino acids were incorporated in their presence. It is not possible to link up the nucleotides in a controlled sequence—yet. In the meantime, less precise methods have proved very useful.

New synthetic RNA molecules were made from a mixture of

nucleotides, predominantly uracil with a little adenine. These synthetic RNAs consisted mainly of U with a scattering of A nucleotides.

The relative proportions of uracil and adenine determine the types of triplets that occur along the resultant RNA molecules. If only a trace of adenine is present, the A nucleotides will be scattered along the molecules, with a very rare chance that two A nucleotides will occur near each other.

U U U U U U A U U U U U U U A U U U U U U A

There are four types of triplets along these RNA molecules. When the RNA was used to direct the incorporation of amino acids, it was found that the amino acid incorporated most often was phenylalanine. This is expected, because most of the triplets of the RNA will be U U U. However, other amino acids are incorporated in small amounts: isoleucine, leucine, tyrosine. This established another step in decoding the code.

UUA		Isoleucine
UAU	———	Leucine
UAA		Tyrosine

If RNA molecules are made from a mixture of uracil and adenine, where the adenine is an appreciable fraction of the mixture, then there will be an appreciable probability that two A nucleotides will occur near each other.

U U A U U A A U U U A U A U U U A U A A U U U

There are eight types of triplets along these RNA molecules. When these RNAs were used to direct the incorporation of amino acids into protein, it was found that six amino acids were incorporated.

UUU		Phenylalanine
UUA		Isoleucine
UAU	———	Leucine
AUU		Tyrosine
AAU		Asparagine
AUA	———	Lysine
AUU		

AAA would occur so rarely that its effect could not be detected.

There are many ways of getting at the code, and all of these ways are being used, sometimes with conflicting results. There is more agreement than disagreement, and it is obvious that a final answer can be expected in the next few years.

The following table is the best available statement on the triplet code at the time of this writing; it may be shown to be incorrect in particular details.

THE TRIPLET CODE

UUU ⎱ Phenyl UUC ⎰	UCU ⎫ UCC ⎪ Serine UCA ⎬ UCG ⎭	UAU ⎱ Tyrosine UAC ⎰ UAA ⎱ Terminator UAG ⎰	UGU ⎱ Cysteine UGC ⎰ UGA ⎱ Trypto- UGG ⎰ phan
UUA ⎱ Leucine UUG ⎰			
CUU ⎫ CUC ⎪ Leucine CUA ⎬ CUG ⎭	CCU ⎫ CCC ⎪ Proline CCA ⎬ CCG ⎭	CAU ⎱ Histidine CAC ⎰ CAA ⎱ Glutamine CAG ⎰	CGU ⎫ CGC ⎪ Arginine CGA ⎬ CGG ⎭
AUU ⎱ Isoleucine AUC ⎰ AUA ⎱ Methionine AUG ⎰	ACU ⎫ ACC ⎪ Threonine ACA ⎬ ACG ⎭	AAU ⎱ Asparagine AAC ⎰ AAA ⎱ Lysine AAG ⎰	AGU ⎱ Cysteine AGC ⎰ AGA ⎱ Arginine AGG ⎰
GUU ⎫ GUC ⎪ Valine GUA ⎬ GUG ⎭	GCU ⎫ GCC ⎪ Alanine GCA ⎬ GCG ⎭	GAU ⎱ Aspartic GAC ⎰ acid GAA ⎱ Glutamic GAG ⎰ acid	GGU ⎫ GGC ⎪ Glysine GGA ⎬ GGG ⎭

Note: Terminator signifies the triplets that may have the function of signifying the end of a particular sequence of nucleic acid.

Problems

1. Draw a map of the path followed by the hereditary information from the parents to the enzymes that produce a given effect in the progeny.

2. Compare the structure and functions of DNA and messenger-RNA.

3. There are three types of RNA. What are they? What are their functions?

ESSAY PROJECT

A useful project at this point is to relate in essay form the main steps in the advance of our knowledge of the gene. This advance did not occur in a simple temporal sequence; often the importance of a discovery was not realized for several years or decades. Simply listing the times at which discoveries were made would not show the inherent logic of this advance; the aim of the essay should be to develop and emphasize this logic, showing how the various discoveries changed our concepts of the nature of the gene.

The following outline gives one view of this sequence. It is not the only one, and some discoveries that are not listed could be argued to have a right to inclusion. It can also be argued that other discoveries that have been included could be left out.

I. Mendel demonstrated:
1. the constancy of genetic units.
2. dominance between alleles.
3. the duality and equiprobability of transmission of genetic units.
4. the independence in heredity of separate pairs of genetic units.

II. Many exceptions to Mendel's laws have been found to be due to the variation of phenotypic expression of the genetic units. The main tenets of Mendel's laws are those concerned with the constancy and transmission of genetic units.

III. The discovery of meiosis and mitosis gave a physical rationalization of Mendel's laws, because:
1. chromosomes are dual in number.
2. chromosomes are homologous in pairs.
3. meiotic reduction is specific within homologous pairs; independent between nonhomologous pairs.

IV. The identification of specific control of hereditary characters by particular chromosomes was shown by:
1. sex in insects: XO and XY types.
2. sex chromosome balance in mice, men, and Drosophila.
3. sex-linkage and its reversal paralleling the reversal from the XY to the ZW type.

V. Morgan demonstrated:
   1. crossing over and recombination.
   2. additivity of crossover values.
   3. equality of number of linkage groups and number of chromosomes.

VI. Chromosomal identification of the location of specific genes was shown by:
   1. nondisjunction of the X chromosomes.
   2. nondisjunction of the IVth chromosomes.
   3. translocations resulting in a change of linkage relations.

VII. Discovery of the salivary-gland chromosomes allowed:
   1. use of overlapping deficiencies to identify the location of specific genes.
   2. demonstration that a single band may contain several genes.

VIII. Chemical structure of the gene was shown by:
   1. Meischer's discovery of the nucleic acids.
   2. use of Feulgen stain to identify the restriction of the DNA to the chromosomes.
   3. correlation of DNA content with chromosomal content—haploid versus diploid, doubling increase of DNA content of the salivary chromosomes with doubling increase of the polyteny of the salivary chromosomes.
   4. transformation of pneumococcus with extracted DNA.
   5. viral infection with radioisotopic tracers identifying DNA as the infective agent.
   6. Watson and Crick's discovery of the double helical structure of DNA.
   7. Meselson and Stahl's experiment demonstrating that the replication of DNA is semiconservative.

IX. The nature of the actions of genes was shown to be based on:
   1. the unitary nature of gene actions underlying complex phenotypic effects (spurious pleiotropy).
   2. genetic control of biosynthetic pathways.
   3. one gene—one enzyme hypothesis.
   4. demonstration that the block of a particular biosynthetic step is coupled with the absence of the requisite enzyme.
   5. mutants produce antigenically similar but enzymatically inadequate proteins, e.g.—tryptophan synthetase.
   6. genetic control of the amino acid sequence of specific proteins, e.g. hemoglobins in man.

X. The determination of protein structure by the DNA-directed synthesis of RNA involves:

1. synthesis of primary RNA in the nucleus; chromosome puffs as sites of active synthesis of RNA.

2. DNA-RNA hybrids showing that DNA directs the synthesis of complementary RNA.

3. Nirenberg's experiments demonstrating that the structure of RNA is specific in the direction of protein synthesis.

4. Crick's use of deletions in T4 phage to demonstrate the existence of a triplet, or "order-of-three" genetic code.

5. The relationship of nucleotide triplets to amino acid specificity.

Chapter 11

MUTATION

A line that is homozygous for a particular set of genes is expected to transmit these unchanged—this is a basic tenet of genetics. Similarly, a line with a particular set of chromosomes is expected to transmit these unchanged. The basis of most genetic studies is the constancy of the genes and chromosomes. They can replicate hundreds of thousands of times without any deviation from the originals. This constancy is remarkable but it is not absolute—both genes and chromosomes can mutate. Mutations are usually recognized by a sudden change of the phenotype which is inherited. Some mutations are very stable; others are unstable. They may be due to the mutation of a gene, but they could also be due to the mutation of the structure or quantity of the chromosomes. Mutations of the chromosomes can result in effects on the phenotype that are not distinguishable from the effects of gene mutation.

Abnormal inheritance of the sex chromosomes has been shown in both man and Drosophila to cause abnormalities of the sexual characteristics. The same effects are also caused by single gene mutations whose occurrence transforms females into sterile males. or into intersexes.

CHROMOSOMAL MUTATIONS IN MAN

Recent advances in the techniques of mammalian cytology have allowed the detection of chromosomal mutations in man. A frequent example of such mutation is *mongolian idiocy* (Down's syndrome), a disease characterized by mental retardation. (Other symptoms are: folds of the eyelids reminiscent of those of orientals; abnormal body growth; and frequent defects of the internal organs, particularly the heart.) Mongolism occurs once in every few hundred births, and it is the major single cause of severe mental deficiency. It has been found to be caused by chromosomal mutations. Mongoloids have an extra chromosome or part of a chromosome. The chromosome concerned is either the 21st or 22d—it is not sure which but, for simplicity, we assume it is the 21st chromosome.

The occurrence of an extra 21st chromosome can be explained by nondisjunction at meiosis. If the two 21st chromosomes do not pair at meiosis, they will separate independently instead of alternatively, and this will result in gametes that contain two 21st chromosomes. Their junction with a normal gamete will then result in an individual with three 21st chromosomes. An interesting feature of mongolism is its increased incidence among the children of older women. Apparently, the pairing of chromosomes at meiosis has a greater chance of failing in older women. Restriction of child bearing to younger women could possibly effect a significant reduction of the incidence of this serious defect.

The occurrence of mongoloids who do not have a complete 21st chromosome but only an extra part of this chromosome cannot be explained by nondisjunction. Their occurrence has been shown to be due first to another type of chromosomal mutation, a translocation, which has no serious effects. Several parents of mongoloids have been found to have such a translocation of part of the 21st chromosome onto the 15th chromosome, producing a 15-21 chromosome. This mutated chromosome does not produce any effect on its carrier, but causes abnormalities in later generations because it can result in mispairing at meiosis. Suppose one of the parents of a translocation mongoloid had the following constitution for the 15th and 21st chromosomes:

$$15\text{-}21, \quad 15, \quad 21$$

When these chromosomes pair at meiosis, the 15th chromosome pairs with the 15-21 chromosome, leaving the 21st chromosome unpaired. This can result in gametes that have both a 15-21 and a 21 chromosome; fertilization of such a gamete by a normal gamete would then result in an individual with the following constitution for the 15th and 21st chromosomes:

$$15, \quad 15\text{-}21, \quad 21, \quad 21$$

The mutation that produced a 15-21 translocation in one generation can lead to individuals with an extra piece of the 21st chromosome in later generations. The essential feature of both types of mongolism is that a part of the 21st chromosome occurs in triplicate. A mutation in Drosophila, the Bar eye mutation, has a similar constitution.

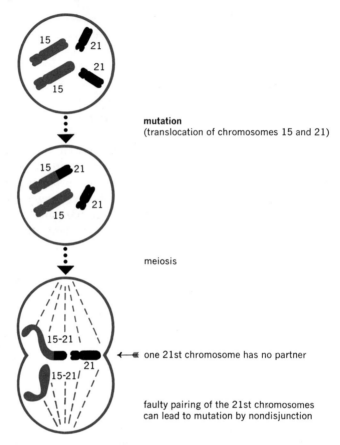

mutation
(translocation of chromosomes 15 and 21)

meiosis

one 21st chromosome has no partner

faulty pairing of the 21st chromosomes
can lead to mutation by nondisjunction

FIGURE 11.1

Mongoloid idiocy. This hereditary defect can be caused by a two-step mutational process. A translocation of a 21st chromosome onto a 15th chromosome can lead to faulty pairing at meiosis, which results in non-disjunction of the 21st chromosomes.

BAR EYES IN DROSOPHILA

The Bar eye mutation causes a drastic reduction of the size of the eye. It has a typical sex-linked inheritance in which Bar is dominant to normal. This dominance is not complete—the effect of the Bar gene is expressed in heterozygotes, but the effect is not as great as that found in homozygotes. The inheritance of Bar has a feature that differentiates it from most other genes: homozygous Bar stocks mutate at a high frequency, producing reversions both to a normal-type eye and to a more exaggerated type, double-Bar, which has an even greater reduction of eye size. The rate of mutation from Bar to normal, and from Bar to double-Bar, is about 1 : 1600 offspring. This is a much greater rate than is normal for sex-linked genes. The explanation came from the salivary-gland chromosomes.

Bar individuals have a duplication of the X chromosome involving several bands. Normal stocks and reversions from Bar to normal do not have this duplication. Double-Bar stocks have even more exaggerated chromosomes—they have a triplication. The mutation that causes the Bar effect is not a gene mutation, but a chromosomal mutation—a duplication of part of the X chromosome. This shows how the high mutation rate can be explained. The phenomenon of recombination involves the point-by-point exact pairing of homologous chromosomes, but in Bar homozygotes each chromosome has two identical sections, and this can lead to incorrect pairing and unequal crossing over. Suppose we call the section of the X chromosome that is duplicated the B section. Homozygous Bar females will then have two B sections in each of their X chromosomes. If the "left" B section in one chromosome pairs with the "right" B section of the other chromosome, pairing will be unequal. A crossover within this segment will lead to recombinants having only a single B section (reversions to normal) and other recombinants having three B sections (the double-Bar mutations).

The initial mutation from normal to Bar involved a change of the quantity of part of the X chromosome. It was a chromosomal mutation. The mutations of Bar back to normal and to double-Bar are a consequence of misplaced crossing over.

POSITION EFFECTS

The effects of the Bar and double-Bar mutations are not solely due to the doubling and trebling of the particular section of the X chromosome. There are variations of the effect on the size of the eyes that cannot be explained in this way. There are two ways to produce individuals with four *B* sections: homozygous Bar (*BB/BB*) and heterozygous normal/double-Bar (*B/BBB*). These have the same number of *B* sections but they do not have the same-sized eyes. The former have, on an average, 50% more facets in their eyes than the latter. There is an effect of position: three *B* sections side by side

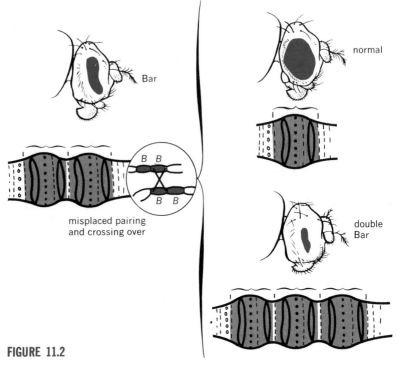

FIGURE 11.2

The Bar mutation in Drosophila is a duplication of a small section of the X chromosome. Misplaced pairing and crossing over in homozygous Bar females can lead to reversions to normal, and "mutations" to a triplication of the segment, which causes an even more marked reduction of eye size.

cause a greater reduction of the eyes than is expected from the simple addition of extra sections of chromosome.

Many examples of position effect have been discovered. A gene that causes breaks in the wing veins of Drosophila is called *cubitus interruptus*, with the symbol *ci*. It is a simple recessive located on the IVth chromosome. Translocations of the *ci* gene to the X, the Y, or the IInd chromosome affect its dominance—changing the position of this gene changes its effectiveness. The chromosome mutations did not involve any changes of the quantity of genetic material; all that has been changed is the position of some genes relative to other genes.

Position effects have been found that are associated with inverted chromosomes. These can be imagined as chromosomes in which a section has been removed, turned over end to end, and then replaced. Many inversions have no detectable effects on the phenotype, but others cause striking effects. In Drosophila the w^+ allele normally functions to determine the red color of the eye. If this gene is inverted to a new position, it may become inconsistent in its effects, resulting in the eyes' having a mixture of white and red facets. If the gene is returned to its normal position, it resumes its normal function. The change of effectiveness is solely a consequence of the change of position.

A feature of inversions is that they can result in further mutations of the chromosomes. The point-to-point pairing of chromosomes in individuals that are heterozygous for an inversion can result in the chromosomes' forming loops. If crossing over occurs within such a loop, chromosomes will be produced with duplicated or deleted sections. The initial mutation of a chromosome to an inverted sequence can lead to other chromosomal mutations in later generations.

DELETIONS

Many mutations have been found to be due to the absence of whole chromosomes, or parts of chromosomes. In corn, it is possible to see a fair amount of detail in the chromosomes during the early stages of meiosis, before the chromosomes condense. The chromosomes of several mutant strains of this crop plant have been found to be characterized by small deletions, with each type of mutant phenotype characterized by a deletion of a particular part of the chromosomes. A particular mutant phenotype, *brown midrib*, is caused in one strain by a small deletion, in another strain by a gene mutation (no abnormality of the chromosomes could be detected in this strain). The locations of the *bm* gene mutation and the *bm* deletions are the same, which suggests that the gene mutation involves a physiological deletion of the *bm* gene.

A similar example in Drosophila involves minute deletions of the left end of the X chromosome which include the locations of the yellow-body and achaete genes. Deletion of the y^+ and ac^+ genes causes the same phenotypic effects as mutations to y and ac. This kind of evidence suggests that gene mutation can involve the inactivation of the wild type allele. The idea has a neat simplicity: mutations are either the loss or inactivation of normal alleles.

The general theme of all this detail is that mutations may involve changes of the quantity or rearrangement of the chromosomes without affecting the internal structure of the gene. The next question is whether the same type of changes can occur within a gene. A major difficulty in answering this question was the nature of the gene. Initially, the gene was thought of as a structure that was not involved in crossing over, which was supposed to be restricted to the regions of the chromosomes between genes. Very detailed studies scoring hundreds of thousands of individuals showed that this concept was naïve—crossing over can happen within genes.

CROSSING OVER WITHIN GENES

The *white* locus in Drosophila has been extensively studied by geneticists, who have discovered dozens of different mutations that are all alleles of the locus, but this does not mean that they are alleles of each other. There is a contradiction here that has been resolved by the demonstration that the white locus has a complicated structure consisting of several parts which, although they act together as a physiological unit, can be recombined by crossing over. Such crossovers are very infrequent, but they do occur, and their frequency can be measured if the experiments are based on very large numbers of individuals. Recombinants between parts of a single gene are usually so infrequent that they can be confused with the occurrence of actual mutations, and special crosses are used to distinguish between rare recombinants within a gene and mutations.

The apricot (w^a) and eosin (w^e) mutations of the white locus are pseudo alleles—they are both allelic to white but they are not allelic to each other. The nonallelism of these two mutants was first inferred from the occurrence of rare *white*-eyed and *red*-eyed individuals in the progeny of *apricot/eosin* heterozygotes. The white-eyed individuals were thought to be the result of the recombination of apricot and eosin onto the same chromosome, and the red-eyed individuals were thought to be the result of the recombination of the normal alleles of apricot and eosin onto the same chromosome. This was demonstrated by studies in which two other mutants were included: yellow body (y) and split bristles (spl). These are located close to and on either side of the white locus. If the occurrence of the exceptional white-eyed and red-eyed individuals *is* due to recombination, the linked genes should also be recombined—this was found. Experiments of this type have been completed for most of the alleles of the white locus, making it possible to draw a linkage map of the internal structure of the locus.

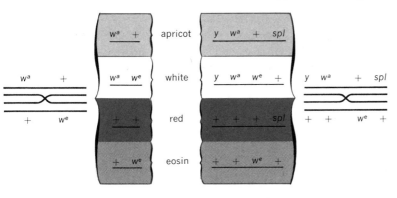

FIGURE 11.3

Apricot-eosin heterozygotes (wᵃ/wᵉ) give rare red-eyed and white-eyed progeny. This could be due to these mutations not being allelic, but rather being mutations of different parts of the white gene. Recombination between them could produce the unusual progeny. This was shown by crosses in which linked markers were used (y and spl); the unusual red and white progeny were found to be recombinants for these other markers.

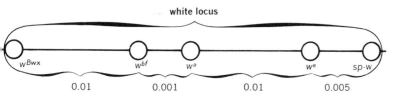

FIGURE 11.4

The white locus in Drosophila has several parts, and recombination can be measured between these parts, resulting in an intragenic linkage map.

Many genes have been shown to have the same complex internal structure. Thus, the rare occurrence of exceptional types cannot be accepted as diagnostic of mutation; such rare exceptional types can occur by rare recombination within genes. Detailed analyses are needed to distinguish between such recombinations and true mutation.

Recombination between the subgenes of the white locus is only part of the complications that have been discovered. Some mutants

of this locus have been shown to be duplications, like the Bar muta
tion. These duplications are too small to be detected microscopically
but they can be demonstrated by genetic methods. A consequence
of such duplications is that misplaced pairing can cause, as it does in
the case of the Bar mutation, reversions (to the normal sequence
and exaggerations (to triplications). These have been shown to
occur. Mutation at the white locus can involve the same types of
change within the gene as those that have been seen to occur in
chromosomes. Mutations of quantity and arrangement occur within
genes just as they do within chromosomes. This situation emphasize
the difficulties of finding an absolute definition of a gene.

DELETIONS IN BACTERIOPHAGES

One of the most important innovations in genetics recently has been
the invention of ways to detect very rare mutations and recombin
ants. This is especially evident in the T4 bacteriophage in which
some genes have been mapped with an almost fantastic precision
If the gene *is* a length of DNA, then it is probable that mutation
within genes have been mapped that are not much more than a few
nucleotides apart.

Some mutations within genes in T4 bacteriophage give confusing
results when attempts are made to locate them along the linkag
map of the gene. These mutations will not recombine with any of
several mutations located at different points along the gene. When
two mutants do not recombine, it is reasonable to consider that they
are alleles, located at the same point of the gene. But how can
mutant be allelic to a series of other mutants that are not themselve
allelic? A simple explanation is that these mutants are really dele
tions that cover the locations of several other mutations. This hypo
thesis is very easy to make, but a considerable amount of very
detailed and subtle genetic experimentation was needed to demon
strate its validity. We will consider only the principles involved i
these experiments.

Suppose m_1, m_2, m_3, m_4, and m_5 are mutations of the *r*II gene i
T4 bacteriophage. These have been shown to have rates of recom
bination that can be explained only if they occur at distinct point
in line along the gene.

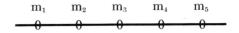

Suppose another mutation, D, does not recombine with m_2, m_3 and m_4. Then the hypothesis is that D is a deletion extending over the locations of these three mutations.

One test of the hypothesis was to determine the recombination of m_1 and m_5 in the presence of D. If D *is* a deletion, then m_1 and m_5 will be much closer together, and they should have a lower recombination rate. Such reductions of the recombination rate were found; this supports the hypothesis that some mutations of genes in bacteriophages are deletions. However, it is possible that the D mutations are not deletions but rather inversions that also cause reductions of recombination.

Another approach has been used in a different bacteriophage, *lambda phage*. Mutant strains of this phage were compared with normal strains in the ultracentrifuge, and some of the mutants were found to cause a reduction of density, just as would be expected if the mutations involved the loss of a section of the DNA.

Throughout this chapter we have developed the idea that mutations can be of quantity and position involving whole chromosomes, parts of chromosomes, or parts of genes. Next we must consider the other aspect of mutations—one that involves changes of quality.

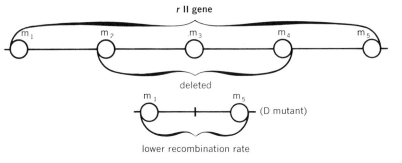

FIGURE 11.5

The rII locus in the T4 bacteriophage has been extensively studied. Some mutants behave as if they are deletions, being allelic with several different mutants (m_2, m_3 and m_4), and causing a reduction of the recombination between other mutants (m_1 and m_5).

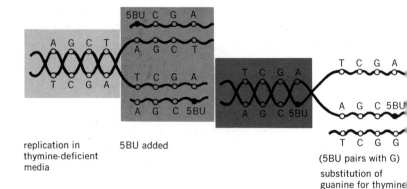

replication in
thymine-deficient
media

5BU added

(5BU pairs with G)
substitution of
guanine for thymine

FIGURE 11.6

Chemical mutagen. If 5BU is incorporated in place of thymine, a DNA molecule is formed in which 5BU is paired with adenine. If this molecule replicates, then 5BU can pair with guanine, resulting in the formation of a strand of nucleic acid in which guanine occurs where initially thymine had occurred. This could result in a detectable mutation.

GENE MUTATION

There is no way, at present, of being absolutely certain that a particular mutation involves a change of the chemical quality of the gene. However, in recent years, several chemicals have been found that cause marked increases of the rates at which mutations occur. These are called *mutagenic* substances, and the whole phenomenon of such mutagenesis will be considered in the next chapter. Here we will mention a few mutagenic substances that appear to cause changes of the chemical quality of the gene.

A substance, 5-bromo-uracil, is a very powerful mutagen—the mutation rate is increased several hundred times after treatment with this substance. This is extremely interesting because 5-bromo-uracil is almost identical with thymine, one of the four main building blocks of DNA. The way in which 5BU (5-bromo-uracil) causes mutations is thought to involve its being incorporated into DNA in place of thymine, which then results in errors of replication of the DNA.

The experiments with 5BU first involved culturing bacteria on media deficient in thymine. Then 5BU was added to the media with the result that 5BU was incorporated in place of thymine in the DNA.

Bacteriophages were then cultured on these bacteria, and these phages were found to include a large number of mutants.

Although 5BU is almost identical with thymine, it is sufficiently different to imagine its presence causing errors in the positioning of the purines and pyrimidines during the replication process. If 5BU replaces T, and if guanine can pair with 5BU, this will result in the substitution of a G-C pair in place of an original A-T pair. This would result in a change of the gene's code, which would then cause a change in the structure of the protein whose synthesis is directed by the gene.

Another mutagenic substance that could be modifying the chemical structure of nucleic acid is nitrous acid. This substance can effect a transformation of *adenine* into *hypoxanthine*. Hypoxanthine will act as if it is guanine, and this will result in errors during the replication process. An A-T pair would be replaced by a G-C pair by this effect of nitrous acid.

These ideas about the actions of substances such as 5-bromo-uracil and nitrous acid are attractive, but that does not mean they are correct. At present, there is no conclusive proof that mutations involve changes of the chemical quality of DNA. We can expect such proof to be produced in the next few years as researches on the genetics of bacteriophages and bacteria attain even greater precision.

Problems

1. What would you consider sufficient evidence to show that a hereditary defect is due to a gene mutation?

2. Albinism is due to a recessive gene. What evidence would you accept to show that the occurrence of a particular albino individual had its origin by mutation in the parents?

3. Pairing in inverted segments during meiosis can lead to mutated chromosomes. How?

Chapter 12

INDUCED MUTATION

Measurements of mutation rates of genes are laborious to make, but enough have been made to show that the average rate is about 1 : 100,000 gametes. Differences do occur from one gene to the next and from one species to another, but this generalization is reasonably valid. In Drosophila, the average mutation rate is 1 : 200,000 gametes; in mice, it is 1 : 100,000; and in man it is about 1 : 50,000 gametes. Considering the small number of genes whose mutation rate has been measured, there is a surprising lack of difference between these very different organisms. This raises an intriguing question: what determines the rate of mutation? For some time it was considered that the rate was an inherent feature of the gene—mutation was considered to be equivalent to the breakdown of radioactive elements and strictly independent of the surrounding environment. It is difficult to reconcile this view with the similarity of mutation rates in organisms with such vastly different generation lengths as Drosophila and man. Man would be expected to have a much greater mutation rate per generation than Drosophila. It would appear that there has been an evolution of genetic stability that has reached the same level per generation in widely varied organisms. Such an evolution would not be possible unless genes differed in their mutation rates, so that selection could favor the more stable alleles, or some genes could control the rate of mutation of other genes. Examples of both types of control of genetic stability have been found.

MUTATOR GENES

A recessive gene on the IInd chromosome in Drosophila causes nearly a fifteenfold increase of the mutation rate. Several such mutator genes have been discovered in Drosophila, showing that the rate of mutation is under genetic control. This is not an iso-

156

lated feature of Drosophila—mutator genes have been identified in bacteria and in corn.

The a_1 gene in corn causes an absence of color in the seed coat. It occasionally mutates to other alleles that cause a range of colors in the seed coat. Some strains of corn that were homozygous for the a_1 gene, and should have had uncolored seed coats, had speckles of color. This was due to frequent mutation of the a_1 gene. Each mutation of the a_1 gene during the development of the seed coat results in a spot of colored cells. Genetic analysis of these strains showed that they were characterized by another gene, *Dt*. This gene has no effect on seed coat color by itself, but it does have an effect on the mutability of the a_1 gene, resulting in the speckled seed coat.

As a result of some exceedingly complicated researches, other mutator genes were discovered in corn. Some of these are like *Dt*, increasing the rate at which specific genes mutate. Others affect the stability of the chromosomes, causing an increased frequency of chromosome breaks.

It is clear that the stability of genes and chromosomes is under genetic control. Other factors have been shown to affect the rate of mutation. A major feature of the researches that showed this has been the construction of special stocks which reduced the work needed in these measurements. The logic behind these measurements was to measure the rate of mutation to a single type of effect— *lethality*—and to measure the mutation to lethality of all the genes in a chromosome. Since a chromosome contains many hundreds of genes, mutations per chromosome will occur far more frequently than mutations per gene, and restriction to lethal mutations saves the labor of having to score hundreds of different characters.

THE ClB CHROMOSOME

Muller perceived that the combination of several mutant features into the X chromosome of Drosophila would allow easy identification of mutations to lethality of genes on the X chromosome. The features were an inversion to reduce or prevent crossing over with the other X chromosome; a lethal chromosome such that this one could only be transmitted from females to female progeny (males inheriting such an X chromosome would die); and a dominant gene to allow identification of the chromosome in heterozygous females. The *ClB* chromosome was such a chromosome.

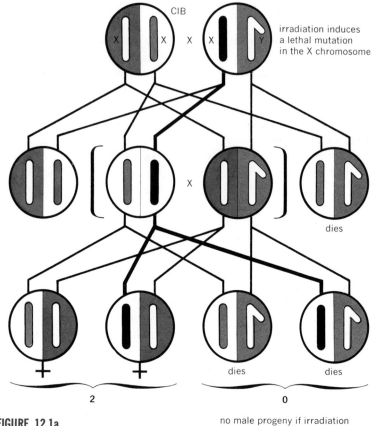

irradiation induces
a lethal mutation
in the X chromosome

dies

dies   dies

2   0

FIGURE 12.1a

no male progeny if irradiation
caused a lethal mutation in the
X chromosome

C = crossing over suppressor (an inversion)
l = recessive lethal gene
B = Bar eye gene

The inheritance of this chromosome has several features that make it peculiarly suitable for studies of mutation rates. Females that carry such a chromosome must be heterozygous for it, and male progeny that inherit it die. Any surviving male progeny from *ClB* females must have inherited the normal X chromosome. Progeny of *ClB* females, therefore, have an abnormal sex ratio of 2 ♀ ♀ : 1 ♂. It is possible to set up mating schemes in which all male progeny are characterized by identical copies of a particular X chromosome. If that X chromosome mutates to lethality, no males will be produced.

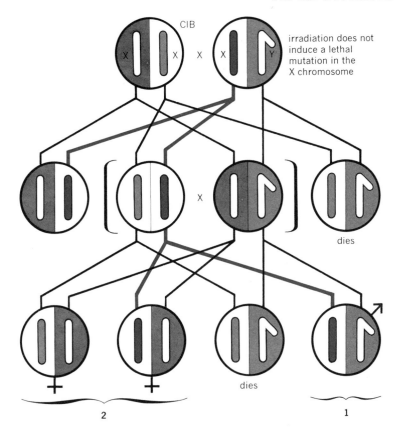

irradiation does not induce a lethal mutation in the X chromosome

dies

dies

2   1

FIGURE 12.1b

Crosses of ClB females with normal males result in 2 ♀ ♀ : 1 ♂ ♂ sex-ratios in the F₂, if the X chromosome from the ♂ ♂ does not carry a recessive lethal mutation. If irradiation of normal males does result in mutations of the X chromosome to recessive lethality, then no male progeny occur in the F₂; the sex ratio is 2 ♀ ♀ : 0 ♂ ♂.

Measuring mutation rates in such matings consists solely of determining between a sex ratio of 2 ♀ ♀ : 1 ♂ ♂ (no mutation) and 1 ♀ ♀ : 0 ♂ ♂ (mutations to lethality on the X chromosome). The intricacies of the *ClB* method are best appreciated by tracing the transmission of chromosomes through a set of crosses. (A subsidiary reason for understanding this method is that it provides an excellent illustration of how a set of genetic oddities can be combined to provide an extremely precise manipulation of the transmission of chromosomes in heredity.)

The *ClB* method showed that the rate of mutation to lethality of the X chromosome is about 0.1% per generation. About 1 : 1,000 X chromosomes have a lethal "gene" that mutated in that generation. The term *gene* has to be used with caution, since structural mutations of the X chromosome are also likely to be lethal in males. For example, a deletion of the X chromosome will be lethal if it involves more than a very short section.

One of the most dramatic results from this method of measuring mutation rates was Muller's discovery that exposure to X rays causes a marked increase of the mutation rate.

X RAYS AND ATOMIC RADIATION

When living tissue is exposed to X rays, it is traversed by high-energy atomic particles. When these are absorbed by an atom in the tissue, an electron is emitted with very high energy. This electron is absorbed by another atom, bouncing off another electron in the process. Effectively, X rays cause tracks of ionization through tissue that has been exposed. A quantitative measure of this effect of X rays is the *roentgen;* this is the amount of exposure necessary to produce a specified amount of ionization in a specified volume of air. (There are a variety of such measures, but the roentgen is adequate for a nontechnical appreciation.)

If a normal male is exposed to X rays, then mated to *ClB* females, each *ClB* progeny from such a mating will contain an X chromosome from the original treated male. If each such *ClB* ♀ ♀ is mated to an ordinary male, and if no male progeny are produced, this will show that a mutation to lethality occurred in an X chromosome from the original male. Many such experiments were performed for a wide variety of dosages of X rays, and an interesting fact emerged. The increase of the mutation rate was proportional to the amount of X irradiation, and almost completely independent of its intensity. If a certain amount of irradiation were applied in one short burst, this produced the same increase of the mutation rate as that amount of irradiation spread over a longer time.

The majority of the work on the mutagenic effect of radiation was based on Drosophila, but measurements have been made in other organisms, particularly in mice. Russell at Oak Ridge found that the intensity of exposure to radiation did affect the rate of mutation, which was much higher for the higher intensities. Irradiation at 90 roentgens per week produced only one-quarter as many mutations

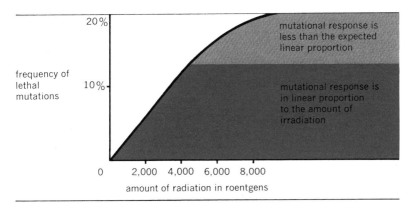

FIGURE 12.2

The relation of amount of irradiation to frequency of mutation is a straight line for most of the range of irradiation studied. At very high amounts of exposure, less mutations are found than is expected; this could be due to the greater chance of a gene being hit twice at these high exposures.

as the same total amount of radiation given at 90 roentgens per minute. One possible explanation of this difference is that newly induced mutations can be "repaired" to normality if the irradiation is at a low intensity, whereas at high intensity exposure after the occurrence of a mutation inhibits the "repair" process. This is a *possible* explanation. Facts like this are of major importance in determining the genetic dangers consequent from the increased exposure to radiation.

A convenient measure of the genetic consequences of irradiation is the "doubling dose." This is the amount of radiation that will double the natural mutation rate. The present measurements of the genetic effects of irradiation place this dose in the range of 50-60 roentgens.

THE TARGET THEORY

The effects of radiation can be considered analogous to a blind rifleman firing at a target. His success in hitting the target will be directly related to how often he fires, and it will be independent of how fast he fires. If we consider the genes as the target and X irradiation as the rifleman, the rate of induction of mutation will be directly related to the number of ionization tracks and independent of the rate at which these tracks are produced.

It is possible to calculate the size of the genetic "target," and this has been found to be of the order of 4-40 mμ. This is smaller than the estimate of the size of the gene made from measurements of the volume of chromosomes and counts of the number of bands in the salivary-gland chromosomes (see page 80). This estimate is 125 $\times$ 25 mμ. A possible explanation is that each salivary-gland band contains several sites of mutation, which act together as a "gene." When this work was done, in the 1940s, it seemed that the methods of direct cytologic examination and the methods of radiation genetics could be integrated to provide decisive information on the size and structure of the gene. This optimism has been shown to be unjustified by a series of experiments in which the increase of the mutation rate caused by irradiation was shown to be affected by other treatments. The temperature, oxygen level, and physiological state of irradiated cells have all been shown to modify the mutagenic effect of irradiation. It is difficult to reconcile these effects with the target theory, and it appears that at least some, if not all, of the mutagenic

FIGURE 12.3

Irradiation can result in the formation of short-lived, highly reactive substances, which may react with genes, leading to mutations.

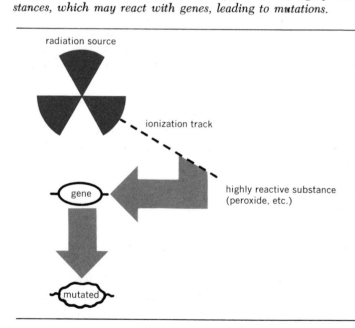

effects of irradiation are consequences of the induction of chemical changes in substances near the genes. Irradiation of watery substances leads to the formation of highly reactive chemicals—peroxides, etc.—which can be imagined as acting on the material of the genes, producing mutations. Very strong support for this concept came from experiments in which sterile bacterial culture media were irradiated, then used to culture bacteria. An increased mutation rate was found in the bacteria. These results can be explained only by the irradiation causing chemical changes in the culture media, which then acts on the genetic material of the bacteria. It logically follows that there must be mutagenic chemicals but, before considering this, there are several other effects of irradiation that are relevant here. The most notable of these is that irradiation causes a marked increase of the frequency of broken and rearranged chromosomes.

CHROMOSOME BREAKAGE

Exposure to X rays and other forms of high-energy particles can cause mutations that are completely analogous to natural "gene" mutations, meaning that no visible changes of the chromosomes can be detected. In addition, irradiation causes increases of the frequencies of deletions, translocations, and other chromosomal mutations which involve breakage. This effect differs from the increased frequency of "gene" mutations in that it is related to the intensity of irradiation. Increasing the rate of irradiation causes an increase of the rate of breakage of the chromosomes. This can be understood for rearrangements like deletions and translocations, since these must involve the simultaneous occurrence of two separate breaks, with the broken chromosomes rejoining in a new sequence. The chance of such simultaneous events will be increased if the density of ionization tracks is increased. In an experiment with Drosophila, irradiation of 2,000 roentgens was given in one minute, and in twenty minutes; the same total amount of irradiation was involved, delivered at two intensities. There were 60% more translocations produced by the high-intensity irradiation.

Many of the experiments of the genetic effects of irradiation have been based on direct examination of the chromosomes. The results of exposure to large doses at high intensity are visually extremely dramatic, showing frequent broken and rearranged chromosomes. Extremely high doses can result in the chromosomes' losing their independence and clumping together into an inchoate mass. The whole problem of the genetic effects of irradiation is extremely complicated, particularly in light of the discovery that many chemicals are also mutagenic. The first substance to be identified as mutagenic was mustard gas. This discovery was made by Auerbach and her colleagues following the observation that mustard gas burns were very similar to X-ray burns.

MUSTARD GAS

Mustard gas is a poison that causes blistering of the skin and of mucous membranes. These injuries heal very slowly, and even after they have healed, recurrences are frequent. X-ray burns are similarly difficult to heal and recur frequently; tests were made to determine whether this similarity extended to the mutagenic effect. Drosophila males were exposed to mustard gas, then mated to *ClB* females, allowing measurements of the rate of induction of X-chromosome lethals. There was a spectacular increase of the mutation rate from the natural rate of 0.2% to 25%. Clearly, mustard gas is highly mutagenic.

FIGURE 12.4

Mustard gas causes two types of mutation: stable mutants, and unstable normals, which later mutate. This latter effect results in progeny with mosaic spots—regions of mutant tissue in otherwise normal individuals.

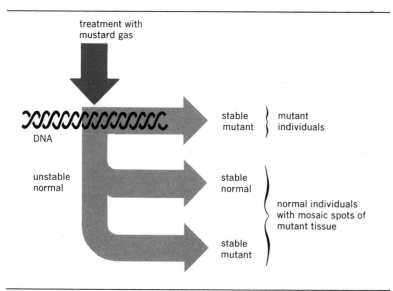

Following this discovery, mustard gas was shown to cause both "gene" mutations and chromosome breaks. An interesting aspect of the effects of mustard gas is that an increased frequency of mutations occurs at times after the treatment; these show as mosaic spots in the offspring. It would appear that treatment with mustard gas makes genes unstable for some time. X rays do not have any such delayed effects.

Hundreds of other chemicals were tested, and the list of mutagenic substances rapidly became very extensive. A variety of quite unrelated substances are mutagenic, many to a very high degree. Some of these have already been mentioned in the preceding chapter, namely, 5-bromo-uracil and nitrous acid, whose mutagenic effects appear to be due to direct chemical effects on nucleic acid. The majority of mutagenic substances do not have structures that suggest such simple effects.

One possibility of the discovery of mutagenic substances was that specific substances would be directive in their effects, causing only specific genes to mutate. This possibility has not been realized; mutagenic substances are as nonspecific in their effects as irradiation. There are differences in the spectrum of effects—mustard gas produces fewer chromosome breaks than do X rays—but the differences are small relative to the general absence of genetic specificity. A few substances are more specific; one substance causes frequent reverse mutations of one allele, having very little effect on other alleles of the same locus. However, such restrictions of the mutational spectrum are the very rare exception rather than the rule.

An intriguing feature of mutagenic substances is that they differ in the frequencies of mutations that they cause at different positions within the gene. The precision possible in bacteriophages like the T4 phage has made it possible to locate the positions of mutations along the length of the gene. Such analyses have shown that natural mutations of the *r*II gene in T4 phage have a different pattern of occurrence along the length of the gene from mutations induced by 5-bromo-uracil. There is more than an indication that the length of a gene can be classified into regions of different sensitivity to mutation, and that this classification can be extended to include sensitivity to different mutagens.

The discovery of chemical mutagenesis has cast considerable doubt on the general validity of the target theory as a final explanation of the induction of mutations by atomic radiation. It appears now that a simple solution to the mechanism of mutagenesis is very unlikely. There are probably dozens if not hundreds of different ways in which mutations may be induced. This is a laborious but rewarding field of research which is being actively pursued toward a target of specifically directed and precisely controlled mutagenesis.

Problems

1. If 1,000 roentgens cause one lethal mutation, and if the mutation rate is simply proportional to the amount of irradiation, which will cause the most mutations:

    (*a*) 1 roentgen to 10,000 people, or 50 roentgens to 200 people?

    (*b*) 5,000 roentgens to 100 people, or 0.1 roentgen to 5,000,000 people?

2. If the mutation rate at 100 roentgens is 1%, and at 1,000 roentgens is 10%, what will the mutation rate be at:

    (*a*) 10 roentgens?

    (*b*) at 0.1 roentgens?

    What assumptions would be involved?

Chapter **13**

GENES IN POPULATIONS

A major aim of genetics is to derive ways of predicting the characteristics of offspring from knowledge of the genetic structure of the parents. This is usually emphasized for small family groups, or for crosses between pure lines, but it is possible to apply the basic laws of genetics to larger groups: to populations, to races, to species. The need for such a wider application has been emphasized recently by the increased exposure to atomic radiation which can be expected to result in an increase of the mutation rate. It is necessary to know what the consequences of such an increase will be, but this is only one of many genetic problems facing mankind that need to be considered in terms of the larger context of populations. Population genetics is that aspect of genetics in which the breeding unit is not a small family but a large group of families. The methods of population genetics are based on the algebra of genetics. Before these problems can be considered, we need to establish the principles and methods of population genetics.

Many students find the word "algebra" to have unpleasant connotations, presumably because the abstract symbolism is uncongenial. This argument should not apply to geneticists since their basic methods involve an intricately abstruse symbology.

GENETIC ALGEBRA

A simple starting point in our consideration of genetics algebra is to express the mating of two heterozygotes. This can be shown by a checkerboard diagram.

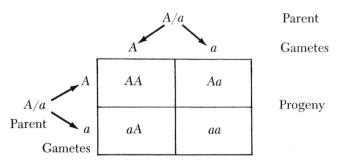

The genetic checkerboard expresses not only the types of progeny that can be produced; it also expresses the probability of their occurrence. Equal probabilities are implicit in the above diagram since a basic principle of genetics is that a heterozygote produces both types of gametes with equal frequency.

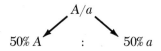

which can be expressed as

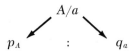

The genetic checkerboard for the mating of two heterozygotes can be redrawn on this new symbology.

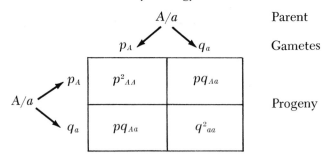

The genetic checkerboard is a visual way of showing that the probability of a certain genotype's occurring is the product of the probability that sperms carry one of the genes involved and the probability that eggs carry the other gene involved. If p_A is the probability that sperms carry the A allele, and p_A is the probability that eggs carry the A allele, then the probability that A-carrying sperms will fertilize A-carrying eggs is p^2_A. Similarly, the probability that A-carrying sperms will fertilize a-carrying eggs is pq_{Aa}, but this does not give the probability of the Aa genotype's occurring in the progeny. The reason is that the Aa genotype can also be produced by a-carrying sperms fertilizing A-carrying eggs. There are two ways of producing the Aa genotype, each way having a probability of pq_{Aa}; the probability of this genotype's occurring is, therefore, $2pq$.

The proportions of the three possible genotypes from this cross are

$$AA \qquad Aa \qquad aa$$
$$p^2 \qquad 2pq \qquad q^2$$

and since $p = q = 0.5$, the frequencies are

$$0.25 \qquad 0.50 \qquad 0.25$$

This will be valid if the parents are heterozygous, and it will be valid for any number of matings if these three requirements are satisfied:

1. All parents are heterozygotes.
2. The two types of gametes are transmitted with equal frequency.
3. The junction of gametes is completely random.

This simple system can be expanded to situations where the two types of gametes are *not* produced with equal frequency. This occurs when the parents are not all of one genotype—when the parents are not a homogenous group, but a heterogenous mixture. It can also occur when the genetic reduction is abnormal, e.g. when meiosis does not follow the standard sequence.

Suppose that an experiment is set up in which the parents are of two types (A/a and a/a) with equal probability. We can represent the frequencies of types of mating by a genetic checkerboard.

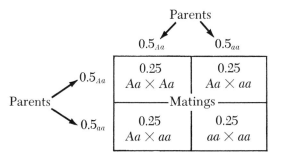

The three types of mating will occur with frequencies of

$$Aa \times Aa = 0.25$$
$$Aa \times aa = 0.50$$
$$aa \times aa = 0.25$$

The types of progeny formed by each type of mating can be found by drawing a checkerboard for each cross. All these checkerboards will, if considered together, give the types and frequencies of progeny expected in this experiment.

Mating	Frequency	Frequencies of progeny		
		AA	*Aa*	*aa*
Aa × *Aa*	0.25	0.0625	0.1250	0.0625
Aa × *aa*	0.50	—	0.2500	0.2500
aa × *aa*	0.25	—	—	0.2500
	Totals	0.0625	0.3750	0.5625

There is another, much simpler way to predict the results expected from this experiment, *if* we assume that mating is completely random.

In this experiment, both the *Aa* and *aa* types of parents occur equally often, and we can assume that they produce equal numbers of gametes. If this is so, we can add their separate contributions to give the frequencies of the different types of gametes produced by the parents.

$$\overbrace{0.5_{Aa}} \qquad + \qquad \overbrace{0.5_{aa}}$$
$$(0.25_A \quad : \quad \underbrace{0.25_a \quad + \quad (0.5_a)}$$
$$(0.25_A \quad : \quad 0.75_a) \quad \text{Conjoint frequencies of types of gametes}$$

These values for the frequencies of the two types of gametes can be introduced into a genetic checkerboard.

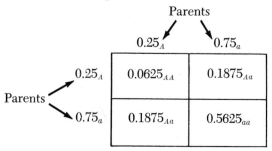

Parents

The frequencies of the three genotypes in the progeny are then

AA	*Aa*	*aa*
0.0625	0.3750	0.5625

This is the same result found by the previous method, which was based on determining the frequencies of the different types of mating, then drawing a separate checkerboard for each type of mating. Essential to this simpler method is the determination of the frequencies of types of gametes produced by a group of parents. Suppose we have a population of parents in which the three genotypes occur in the ratio

$$0.1_{AA} \quad : \quad 0.8_{Aa} \quad : \quad 0.1_{aa} \quad \text{Parents}$$

$$(0.1_A) \quad + \quad \underbrace{(0.4_A \quad : \quad 0.4_a)} \quad + \quad (0.1_a) \quad \text{Gametes}$$

$$(0.5_A \quad : \quad 0.5_a) \quad \text{Gametic frequencies of population}$$

We have already seen that if gametes occur with these relative frequencies, the frequencies of progeny will be

AA	Aa	aa
0.25	0.50	0.25

This is the same result found from the cross $Aa \times Aa$, and a simple conclusion can be drawn: the frequencies of different genotypes in the progeny of a cross are *not* determined by the frequencies of genotypes among the parents, but by the frequencies of types of gametes produced by these parents. All the preceding can be considered, rightly, as rather trivial arithmetic, but it does show how to proceed to a genetic algebra. A population can be described by the frequencies of different genotypes, *or* by the frequencies of different types of gametes produced, considering the population as a reproductive unit.

Suppose, for a single pair of genes, that the two possible types of gametes are produced in the ratio $p_A : q_a$; then the genetic checkerboard is

	p_A	q_a	Gametes
p_A	p^2_{AA}	pq_{Aa}	
Gametes			Progeny
q_a	pq_{Aa}	q^2_{aa}	

The frequencies of the three possible genotypes are

$$p^2_{AA} \qquad 2pq_{Aa} \qquad q^2_{aa}$$

At this point (fairly early in genetics) a very interesting question was asked by Hardy and by Weinberg. Will the frequencies of types of gametes produced by these progeny be different from those of the parents?

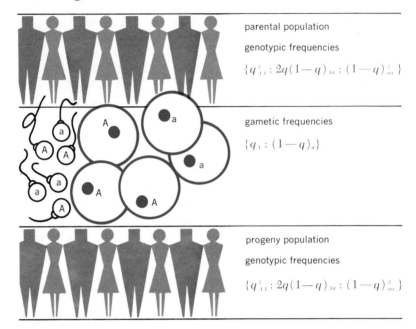

parental population

genotypic frequencies

$\{q^2_{AA} : 2q(1-q)_{Aa} : (1-q)^2_{aa}\}$

gametic frequencies

$\{q_A : (1-q)_a\}$

progeny population

genotypic frequencies

$\{q^2_{AA} : 2q(1-q)_{Aa} : (1-q)^2_{aa}\}$

FIGURE 13.1

A parental population with the Hardy-Weinberg proportions of genotypes will produce gametes at equivalent frequencies. The random assortment of these gametes will produce a progeny population in which the various genotypes are in the Hardy-Weinberg proportions.

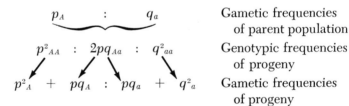

Gametic frequencies
of parent population

Genotypic frequencies
of progeny

Gametic frequencies
of progeny

The question that Hardy and Weinberg asked can be stated as follows:

(The frequency of the A allele in the parental gametes)	Does $p_A = p^2_A + pq_A$ $= p_A(p_A + q_a)$ $= p_A$	(The frequency of the A allele in the gametes produced by the progeny)

The answer to the question was that the relative frequencies of the two alleles are the same in the gametes produced by the progeny as they were in the gametes produced by the parents. This is now known as the Hardy-Weinberg law.

THE HARDY-WEINBERG LAW

There are two aspects of the Hardy-Weinberg law.

1. The relative frequencies of the two alleles remain constant from one generation to the next.
2. The three genotypes occur in quadratic proportions in populations that are at equilibrium.

Mendel deduced his first law of segregation from the $3 : 1$ ratio of hereditary alternatives in the F_2 of a cross between homozygous lines. This is a special case of the Hardy-Weinberg law in which all the parents are experimentally constrained to be heterozygous, thus setting the relative gene frequencies to equality. The frequencies of the three possible genotypes will be $1 : 2 : 1$ when the gene frequencies are equal, giving in the case of full dominance the ratio $3 : 1$. It is possible to deduce the same law without recourse to the experimental constraint of equal gene frequencies. The occurrence of the three genotypes in the quadratic proportions is a consequence of genetic segregation and random junction of gametes, and this can be generally stated as

$$p^2_{AA} \quad : \quad 2pq_{Aa} \quad : \quad q^2_{aa}$$

which is $1 : 2 : 1$ when $p = q = 0.5$.

Blood-group types in man have been very widely described, and there are extensive data on the frequencies of different types, which are known to be due to allelic genes. The M and N blood group genes constitute a very simple system in which all three possible genotypes (MM, MN, NN) can be separately recognized. Race and Sanger give some frequencies of these three types of blood in an English population:

M	MN	N	Total
363	634	282	1,279

If these three types are due to segregation of two alleles (M and N), and if mating was random in the production of this population, then they are expected to occur in quadratic proportions. The first step in testing whether these frequencies are in the quadratic proportions is to calculate the frequencies of transmission of the M and N alleles by this population. The relative frequencies of the three genotypes are

MM	MN	NN
28.4%	49.5%	22.1%

Individuals of the MM genotype produce 28.4% of the gametes, all containing the M gene. Individuals of the MN genotype produce 45.9% of the gametes, but only half of these will contain the M gene. The frequency of gametes carrying the M gene is, therefore, 28.4 + 24.7% = 53.1%.

The same logic can be used to show that the frequency of gametes carrying the N gene is 24.7 + 22.1% = 46.8%.

The expected quadratic proportions are then

$$(0.53)^2 \quad : \quad 2\,(0.53 \times 0.47) \quad : \quad (0.47)^2$$
$$= \quad 0.28 \quad : \quad 0.50 \quad : \quad 0.22$$

These proportions can be transformed into the numbers of individuals that are expected of each genotype.

M	MN	N	
361	637	281	Expected
363	634	282	Actual

The agreement is extremely close. Stern (1960), in his excellent textbook, quotes results for several populations in which the frequencies of M and N range from the M gene's being infrequent to the N gene's being infrequent. In all this wide range, the frequencies of the three genotypes agree with the quadratic proportions.

	M	MN	N	p_M	q_N	
Australian	3.0	29.6	67.4	0.18	0.82	Actual
aboriginal	3.2	29.3	67.6			Expected
Ainus	17.9	50.2	31.9	0.43	0.57	Actual
	18.5	49.0	32.3			Expected
White (U.S.)	29.2	49.6	21.3	0.54	0.46	Actual
	29.2	49.7	21.2			Expected
Indians (U.S.)	60.0	35.1	4.9	0.78	0.22	Actual
	60.2	34.8	5.0			Expected
Eskimos	83.5	15.6	0.9	0.91	0.09	Actual
	83.4	15.0	0.8			Expected

This is a convincing demonstration of the second aspect of the Hardy-Weinberg law: the three genotypes will occur in quadratic proportions. The Hardy-Weinberg law is basic to the understanding of the genetic structure of populations, and much effort has been given to determining the conditions under which it is, or is not, valid.

The effects of mutation, of migration, of selection, of inbreeding have all been examined to determine how they affect the prediction that gene frequencies will remain constant, and that the frequencies of genotypes will occur in quadratic proportions.

Problems

1. The frequency of albinos in the population is 1 : 20,000. If this character is due to a single recessive gene, what is its frequency?

2. Blue versus dark-colored eyes in man could be due to a recessive genetic difference: bb = blue, bB and BB = dark. If the frequency of blue-eyed individuals in a population is 16%, what is the frequency of heterozygotes? In what percentage of marriages would both parents be heterozygotes?

Chapter 14

INBREEDING AND THE GENETIC LOAD

The Hardy-Weinberg law is only valid in very large populations where mating is random. One factor having a marked effect on the genetic constitution of populations is *inbreeding*. Populations in which inbreeding occurs have a different structure from those in which there is no inbreeding. Inbreeding is defined as the mating of relatives, but this definition is not useful since every individual of a species is to some degree or another related to every other individual. Each individual, theoretically, has

2 parents
4 grandparents
8 great-grandparents
16 great-great-grandparents
32 great-great-great-grandparents
64 great-great-great-great-grandparents
128 great-great-great-great-great-grandparents
and so on.

Consider the present population of the United States (about 190,000,000), seven generations ago (about 200 years) these should have had a population of 25,000,000,000 great...grandparents, if no mating of relatives occurred. Since the ancestral population of the present U.S.A. population clearly was not of this size, it follows that there must be a much greater degree of relationship between individuals than is normally envisaged.

A more useful definition of inbreeding is that it is mating between *close* relatives, and there is a considerable volume of both civil and religious law defining what is meant by close relatives. Matings of parents with progeny, or brothers with sisters, are almost universally prohibited. Matings of second-order relatives (first cousins, uncle–niece, aunt–nephew) are prohibited fairly widely, but not generally. (There have been periods in history

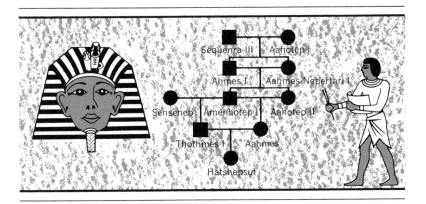

FIGURE 14.1

Pedigree of the Pharaohs of Egypt.

when inbreeding was not considered a crime. The Pharaohs of Egypt favored marriages of brothers with sisters.) This raises the question of the validity of the proscriptions against inbreeding: does inbreeding have effects that are detrimental? There is no general answer to this question. Many species of plants reproduce by self-fertilization, which is one of the most intensive forms of inbreeding, and yet they seem no less vigorous or healthy than related plants that reproduce by cross-fertilization. However, if the question is restricted to species that normally reproduce by cross-fertilization, then there is no doubt that inbreeding has detrimental effects; but even this statement has to be qualified. The detrimental effects are statistical, not absolute. The probability of stillbirths or infantile and juvenile deaths is greater in the offspring of the mating of close relatives. Inbreeding reduces the probability of survival. It also affects the probability that offspring will have physical or mental defects. Such defects are more frequent in offspring of matings between close relatives.

PARENT RELATION	EARLY DEATH OF OFFSPRING		MENTAL AND PHYSICAL DEFECTS
	Stillbirths	*Infantile and juvenile*	
First cousins	0.087	0.138	0.117
Second cousins	0.060	0.093	—
Unrelated	0.038	0.072	0.046

The incidence of early death and of physical and mental defects has been measured in various populations. These figures cannot be accepted as precise and definitive, but even allowing for various inaccuracies, marriages between first cousins clearly have a greater physical or mental defects.

Several questions are raised by these facts. Why is inbreeding detrimental in crossbreeding organisms but not in self-fertilizing organisms? Why do the deleterious effects of inbreeding show in some offspring and not in others? What is the cause of the detrimental effect of inbreeding? The answers to these questions are apparent from a consideration of the effects of inbreeding on the genetic constitution of populations.

HOMOZYGOSITY AND INBREEDING

In a large population where mating is random, the frequencies of genotypes for a single segregating genetic difference are:

$$p^2_{AA} : 2pq_{Aa} : q^2_{aa}$$

Suppose this population suddenly changes from random mating to self-fertilization, then the AA and aa individuals will produce only AA and aa progeny respectively. The Aa individuals will segregate, producing all three types, in the ratio of $1 : 2 : 1$.

After one generation of self-fertilization, the frequencies of the three types will be:

$$\left(p^2 + \frac{pq}{2}\right)_{AA} : pq_{Aa} : \left(q^2 + \frac{pq}{2}\right)_{aa}$$

The proportion of heterozygotes has halved after one generation of self-fertilization, and the proportion of homozygotes has increased. The proportion of heterozygotes will continue to halve at every generation, and eventually there will be no heterozygotes in the population.

$$(p^2 + pq)_{AA} : --_{Aa} : (q^2 + pq)_{Aa}$$

Clearly, inbreeding in the form of self-fertilization has resulted in a marked change of the genetic constitution of the population. The Hardy-Weinberg expectation that the three genotypes will occur in the quadratic proportions no longer holds; instead, only the homozygous genotypes occur, in the following proportions:

$$(p^2 + pq)_{AA} : (q^2 + pq)_{aa}$$
$$= [p(p + q)]_{AA} : [q(q + p)]_{aa}$$

but since $(p + q) = 1$, the frequencies are

$$p_{AA} \quad : \quad q_{aa}$$

These proportions are the original gene frequencies, and a second aspect of the effect of self-fertilization can be added. Self-fertilization does not affect the Hardy-Weinberg expectation that the frequencies of genes will remain constant—this is still valid. The effects of inbreeding are to increase the proportions of homozygotes without affecting the proportions of transmission of genes. This applies to the inbreeding of a population, and we need to make a distinction between this and an inbred line of descent.

INBRED LINES

The mating of brothers and sisters in the Pharaoh dynasty is an example of an inbred line of descent.

Suppose a population suddenly changes from random mating to brother-sister mating (sib mating); after a few generations, the population will have separated into a number of separate inbred lines of descent. Each line will eventually, in the absence of genetic complication, be pure for a particular homozygous type: some will consist only of *AA* individuals, others will consist only of *aa* individuals. The proportions of *AA* and *aa* lines will be the same as the original frequencies of *A* and *a*. Brother-sister mating, like self-fertilization, results in an increase of the frequencies of homozygotes, without affecting the frequencies of the genes over the whole population of inbred lines.

The fastest possible way of forming an inbred line of descent in a bisexual organism, such as the mouse or man, is by brother-sister mating. Many such inbred lines have been formed in mice in this way, in which brother-sister mating has been continued for more than 50 generations. A marked feature of such inbreeding has been that many lines are lost in the early generations due to their low viability. The surviving lines are not as viable as normal, crossbred populations, nor are they as fertile, and there is a decreased probability of survival to maturity. The inbred lines are remarkably uniform in many of their characteristics in comparison with normal, crossbred lines. Conversely, they are noticeably more variable in other characteristics. It appears that the homozygosity consequent from inbreeding can result in an increased uniformity for some characteristics and a decreased uniformity for others. This feature of inbreeding will be considered again later.

The genetic consequences of inbreeding can provide an explanation of the detrimental effects of inbreeding. This is based on a widespread occurrence of recessive genes which have detrimental or lethal effects when homozygous.

RECESSIVE LETHALS

Juvenile amaurotic idiocy in man is caused by a recessive gene. Its primary effect is to cause the accumulation of fatty substances in nervous tissue, which leads to mental degeneration and early death. The gene for this defect can be represented as *ami*, and its normal allele by $+^{ami}$. We will consider a pedigree in which mating occurred between cousins with a common grandparent who was heterozygous for these genes. The grandparent could transmit the *ami* gene to two children, who could in their turn transmit it to one each of their children. These children would then be first cousins and, if they mated to produce offspring, there would be a probability of 0.25% that each child from such a mating would be homozygous for the *ami* gene. Inbreeding in a line of descent can result in the junction of two lines of transmission of a lethal gene with the increased probability of production of offspring who are homozygous for the gene.

It is relatively simple to place this situation on a numerical basis, remembering that the probability of transmission of a specific allele is 50% (see Figure 14.2).

The calculation from Figure 14.2 shows that the offspring of the mating of first cousins have $\frac{1}{64}$ chance of being homozygous for a recessive lethal gene carried by one of the common grandparents as a heterozygote. Clearly, this is a way to understand the detrimental effects of inbreeding: if there is a recessive detrimental gene in an inbred line of descent, the mating of close relatives can result in offspring that are homozygous for this gene. These offspring can have a lowered chance of survival, or mental or physical defects caused by the detrimental gene. Conversely, if there are no such recessive detrimental genes in a line of descent, inbreeding will have no effect. This can explain how inbreeding can have a detrimental effect in some cases and not in others. Inbreeding is not detrimental except in the increased homozygosity of recessive genes that it causes. This is a logical, convincing explanation, which raises the question: how frequent are such recessive detrimental genes in populations?

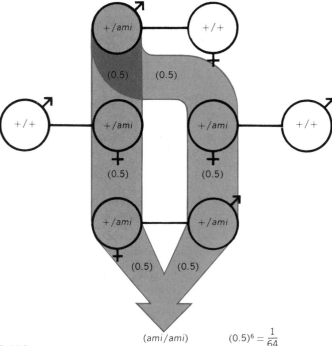

$$(ami/ami) \qquad (0.5)^6 = \frac{1}{64}$$

FIGURE 14.2

Transmission of the ami gene in a hypothetical pedigree involving first-cousin marriage. The probability of such a marriage resulting in ami/ami offspring can be found by tracing the possible lines of descent of the ami gene from the common grandparent.

THE GENETIC LOAD

Some idea of the frequency of lethal genes in a population can be gained from measurements of the rate of mutation to recessive lethality, which is about 0.1% for the X chromosome in Drosophila. About 1:1,000 X chromosomes has a lethal gene that mutated in that generation. If such a lethal X chromosome joins with a Y chromosome to form a male zygote, the line of descent is terminated by the lethality. If, on the other hand, the lethal X chromosome joins with a nonlethal X chromosome to form a female zygote, the line of descent will continue. The mutation of the X chromosome will then result in the initiation of lines of descent of recessive lethality: some of these will be terminated by the chance nontransmission of the chromosome; others will be terminated by transmission into males; still others will continue by transmission from heterozygous females to heterozygous female offspring. A population of Drosophila will, therefore, contain 0.1% newly mutated X chromosomes, and a greater percentage of lethal X chromosomes that were produced by mutation in earlier generations.

The X chromosome is only one of the four chromosomes of the Drosophila genotype. Two of these are the same order of size as the X chromosome, and they can be expected to have the same order of mutation to lethality. The IVth chromosome is very small and will, presumably, have a much lower rate of mutation to lethality. Mutation of the genes of chromosomes other than the X chromosomes will result in the addition of further lines of descent of lethality. These will involve autosomal genes, and there will be a much lower rate of termination of these lines of descent by lethality, because the lethality will only be expressed when the same lethal chromosome is inherited from both parents.

A population should, therefore, contain an appreciable proportion of individuals that are heterozygous for lethal chromosomes. Measurements of the frequency of such chromosomes in natural populations of Drosophila have shown that the conclusion is correct —natural populations do contain a very high frequency of lethal genes. Over 1,000 X chromosomes were tested in one experiment, and 55% of these were found to be lethal when homozygous. Tests of several thousand IIIrd chromosomes showed that approximately one-third were lethal when homozygous. The great majority of both the X and the IIIrd chromosomes which contained lethal genes were independent in their lethality, which is expected if there are many different genes that can independently mutate to lethality. Tests were also made for the frequency of chromosomes that were not lethal, but that did have recessive deleterious effects causing infertility, decreased rate of growth, etc. Such chromosomes were also found to occur at a high frequency.

Clearly, the occurrence of lethal and deleterious genes at such high frequencies will result in almost every individual's being heterozygous for such genes. Normally, these genes will have no effect unless both parents are heterozygous for the same lethal or deleterious genes. In a random-mated, large population, this will occur rarely. If mating is not random, but is between close relatives, the same lethal or deleterious gene (transmitted to both relatives by a common ancestor) can be combined in the offspring. This will result in genetic death, either directly, or by infertility or lowered

every individual heterozygous for a lethal or deleterious gene

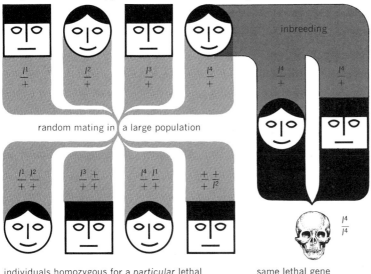

individuals homozygous for a *particular* lethal
gene are very infrequent—genetic deaths are rare

same lethal gene
transmitted to and by
both parents

homozygotes for a
particular lethal are
frequent—genetic deaths
are common

FIGURE 14.3

Inbreeding. There is a high probability that every individual is heterozygous for lethal or deleterious genes. Since these are recessive, the occurrence of individuals homozygous for a particular gene is very low in large, random-mating populations. Inbreeding will often result in such harmful homozygosity.

viability. The deleterious effects of inbreeding can be understood as a consequence of populations' containing a high frequency of genes that are deleterious when homozygous. This has been called the "genetic load."

INBREEDING AND RECESSIVE GENES

The frequency of matings between close relatives is not very high; for example, in Austria, the frequency of first-cousin marriages was found to be 0.5%. Similar values were found for large cities in Brazil and Spain but if the frequency of such matings is determined for parents of offspring with homozygous recessive defects, it is found to be much higher. The incidence of first-cousin marriages between parents of juvenile amaurotic idiots is 15%. Another recessive defect, phenylketonuria, is marked by 5 to 15% of first-cousin marriages between the parents. It is now accepted that if offspring with a particular trait have an increased frequency of inbreeding in their ancestry, the trait probably is heritable and recessive.

POPULATION SIZE AND INBREEDING

The frequency of inbreeding increases as the size of the population decreases. Where a population is broken up into small, isolated villages, the frequency of first-cousin marriages can be as high as 10% (Swiss Alpine communities). It reaches 30% in Fiji Island villages, but this is also due to social pressure in favor of such marriages. As can be expected, the frequency of progeny with homozygous recessive defects is markedly higher in such communities

One way to study the effects of population size would be to set up a number of populations differing in size, but having the same gene frequency. If records were maintained for a number of generations, it would be possible to determine the relative effects of population size on genetic structure. This experiment has only been done with small populations, but an equivalent experiment with much larger populations has been done using electronic models of genetic systems. An automatic electronic computer can be set to imitate all the genetic essentials of reproduction. The machine can be set to imitate meiosis, fertilization, and so forth. Figure 14.4 shows the results of such "experiments" where populations segregating for a single genetic difference were started at a gene frequency of 50% for each allele, and allowed to reproduce without any selection. A number of different populations of the same size and of different sizes were maintained in this way. When the number of individuals was small, the gene frequency fluctuated widely

FIGURE 14.4

Artificial computer populations. The frequencies of a single genetic difference are shown vertically from 0−1 for one allele (the complementary values are the frequency of the other allele). The number of generations of random mating is given horizontally, and each block represents a different-sized breeding group, from 4 to 1,024 individuals. The random changes of gene frequency are less in the large than in the small populations.

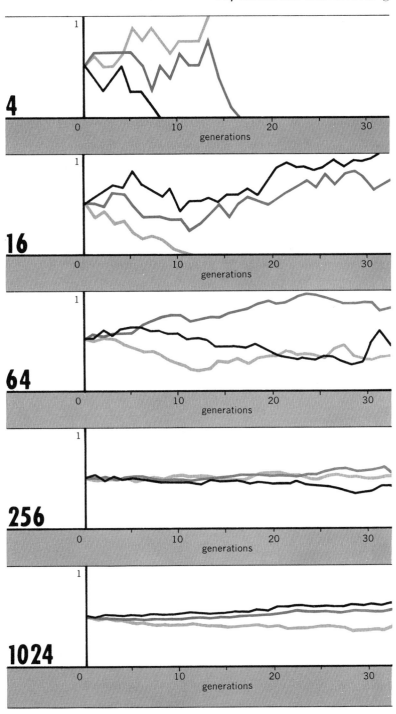

from one generation to the next, and eventually each population lost one or the other of the segregating alleles. The populations became genetically fixed—all individuals were homozygous for the same allele. In the larger populations the fluctuation was less noticeable, and it took longer for the loss of one or the other allele to occur. In the largest populations where the number of individuals was 1,024, the fluctuation was very small, and there was a very reasonable agreement with the Hardy-Weinberg expectation of constant gene frequencies. However, even in these large populations there is a noticeable change of gene frequencies over the duration of the experiment. If such populations are maintained for hundreds of generations, then even in large populations there is a dispersion away from the original gene frequency toward fixation.

Inbreeding causes an increase of homozygosity; decrease of population size causes an increase of inbreeding, so decrease of population size will cause an increase of homozygosity. If a large population is separated into a number of isolated small populations, the eventual result will be an increased frequency of homozygotes and a decreased frequency of heterozygotes, but no change of the frequencies of genes over the whole group of populations. Gene frequencies for each little population will be changed, but the average over all populations will be unchanged. Inbreeding and decrease of population size modify only one of the features of the Hardy-Weinberg law: the expectation that genotypes will occur in the ratio of quadratic proportions. Inbreeding can be considered as causing a redistribution of genetic variability.

Problems

1. If a plant that is heterozygous for 1,000 separate genes is taken as the starting point for a self-fertilized line, how many of these loci will be heterozygous after (a) one, (b) two, (c) ten, and (d) 100 generations?

2. If the frequency of the gene for juvenile amaurotic idiocy (*ami*) is 0.01 (1%):
   (a) What is the frequency of heterozygous individuals?
   (b) What is the frequency of *ami/ami* individuals?

3. Is it possible to distinguish between genetically large and small populations? How many individuals comprise a small population? What is the smallest number of individuals that will comprise a large population?

QUICK QUIZ *Chapters 10 through 14*

1. Cells without nuclei:
   (a) die.
   (b) live for a long time.
   (c) cannot divide.
   (d) synthesize proteins (if they contain RNA).

2. RNA differs from DNA in:
   (a) being single- instead of double-stranded.
   (b) containing uracil instead of thymine.
   (c) containing ribose instead of deoxyribose.
   (d) occurring in both the nucleus and the cytoplasm.

3. Messenger RNA is:
   (a) the basic material of the ribosomes.
   (b) capable of forming hybrid molecules with DNA.
   (c) capable of joining with amino acids to locate them on the ribosomes.

4. Mongoloid idiocy is caused by a trisomic condition. This means that:
   (a) cells of Mongoloids have three nuclei.
   (b) cells have three sets of chromosomes.
   (c) cells have three instead of two of a particular chromosome.

5. The Bar mutation involves the duplication of a region of the X chromosome containing several bands. This mutation frequently mutates to double-Bar, or to wild type. This mutation rate is high because:
   (a) Bar is inherently an unstable gene.
   (b) Bar involves several genes, any one of which can mutate.
   (c) misplaced pairing at meiosis results in unequal crossing over.

6. The use of the *ClB* chromosome to detect mutations to lethality of the X chromosome depends on:

   (*a*) its containing an inversion.

   (*b*) its containing a recessive lethal gene.

   (*c*) its containing the Bar duplication.

   (*d*) all of the above.

7. The Hardy-Weinberg equilibrium can be expressed as $p^2 : 2pq : q^2$. Which of the following populations do not fit this equilibrium?

	AA	Aa	aa
(*a*)	0.25	0.50	0.25
(*b*)	0.36	0.54	0.10
(*c*)	0.64	0.10	0.26
(*d*)	0.81	0.18	0.01

8. Mating of cousins is invariably a bad thing because:

   (*a*) inbreeding is deleterious.

   (*b*) there is an increased probability of the parents' being heterozygous for the same recessive deleterious gene.

   (*c*) relatives should not marry.

9. The separation of a large population into a number of isolated small populations results in:

   (*a*) an increased frequency of homozygotes.

   (*b*) no detectable genetic effects.

   (*c*) an increased frequency of recessive defects.

Chapter 15

MIGRATION AND MUTATION

The Hardy-Weinberg law predicts that the frequencies of genes in a population will remain constant from generation to generation, *yet* any set of related populations characteristically differs in its frequencies of the same genes.

BLOOD GROUPS

Several simple tests have been devised that allow description of genetic differences affecting the chemical structure of the blood. Many different genetic loci are involved: the M and N alleles of one locus affect one feature; the A, B, and O alleles of another locus affect another feature; the Rh^+ and Rh^- alleles of a third locus determine yet another feature. The simplicity of the testing methods and the widespread introduction of blood transfusion have resulted in the accumulation of extensive descriptions of the frequencies of these genes in human populations. These data have been extremely important in understanding the effects of migration ,on the genetic geography of man.

The M and N genes have been shown to vary markedly from one human population to another. The M allele has a low frequency in Australian aboriginals, whereas it has a very high frequency among Eskimos. The frequencies of the A, B, and O alleles also vary widely between populations. The B allele has a high frequency among Mongolians (as high as 30%), which contrasts with the low frequency of this allele in Icelanders. If a number of genes are studied, it is reasonably safe to say that any isolated population will have a characteristic set of frequencies of those genes, which will be different from that of any other population of the same species. Since all populations of the same species trace back to some initial population, this raises

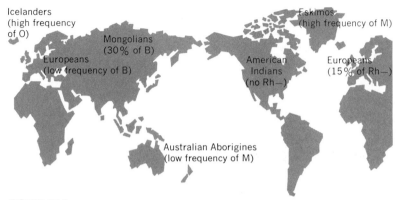

FIGURE 15.1

A few illustrations of differences that have been found in the frequencies of blood group genes in man.

an interesting paradox. The Hardy-Weinberg prediction of the *constancy* of gene frequencies contrasts with the genetic variation found between populations.

Migration is a possible explanation of how related populations may have very different gene frequencies. Suppose a small group migrates from a main population; the gene frequencies in this small group may differ from those of the parental population by chance, and this will lead to the new population having a different set of gene frequencies. This has been called the *founder effect*.

THE FOUNDER EFFECT

Suppose a single population of a species is evolved on an island, separated from the continents by long expanses of ocean. The species will be restricted to the island unless a rare accident results in a few individuals' surviving the journey to the mainland. They will then set the genetic pattern for a new population that will not necessarily have the same set of gene frequencies as the parental population on the island. This is just one example of isolation; communities may be separated by impassable tracts of ice, as are the Eskimos who occur in a number of small isolated groups. The frequencies of the A, B, and O genes fluctuate markedly from one group of Eskimos to the next, which is what would be expected if each of these populations were founded by a small group of migrants. The same fluctuation is found in the tribes of the Australian aboriginals, who also exist in small isolated populations.

The founder effect can result in genetic diversity when migration is sporadic, in small groups. This can reconcile the apparent paradox between the genetic variability of actual populations and the genetic constancy predicted by the Hardy-Weinberg law.

MIGRATION STREAMS

The founder effect can result in large differences of gene frequency between populations. A continued migration stream would not, however, have this effect; eventually the daughter population would have the same gene frequency as the parent population. Migration can originate genetic differences, but it can also reduce and remove them, depending on the amount of migration.

American Indian populations differ from European populations in the frequencies of the Rh⁺ and Rh⁻ alleles. The Rh⁻ allele does not occur in American Indians, whereas it occurs at a frequency of 15% in Europeans. The dramatic migrations of Europeans into North America, with intermarriage between them and the American Indians, will eventually result in introduction of Rh⁻ allele into American Indian populations and its increase to the same frequency as in the Europeans. By then, of course, the American Indian populations will be only a matter of history, perpetuated solely by surnames. A genetic difference can be obliterated by a migration stream.

GENETIC GEOGRAPHY

The map of Europe is crisscrossed by national boundaries, but it is possible to superimpose new lines separating regions in which the populations are characterized by different frequencies of the A, B, and O alleles. There is a high frequency of the B allele in Eastern Europe, which grades down to a low frequency in Western Europe. Mongolians have a high frequency of the B allele, and there have been repeated invasions by them into Eastern Europe. The graded increase in frequency of the B allele from West to East possibly resulted from this migration.

Another feature of the genetic geography of Europe is the high frequency of the O allele in the Western periphery: Ireland, Scotland, Iceland. The Celtic peoples of these regions can be considered as the original occupants of the whole of Western Europe. They were supplanted or genetically overrun by a migration stream of the present type who do not have a high frequency of the O allele.

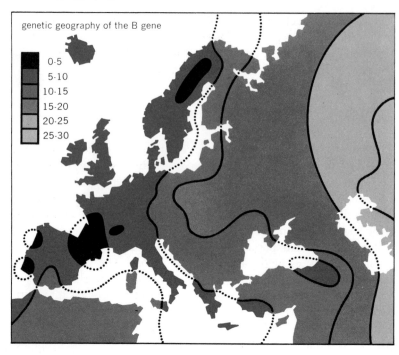

genetic geography of the B gene

■	0-5
	5-10
	10-15
	15-20
	20-25
	25-30

FIGURE 15.2

The genetic geography of Europe in terms of the B blood group gene. There is a trend of decreasing frequency from East to West, considered to be a result of the frequent invasions in that direction by Mongolians who have a high frequency of this gene.

Patterns of migration have been studied extensively in many organisms, but it is difficult to evaluate the genetic consequences of migration unless information is available on genetic relationships. One group of organisms whose patterns of migration have been studied extensively at the genetic level are domestic livestock: cattle, sheep, pigs, poultry. The Merino breed of sheep in Australia exists in a very large population divided into separate flocks ranging in size from a few hundred to tens of thousands. The division is not only geographical; it is also genetic. A small number of large flocks have been isolated from the main population for many decades— these are the elite stud flocks which do not accept any immigrants from other flocks. Although the elite stud flocks have been isolated, the reverse is not true. Many production stud flocks buy their rams from the elite stud flocks, and these in turn sell their rams to the rest of the population. The migration is from the elite stud flocks to the production stud flocks to the main population. Thus any genetic changes that occur or are produced by selection in the elite stud flocks will eventually be spread through the whole population.

The genetic effects of migration are a complex and not fully understood aspect of the variability occurring between populations. The reason for this complexity is that migration seldom, if ever, occurs in the absence of the other factors that affect genetic variation. Mutation is one of these factors.

MUTATION

Migration can increase genetic diversity, but only for populations that are already variable. If all the individuals of a species are genetically identical, no amount or manner of migration can result in genetic diversity. Mutation is the only mechanism that can introduce genetic variability.

Consider a situation where the human species contained only the O allele of the A, B, O set of alleles. Migration around the world would not affect this situation. The only way for the A and B alleles to appear would be by mutation of the O allele into A or B. These three alleles are of widespread occurrence, which raises the question: could the genetic diversity for the A, B, O alleles have originated from unique mutational events? If the mutation of O → A, or B → O, or A → B involved such complicated changes of the gene that they can only be expected to occur a few times in the history of man, could the actual diversity be explained by such unique mutations?

UNIQUE MUTATIONS

Suppose in a human population that all individuals are OO, and that a mutation occurs to the A allele. The new gene will exist in a single OA individual. What is the probability that this new gene will become a feature of the population? If the population is static in size, an individual will produce, on an average, two progeny. There is a 50% chance that the A gene will be transmitted to one or other of these progeny; a 25% chance that it will be transmitted to neither; and a 25% chance that it will be transmitted to both. The chance that the new gene will be lost in the first generation is 25%. One-quarter of such unique mutations will be lost in the first generation. This loss by chance can occur every generation, but so can an increase in the number of heterozygotes—

the chance that the A gene will be transmitted to two individuals is also 25%. Such a chance increase will decrease the possibility that the gene will be lost in a later generation. However, the possibility that a unique mutation will become a feature of the population is small. The calculation of such degrees of improbability involves some fairly sophisticated algebra which has no place here. Chance can operate in both ways—the great majority of new mutations will be lost, but a very few will become incorporated into the genetic structure of populations as something more than rare oddities. Considering that there are many thousands of loci, which can probably each mutate in dozens of different ways, it is probable that some features of genetic diversity are chance incorporations of unique mutations. However, it is unlikely that this process can be accepted as responsible for more than a minor part of the genetic diversity that actually exists. We need to consider other possibilities.

REPEATED MUTATIONS

Most genes seem to mutate repeatedly to similar or identical mutant alleles and, conversely, most mutant alleles seem to have the potential to mutate back to the original allele. Suppose, once again, a population of OO individuals in which mutation from O → A occurs repeatedly at a rate of 1 : 100,000 gametes. Each specific mutational event will have the same low chance of survival as if it were a unique mutation, but repetition over enough time will eventually result in the whole population's becoming AA. This would clearly take an extremely long time. Now consider the situation where the A allele mutates to 0 at the same rate as O mutates to A. Initially, since the whole population is OO, the only mutations will be of O → A, but later, as the effect of this process builds up, there will be mutations of A → O. At first, there will be only a few A alleles in the population, and this mutation from A → O will be unimportant compared to the mutation of O → A. However, as the frequency of A increases, so the importance of the mutation of A → O will also increase. Eventually, the frequency of A will equal that of O, and the number of mutations from O → A will equal that of A → O. The effects of forward-and-back mutation will be balanced, and no further change of the frequencies of the O and A genes will occur. This balancing of the effects of mutation rates in the forward-and-back directions does not depend on the mutation rates' being equal. They can be quite different and still result in a genetic equilibrium.

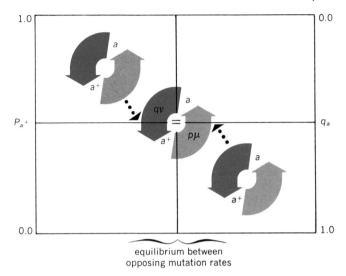

0.0 — 1.0 — 0.0 — 1.0

P_{a^+} — q_a

qv — $p\mu$ — =

equilibrium between
opposing mutation rates

FIGURE 15.3

When the a^+ allele is the most frequent, mutations will be predominantly $a^+ \to a$. The converse is true when the a allele is the most frequent. There will be a balance when the two alleles occur in frequencies inversely proportional to their mutation rates.

GENETIC EQUILIBRIUM

Suppose the frequency of the O allele is p, and that of A is q, i.e. the B allele does not occur in this hypothetical population. Further, suppose that

O mutates to A at a frequency of μ

and that

A mutates to O at a frequency of v

then when

$$p\mu = qv$$

as many O alleles will have mutated to A, as A alleles have mutated to O; the population will be at equilibrium,

and

$$p/q = v/\mu$$

Suppose $\mu = 1/100,000$, and $v = 1/50,000$, then

$$p/q = \frac{1/50,000}{1/100,000} = 2.0$$

and

$$p = 0.66 = \text{frequency of O}$$
$$q = 0.33 = \text{frequency of A}$$

which is simply an algebraic way of saying that if O mutates to A only half as frequently as A mutates to O, the accounts will balance when there are twice as many O alleles as there are A alleles.

Mutation can account for genetic diversity, but it will take so long for this to effect a change that we can exclude it as a major force in shaping genetic diversity. Mutation is the origin of genetic diversity—migration can modify it, inbreeding can redistribute it —but the main force in shaping the genetic structure of populations is selection.

Problems

1. Consider an island population of an insect in which there is no overlap of generations—the parents all die before their offspring reach reproductive age. The island has only sufficient resources for 1,000 individuals to mature. Initially the population is homozygous for a recessive dark coloration, but in each generation there is an immigration of 100 individuals who are homozygous for a dominant light allele.

   What will the proportions of dark-colored and light-colored individuals be after one generation of this immigration? After a very long period of this immigration?

2. Suppose the frequency of albinism is 1 in 3,000 and that this character is due to a recessive gene. If albinism is genetically lethal, and the mutation rate is doubled, what will the frequency of albinism become when the conditions have stabilized?

3. Migration can be imagined as a stream of individuals moving in one direction; it can be imagined as a few small groups moving into uninhabited areas; and it also can be imagined, particularly today, as a general movement in all directions. Do these different views of migration have different genetic connotations?

4. What evidence would you require to demonstrate that a national difference had a genetic basis?

5. To what degree would the fact that the Rh⁻ does not occur in American Indians allow you to identify an individual as belonging to this race?

Chapter **16**

GENETIC SURVIVAL

Some genetic differences cause effects that are clearly more important than others. The genes for red-green color blindness and for muscular dystrophy are similar, both being sex-linked recessives, but they differ markedly in the importance of their effects. Inheritance of red-green color blindness has very little effect on the probability of survival, whereas inheritance of muscular dystrophy involves a crippling defect with survival rarely prolonged beyond 25 years. Some common measure of the myriad kinds of genetic effects is needed. Their effect on the duration and probability of survival could be such a common denominator, and it would have its uses, but it is easy to specify genetic differences that have drastic effects on reproductivity without having any effects on the probability of survival. Conversely, a lethal dominant gene that acts late in life would have no effect on genetic survival.

A simple common denominator of the importance of genetic differences is the probability that one allele will be transmitted more often than another. Examples of this are the "genes" affecting the virulence of the myxomatosis virus.

MYXOMATOSIS

The myxomatosis virus causes a disease in rabbits that is lethal in almost every case. Mosquitoes spread the disease by feeding on infected animals and carrying the virus to uninfected individuals. The virus was released in Australia where large areas had been effectively taken over by rabbits. The synthetic epidemic expanded with spectacular success, leaving only a few odd survivors here and there. It seemed that a final answer had been found, but in subsequent epidemics it became apparent 197 that the frequency of survivors was increasing. Collections of virus were made; these were less virulent than the original strain. With these strains the disease took longer to develop; therefore, each infected animal acted as a focus of infection for a longer period of time. Mutations must have occurred that extended the duration of the disease. These mutations then increased in frequency because they had a greater chance of being transferred by mosquitoes to uninfected animals. An exaggerated example will emphasize how this works. Suppose a mutation occurred that resulted in such extreme virulence that the infected rabbit died in a few minutes. There would be very little chance that mosquitoes would feed on the animal before it died, and the mutated virus would have a very low genetic survival. Conversely, a mutated virus that took a long time to kill its host would act as an infection center for a long time and would, obviously, have a very high genetic survival compared to the quick-killing type.

In this example there are no complexities due to sexual reproduction, diploidy, dominance, etc. Differences between strains of viruses, bacteria, etc., are the simplest illustrations of genetic survival. (The term *reproductive fitness* is usually used for genetic survival.)

POLLEN-TYPE COMPETITION

A slightly more complicated illustration is that of genes whose effects are restricted to the gametes. Suppose in some plant species that the a and a^+ genes affect the rate of growth of the pollen tube down the style to the ovule, with a causing a faster rate of growth than a^+. Pollen carrying the a allele will then have a greater probability of effecting fertilization than pollen carrying a^+. This would result in the a allele being transmitted more frequently than the a^+ allele.

Consider a population in which the two allelic genes are at equal frequencies. And suppose that the genetic survival of a is twice that of a^+. We can then ask the question: what will the frequency of the a allele be in the next generation?

	a	a^+
Frequency	0.5	0.5
Genetic survival	1.0	0.5
Frequency of fertilizations	$\overline{0.5}$	$\overline{0.25}$

The multiplication of frequency by genetic survival gives the relative genetic transmissions of these genes in the pollen. If there are no effects on the ovules, we can find the frequencies of genotypes in the next generation.

	Pollen	a	a^+
Ovules		0.5	0.25
a	0.5	0.25_{aa}	0.125_{aa^+}
a^+	0.5	0.25_{aa^+}	$0.125_{a^+a^+}$

The frequencies of the three genotypes are

$$0.25_{aa} \qquad 0.375_{aa^+} \qquad 0.125_{a^+a^+}$$

These frequencies are not percentages, but they can be converted by dividing by the total frequency:

$$\frac{0.25}{0.25 + 0.375 + 0.125} = 0.33_{aa}$$

$$\frac{0.375}{0.25 + 0.375 + 0.125} = 0.50_{a^+a}$$

$$\frac{0.125}{0.25 + 0.375 + 0.125} = 0.17_{a^+a^+}$$

The frequencies of the two alleles in this population are

$$(0.33 + 0.25)_a \quad \text{and} \quad (0.25 + 0.17)_{a^+}$$
$$= \qquad 0.58_a \qquad \text{and} \qquad 0.42_{a^+}$$

There has been an increase of 8% in the frequency of the a allele. The increase will continue in each generation, with the frequency of the a allele increasing and that of the a^+ allele decreasing.

Even very small differences of genetic survival can produce appreciable changes of gene frequency which, if continued for enough generations, can account for genetic diversity. However, very few genes act on gametes; most produce their effects in diploid body cells. Is selection equally effective for such genes?

RECESSIVE LETHALS

Many mutant genes have recessive effects that result in early death, before reproductive maturity. Other mutants have recessive effects that result in complete sterility. Although these are clearly different types of effects, they have in common a zero genetic survival. (They transmit no genes to offspring). Similarly, society may impose a complete sterility on particular genotypes—these would also have a zero genetic survival. All of these can be considered as a single problem: what are the genetic effects of zero genetic survival of recessive genes?

Suppose we have a population segregating for a pair of genes a and a^+, where a has a recessive zero genetic survival. We can now determine whether this will affect the frequency of the a gene, first by an arithmetic example, then algebraically, to give a general statement. Suppose the frequencies of a and a^+ are equal, i.e., they are both at a frequency of 50%. The frequencies of the three genotypes will be as tabulated here.

	a^+a^+	aa^+	aa
Frequency	0.25	0.50	0.25
Genetic survival	1.0	1.0	0.0
Frequency of genetic transmission	0.25	0.50	0.0

$$\text{Frequency of } a^+ = \frac{0.25 + 0.25}{0.75} = 0.66$$

The frequency of the a^+ gene has increased from 50% to 66% in a single generation. What will be the frequencies of the three possible genotypes in the next generation?

	a^+a^+	a^+a	aa
Frequency	0.44	0.44	0.11
Genetic survival	1.0	1.0	0.0
Frequency of genetic transmission	0.44	0.44	0.0

$$\text{Frequency of } a^+ = \frac{0.44 + 0.22}{0.88} = 0.75$$

The frequency of the a^+ gene, which increased from 50% to 66% in the first generation has increased from 66% to 75% in the next generation. It increased 16% in the first generation, but only 9% in the next generation. If we continued for further generations we would find that the increase in frequency of the a^+ allele would be 5%, 3%, 2.5%, and so on. Here is a clear example of the "law of diminishing returns": As the frequency of a decreases there is a proportionately greater decrease in the frequency of aa individuals. Because the decreased genetic survival is only manifested in these individuals, the difference between a^+ and a has a decreasing effectiveness as a becomes rare.

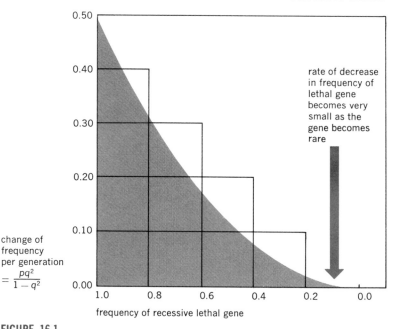

FIGURE 16.1

The rate of decrease in frequency of a recessive lethal gene is not constant —it varies with gene frequency, becoming less and less as the recessive lethal gene decreases in frequency.

The action of selection against the a allele can be represented by algebraic symbols, and an equation derived to express, in general terms, the effectiveness of selection.

Suppose that the frequencies of a^+ and a are p and q, then:

	a^+a^+	a^+a	aa
Genotype frequencies	p^2	$2pq$	q^2
Genetic survivals	1	1	0
Frequencies of parents	p^2	$2pq$	0

And we can calculate the new frequency of the a^+ allele as:

$$\text{Frequency of } a^+ = \frac{p^2 + pq}{p^2 + 2pq}$$

$$\text{Increase in frequency of } a^+ = \frac{pq^2}{1 - q^2}$$

This is a pleasantly simple expression that allows us to determine the rate at which the a^+ allele would increase in populations having any specific values for p and q.

Algebraic expansion

Increase in frequency of a^+

$= $ New frequency $(p^2 + pq)/(p^2 + 2pq)$ $-$ initial frequency (p)

$$= \frac{p^2 + pq}{p^2 + 2pq} - p$$

$$= \frac{p^2 + pq - p(p^2 + 2pq)}{p^2 + 2pq}$$

$$= \frac{p^2 + pq - p^2(p + 2q)}{p^2 + 2pq}$$

$$= \frac{p^2 + pq - p^2(1 + q)}{p^2 + 2pq}$$

$$= \frac{p^2 + pq - p^2 - p^2 q}{p^2 + 2pq}$$

$$= \frac{pq - p^2 q}{p^2 + 2pq}$$

$$= \frac{pq\,(1 - p)}{p^2 + 2pq} \qquad \text{Remember that } 1 - p = q$$

$$= \frac{pq^2}{p^2 + 2pq} \qquad \begin{array}{l}\text{Remember that } p^2 + 2pq + q^2 = 1 \\ \text{so } p^2 + 2pq = 1 - q^2\end{array}$$

$$= \frac{pq^2}{1 - q^2}$$

GENETIC CHECKS AND BALANCES

A recessive lethal allele will decrease in frequency because of selection acting against it in favor of the normal allele. This effect of selection will be countered by mutation. As the recessive lethal allele becomes rare, the majority of mutations will be from the normal allele to the lethal allele. Mutation will act directionally against the effect of selection. Eventually, these two forces will balance each other, and no further change of gene frequency will occur.

The increase in frequency of the normal allele to a recessive lethal gene is given by

$$\frac{pq^2}{1 - q^2}.$$

The decrease in frequency of the normal allele, due to its mutation to the recessive lethal gene, is given by μp (where μ is the rate of mutation of $a^+ \to a$).

We can now ask the important question: at what frequency of a recessive lethal allele will the selection against it be counterbalanced by the mutation from the normal allele to it? In our algebraic representation, this will be when:

Increase in frequency of the normal allele by *selection*	=	Increase in frequency of the recessive lethal allele by *mutation*

or when does $\quad \dfrac{pq^2}{1 - q^2} \quad = \quad \mu p$

Since q^2 will be a very small number when such a balance is reached, we can ignore $(1 - q^2)$ as being effectively 1.

Therefore $\qquad\qquad pq^2 \;=\; \mu p$

and so $\qquad\qquad\quad q^2 \;=\; \mu$

Thus the equilibrium between mutation and selection will be reached when the frequency of recessive lethal homozygotes is equal to the mutation rate. Since mutation rates are of the order of 1 : 100,000 gametes, we can say that a population produces:

> one homozygous lethal individual
> per hundred thousand individuals
> per gene that mutates to recessive lethality.

Suppose, in humans, that there are 1,000 such genes; we would expect one homozygous lethal individual per hundred individuals. This is 1%, but remember that most lethal genes would be expected to act early in development, resulting in miscarriages and abortions.

So far, we have considered only the case of genes that have a zero genetic survival in homozygotes. What about genes that reduce the survival less drastically?

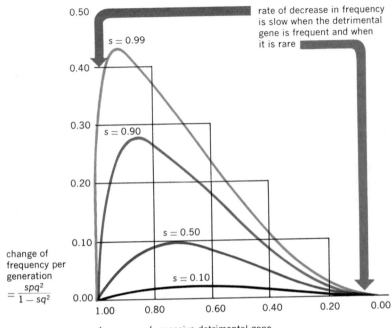

FIGURE 16.2

The rate of decrease in frequency of a recessive detrimental gene is proportional to the inadequacy caused by the gene.

DETRIMENTAL GENES

The algebra follows the same pattern as before and leads to the following expression:

$$\text{Increase in frequency of normal allele} = \frac{spq^2}{1 - sq^2}$$

If we balance this against the effect of mutation, as before, then

Increase in frequency of the normal allele by *selection*	=	Increase in frequency of the recessive detrimental allele by *mutation*
or when spq^2	=	μp
and so q^2	=	$\dfrac{\mu}{s}$

The importance of this can be seen best when substituting some real numbers. If the mutation rate is 1 : 100,000, and if the genetic survival is 50%, then

$$q^2 = \frac{0.00001}{0.5} = 0.00002$$

If the genetic survival is not zero, but is 50%, the frequency of homozygous recessive detrimentals is twice the mutation rate. If the genetic survival is 90%, only 10% less than that of normals, the frequency of homozygous recessive detrimentals would be ten times the mutation rate. If we now use the same argument as before, this will lead to an estimate of one homozygous detrimental individual per ten individuals.

This kind of genetic juggling with numbers is not sterile academic play. Consider the effect of doubling the mutation rate!

THE DOUBLING DOSE

If the amount of radiation were increased to an amount that would double the mutation rate, we could expect

one homozygous lethal individual
per 50 individuals

and

one homozygous detrimental individual
per 5 individuals.

These are the frequencies we could expect *if* the mutation rate were doubled. *if* there were 1,000 genes that could mutate to lethality at a rate of 1 : 1,000, and *if* the same set of genes or another set of 1,000 genes could mutate to a 10% level of detrimental effect at the same frequency. There are a lot of "ifs" in this sentence—far too many. The mutation rate is unlikely to increase by more than some small fraction except in the event of an atomic war, but an increased mutation rate of even a few per cent will cause an increased frequency of genetic deaths. The problem is to evaluate this increase exactly, and for this it is necessary to have accurate measurements of the genetic structure of the human race in terms of mutation rates, numbers of genes, and genetic survivals. The radiation problem is only one reason for obtaining these facts. Medicine is improving the survival of many genetically defective types, and the question can be asked: what effect will such medical advances have on the genetic structure of the human population?

Algebraic expansion

	a^+a^+	a^+a	aa
Genotypes	p^2	$2pq$	q^2
Genetic survivals	1	1	$1-s$
Parents	$\overline{p^2}$	$\overline{2pq}$	$\overline{(1-s)q^2}$

New frequency of a^+

$$= \frac{p^2 + pq}{p^2 + 2pq + (1-s)q^2}$$

$$= \frac{p(p+q)}{p^2 + 2pq + q^2 - sq^2}$$

$$= \frac{p(p+q)}{(p+q)^2 - sq^2} \qquad \text{Remember that } p + q = 1$$

$$= \frac{p}{1 - sq^2}$$

Increased frequency of a^+

$= $ New frequency $(p/1 - sq^2) - $ initial frequency (p)

$$= \frac{p}{1 - sq^2} - p$$

$$= \frac{p - p(1 - sq^2)}{1 - sq^2}$$

$$= \frac{p - p + spq^2}{1 - sq^2}$$

$$= \frac{spq^2}{1 - sq^2}$$

DIABETES

Diabetes is often genetically caused, probably as a recessive homozygosity. Its frequency is about 2%, but it is probable that many cases are not genetic in origin. Its effects can be masked partially or completely by medication with insulin. Suppose the incidence of genetically caused diabetes is 1%, and that the mutation rate is 1 : 100,000. We can then ask the question: what *is* the effect of this defect on genetic survival?

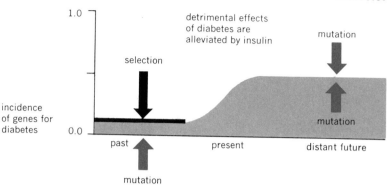

FIGURE 16.3

The frequency of genes causing diabetes was held at a low value by the balance between mutation and selection against the effects of the defect. Insulin treatment alleviates the effects of the defect, and mutation will increase the frequency of the genes for diabetes until this is balanced by countermutation.

Since	q^2	$=$	$\dfrac{\mu}{s}$
then	s	$=$	$\dfrac{\mu}{q^2}$
and	s	$=$	$\dfrac{0.00001}{0.01}$
so	s	$=$	0.001

The genetic survival is then 0.999, but it is not unlikely that more that one gene can mutate to this defect; suppose there are ten such genes. The incidence of diabetes due to any one of these genes would be 0.1%, which would result from a genetic survival of 0.99. Diabetics would be 1% less liable to produce offspring than non-diabetics. This slight defect in genetic survival would be enough to keep the frequency of the gene down to 0.1%. What would happen— what *will* happen—as the widespread use of insulin masks the detrimental effect of the gene? The mutation rate will not be countered by selection, and the frequency of the gene or genes for this defect will rise, eventually reaching an equilibrium when mutation in one way *from* normal is counterbalanced by mutation in the other way *to* normal. This frequency can be expected to be fairly high—somewhere near 50%—resulting in a large fraction of the population's being diabetic.

Diabetes is only one of many genetic diseases that can be treated partially or completely; eventually, we could expect every individual to be characterized by one or more of these defects and therefore to be in need of repairative medicine. "Eventually" is, for these genetic terms, a very long time; by then medicine will need methods not only to repair the effects of genetic defects, but also to repair or remove the genes concerned. The time involved is measured in hundreds of thousands of years. Considering how fast genetics has progressed in its short history, it is likely that a solution will be found well before the need becomes apparent.

These sections on selection against lethal and detrimental genes are a fairly dramatic illustration of one aspect of selection—its role in countering mutation pressure. This is a negative view of selection. The facts of evolution indicate that selection can also be viewed positively, which we will do in the next chapter.

Problems

1. The formula for the increase in frequency of the normal allele to a recessive lethal gene is:

$$\frac{pq^2}{1-q^2}$$

What is the formula for the decrease in frequency of the recessive lethal allele?

2. The formula for the increase in frequency of the normal allele to a recessive detrimental gene is:

$$\frac{spq^2}{1-sq^2}$$

If the frequency of the recessive allele is 90%, 50%, or 10% in the parents, what will be the frequencies of this allele in the next generation?

3. A recessive detrimental gene has a genetic survival of 80%, and the mutation rate from the normal allele is 0.000005. What will be the frequency of the recessive detrimental gene at equilibrium?

4. Compare the effects of mutation and selection on the genetic structure of a population.

5. Research in diseases such as muscular dystrophy and hemophilia promise the alleviation or "cure" of these diseases. What will be the effects of such advances?

6. Rewrite the equation, $spq^2 = \mu p$, in words.

Chapter 17

THE PRICE OF VARIABILITY

The picture of the genetic structure of populations that has emerged so far shows two types of genetic diversity. In one type, selection against recessive genes that reduce genetic survival is balanced by mutation. Populations contain large numbers of such genes, each at a very low frequency. In another type, exemplified by the ABO blood group genes in man, there is a wide-ranging diversity: in some populations one allele may be predominant, contrasting with other populations where it may be rare, and in yet other populations variations between these extremes occur. The simplest explanation for this type of genetic diversity is that ABO genes have no effect on genetic survival, the genetic diversity being the consequence of mutational equilibrium compounded by the effects of migration. (It is possible that the ABO genes do affect genetic survival, and many researches have indicated possible effects, but none can be accepted as conclusive.)

These are two types of genetic diversity—there are others. So far, we have considered only selection as it acts against genes, reducing the frequencies of the genes that decrease genetic survival. There is a converse to this: for every *detrimental* gene whose frequency is reduced by selection, there is an *advantageous* allelic gene whose frequency is increased by selection.

TRANSITIONAL DIVERSITY

A gene may have effects that are detrimental in one set of conditions, advantageous in other conditions. A change of conditions will result in a change of the genetic structure of a population: genes that were rare will become frequent, and vice versa. This is another cause of genetic diversity—changing conditions.

FIGURE 17.1a

The pollution consequent from heavy industrialization appears to have produced a change of genetic structure in some species of moths in England. Normally, these moths have a light color with streaks of dark color that very effectively camouflage the moths when they are resting on lichen-covered tree trunks. The camouflage protects them against the predatory attentions of birds. Dark-colored variants occur, but their lack of camouflage results in a low survival, and it is not surprising that they occur at a low frequency (less than 1%). The dark-colored variants appear to be caused by a dominant gene.

FIGURE 17.1b

The light and dark variants of moths have very different camouflage values in different environments. Light-colored moths are well camouflaged in unpolluted areas, whereas dark-colored moths are well camouflaged in polluted areas. (Photographs from the experiments of Dr. H. B. D. Kettlewell, University of Oxford.)

Industrial pollution kills the lichen and darkens the bark, which reverses the effectiveness of light and dark colors as camouflage. In industrial areas, the dark variants are better camouflaged than the light-colored moths, and this has resulted in dramatic increases of the frequency of dark-colored types. In heavily polluted areas the light-colored types occur at a low frequency (less than 1%). The change from predominant light color to predominant dark color did not take long—about 50 years. It has been called *industrial melanism*.

The variation in frequency of dark-colored and light-colored types is similar to those found for the blood group genes in man but, unlike the blood group genes, there is a clear relationship to survival. This was demonstrated by experiments in which mixtures of dark-colored and light-colored moths were released in polluted and in unpolluted areas. In the polluted areas the birds were seen to eat predominantly the light-colored moths. The reverse was found in the unpolluted areas, where more dark-colored moths were eaten by the birds.

Industrial melanism is an example of how selection can effect a change of gene frequency, resulting in the substitution of one gene for another. The change was rapid, proceeding from start to completion in about a half century, but it is possible to imagine similar substitutions occurring over much longer periods of hundreds or thousands of years. This provides another explanation of diversity: gene frequencies may be intermediate because a selective substitution has not yet progressed to completion.

Each substitution of a favorable for an unfavorable allele is a step forward in evolution, resulting in the species' being better formed to its function—better adapted to its habitat. Such adaptation does not necessarily need to involve the substitution of one allele for another, it can involve the maintenance of genetic diversity. If segregation at a specific locus means that both homozygotes are less well adapted than the heterozygotes, it is possible for a population to be best adapted by two alleles existing at intermediate frequencies.

SICKLE-CELL ANEMIA

The Hb^A and Hb^S genes determine a difference of the structure of human hemoglobin. The Hb^A gene causes the formation of normal hemoglobin, whereas Hb^S causes the formation of an abnormal hemoglobin. Individuals that are homozygous for the Hb^S gene are characterized by a hemolytic anemia, which usually leads to early death. Heterozygotes are characterized by a much milder anemia.

FIGURE 17.2

The incidence of the Hb^S gene is correlated with the incidence of malaria.

Up to this point, the description of this genetic difference is that of a lethal gene. The Hb^S gene appears to have a low genetic survival, and it should, therefore, occur at a low frequency determined by the balance between mutation and selection against homozygotes. It should have a low frequency, but there are many populations in which the Hb^S gene occurs at very high frequencies. Many African Negro tribes contain up to 40% heterozygous individuals. The gene has frequencies nearly as high in parts of India, in Greece, and in areas of Italy. These frequencies are far too high to be explained by mutation; the mutation rate would need to be of the order of 10^{-1}—one mutation from Hb$^A \rightarrow$ Hb^S in every ten gametes. It is unreasonable to rest any explanation of the high gene frequencies of the Hb^S on such an improbable mutation rate; researches were initiated to find a more reasonable explanation.

Populations with a high frequency of the Hb^S gene have a feature in common: they are located in areas where malaria is, or has been, a common disease. This is particularly evident in Sardinia—the gene is frequent in the malaria-prone lowlands, and rare in the malaria-free highlands. It appeared that the Hb^s gene confers some advantage against the malarial parasite; if this advantage were sufficiently great, it could counteract the disadvantage of the homozygous lethality of the gene.

The advantage of the Hb^s gene in heterozygotes could rest in its inadequacy. The red blood cells of Hb^A/Hb^s individuals have an increased fragility—they become distorted in conditions of abnormal oxygen tension. Red blood cells have a short life; they are removed from the blood as they become "worn out." Now consider that the malarial parasite enters the red blood cells. If Hb^A/Hb^s cells are sensitive to this parasitism, they will be removed from the circulation, and this would decrease the intensity of the disease.

Measurements of the incidence of malarial parasites in the blood Hb^A/Hb^A and Hb^A/Hb^s children in Africa showed that there is a much higher incidence in Hb^A/Hb^A than in Hb^A/Hb^s. This is convincing, but an experiment was performed involving experimental infection with malaria. The Hb^A/Hb^A volunteers almost all showed the establishment of the parasite in their blood, but the Hb^A/Hb^s volunteers showed either no infection or, at most, only a slight establishment in their blood. (All the volunteers were given a prolonged course of antimalarial chemotherapy after the experiment.)

SUPERIORITY OF HETEROZYGOTES

The genetic algebra for the example of sickle-cell anemia involves three different terms for genetic survival, one for each of the three genotypes:

Hb^s/Hb^s	die young because of the anemia
Hb^A/Hb^s	are resistant to malaria, with only slight anemia
Hb^A/Hb^A	are susceptible to malaria, with no anemia

If populations occur in nonmalarial regions, there is no advantage of the Hb^s gene in heterozygotes. It is a simple recessive lethal, and selection against it on the basis of this homozygous lethality will decrease its frequency. Conversely, in malarial regions, if a cure were found for the anemia of Hb^s/Hb^s, the prime action of selection would involve the decrease in frequency of the Hb^A gene. In either case, selection would result in the population's being characterized by only one allele, with the other allele maintained as a mutational oddity. Since selection operated against both sickle-cell homozygotes and normal homozygotes, we can ask the question: would such selection lead to a genetic equilibrium?

Consider an exaggerated example where both homozygotes die young, having a zero genetic survival. The only parents will be heterozygotes; both genes will occur at equal frequencies.

Hb^A/Hb^A	Hb^A/Hb^S	Hb^S/Hb^S
Die of malaria	Survive as parents	Die of anemia

Hb^A/Hb^A	Hb^A/Hb^S	Hb^S/Hb^S
Die of malaria	survive as parents	Die of anemia

and so on.

Complete selection against both homozygotes will lead to a genetic equilibrium. The next question is whether incomplete selection against homozygotes will also lead to an equilibrium. Suppose the genetic survivals of the homozygotes are not zero, but are both less than that of the heterozygote. As an illustration, consider a situation where Hb^A/Hb^A has a genetic survival of 0.5, Hb^A/Hb^S has a survival of 1.0, and that of Hb^S/Hb^S is 0.1. The effect of these different survivals can be seen if we compare two populations that differ in the frequency of the Hb^A gene. This is shown in the accompanying table.

The table shows that the frequency of the Hb^A gene will *decrease* in the population where it was predominant, and *increase* in the population where it was infrequent. There must be a particular frequency of the Hb^A gene when the selection against the homozygotes causes no change of gene frequency. This is also shown in the table: when the frequency of Hb^A is 0.64, selection has no effect on the gene frequency. The population is at equilibrium, maintained by selection.

An algebraic statement of this situation can be derived by the same approach, using symbols to represent the different values of gene frequency and genetic survival.

	Hb^A/Hb^A	Hb^A/Hb^S	Hb^S/Hb^S
Frequency	p^2	$2pq$	q^2
Genetic survival	$1 - s_1$	1	$1 - s_2$
Parents	$(1 - s_1)p^2$	$2pq$	$(1 - s_2)q^2$

Hb^A predominant
($p_A = 0.9$, $q_S = 0.1$)

	Hb^A/Hb^A	Hb^A/Hb^S	Hb^S/Hb^S
Frequency	0.81	0.18	0.01
Genetic survival	0.5	1.0	0.1
Parents	0.405	0.18	0.001

($p_A = 0.84$, $q_S = 0.16$)

Decrease of frequency of Hb^A

$p_A = 0.64$, $q_S = 0.36$

	Hb^A/Hb^A	Hb^A/Hb^S	Hb^S/Hb^S
Frequency	0.413	0.459	0.128
Genetic survival	0.5	1.0	0.1
Parents	0.206	0.459	0.0128

$p^A = 0.64$, $q_S = 0.36$

Population is at equilibrium.

Hb^S predominant
($p_A = 0.1$, $q_S = 0.9$)

	Hb^A/Hb^A	Hb^A/Hb^S	Hb^S/Hb^S
Frequency	0.01	0.18	0.81
Genetic survival	0.5	1.0	0.1
Parents	0.005	0.18	0.081

($p_A = 0.35$, $q_S = 0.65$)

Increase of frequency of Hb_A

Frequency of Hb^A in the next generation is then:

$$\frac{(1 - s_1)p^2 + pq}{(1 - s_1)p^2 + 2pq + (1 - s_2)q^2} = \frac{(1 - s_1)p^2 + pq}{1 - s_1p^2 - s_2q^2}$$

If the population is at equilibrium, the frequency of Hb^A after selection should be equal to its frequency before selection.

Initial frequency of Hb^A = Frequency of Hb^A after selection

Algebraically:

$$p = \frac{(1 - s_1)p^2 + pq}{1 - s_1p^2 - s_2q^2}$$

These gene frequencies will only be equal when

$$s_2/s_1 = p/q$$

Suppose $s_2 = 0.9$ and $s_1 = 0.5$; then the values of p and q will be 0.36 and 0.64 respectively.

Any example of intermediate gene frequencies *may* be explained by such selection against homozygotes. The existence of a genetic equilibrium due to heterozygotes' having an advantage is not so much a matter of the *intensity* of selection against homozygotes, as the *ratio* of the two selections. Weak selection can result in the same genetic equilibrium as strong selection.

BALANCED LETHALS

A genetic equilibrium due to heterozygote advantage does not need to be based only on the alleles of a single genetic locus. It can involve linked genes. Two separate, closely linked loci, each having a recessive lethal allele, will segregate lethal homozygotes in the absence of crossing over between the two genes. The only survivors will be the double heterozygotes. This is called a *balanced lethal system,* but crossing over in such a system can result in homozygotes' lacking either lethal allele; eventually, any balanced lethal system will shift away from equilibrium unless the crossing over is prohibited in some way. Inversions both reduce the occurrence of crossovers and result in recombinant chromosomes' being lethal. A balanced lethal system that involves inversions covering the locations of the balanced genes will be permanent. Such "inversion, balanced lethal" systems are widely used in Drosophila genetics.

The *Curly* chromosome in Drosophila contains: (1) a recessive lethal, (2) an inversion that reduces crossing over to near zero in heterozygotes, and (3) a dominant effect on wing shape. The *Plum*

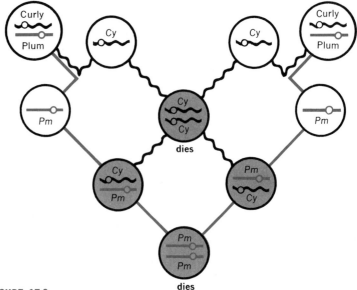

FIGURE 17.3

Balanced lethals. The Curly and Plum IInd chromosomes in Drosophila each contain an inversion and a separate recessive lethal. Crossing Cy/Pm heterozygotes produces only Cy/Pm living offspring.

chromosome also contains a recessive lethal, an inversion, and a dominant effect on eye color. Heterozygotes for those two chromosomes are viable since their recessive lethalities are not allelic, and no effective recombination occurs because the inversions are not identical. A population of Curly/Plum heterozygotes will stay in equilibrium because of homozygote lethality.

The use of "inversion, balanced lethal" systems in Drosophila genetics is an esoteric example of how geneticists can manipulate chromosomes. Dobzhansky found that similar systems of "inversion polymorphism" occur as characteristic features of many species of Drosophila.

INVERSION POLYMORPHISM

Dobzhansky found that a high frequency of individuals of *Drosophila pseudo obscura* were heterozygous for inversions of the IInd chromosome. The salivary-gland chromosomes of such heterozygous individuals are characterized by abnormal pairing—the inverted sections form loops to maintain point-to-point pairing. These abnormal configurations of the salivary chromosomes allow the location of the inverted segment to be identified. It was found that there were several inversions, not just one. The whole story rapidly became very complicated and we will restrict ourselves to a simplified version involving just three IInd chromosomes. These are called Standard, Arrowhead, and Pike's Peak (*ST*, *AR*, and *PP*).

The *ST*, *AR*, and *PP* chromosomes can be considered as a set of triple "alleles," analogous to the A, B, O set of allelic blood group genes, and the frequencies of the inversion chromosomes can be measured and compared in the same way. The frequencies of these chromosomes in a number of populations across the western United States showed the same kind of patterns that were found for the frequencies of the A, B, O genes in Europe. This could be explained by mutation and migration, as in the A, B, O alleles, but Dobzhansky showed that the real explanation involved a different kind of mechanism, one closely analogous to the mechanism of heterozygote superiority.

The first evidence that an explanation in terms of mutation and migration was not valid came from the observation that the frequencies of the three chromosomes varied regularly with season. This variance can be explained by each chromosome's having a high

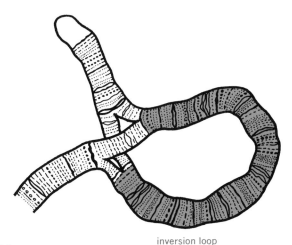

inversion loop

FIGURE 17.4

Pairing between chromosomes that are heterozygous for an inversion can result in the formation of a loop whose position is diagnostic for each particular inversion.

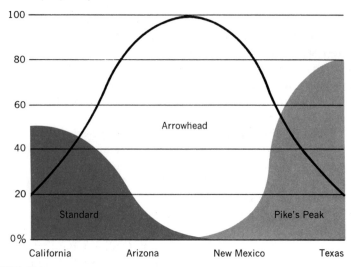

FIGURE 17.5

The relative frequencies of three inversion chromosomes—Standard, Arrowhead, and Pike's Peak—vary in a fairly simple pattern across the Southwestern States.

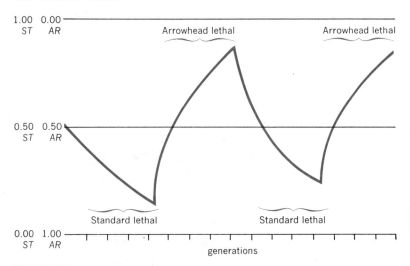

FIGURE 17.6

A theoretical population in which the ST and AR inversions occur will show cyclic changes of their relative frequencies if there is an alternation of lethality with ST/ST being lethal for one "season" of four generations, followed by AR/AR being lethal for the next "season" of four generations, and so on.

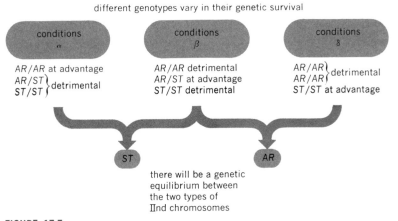

different genotypes vary in their genetic survival

conditions α	conditions β	conditions δ
AR/AR at advantage AR/ST ⎱ detrimental ST/ST ⎰	AR/AR detrimental AR/ST at advantage ST/ST detrimental	AR/AR ⎱ detrimental AR/AR ⎰ ST/ST at advantage

ST   AR

there will be a genetic
equilibrium between
the two types of
IInd chromosomes

FIGURE 17.7

The balanced equilibrium between the ST and AR inversions could be due to a population existing over a range of environments, with the three possible genotypes having different survivals in the different genotypes.

genetic survival in one season, low in another. Drosophila have many generations of reproduction each year, and they have a very high fecundity—enough for a minority genotype in one generation to become a predominant type in later generations. This can be illustrated for just two of the inversion chromosomes: *ST* and *AR*. Suppose, as a possible model, that Standard is a recessive lethal for a sequence of four generations, and that this is reversed in the next four generations, with Arrowhead a recessive lethal. This model would result in a regular fluctuation of the frequencies of the alternative chromosomes.

Dobzhansky placed small populations of *Drosophila pseudoobscura* in cages kept at a constant temperature with a regulated supply of food. The seasonal fluctuation of conditions had been removed, and the fluctuation in frequency of the inversion chromosomes was found to disappear; the frequencies of the different types of chromosomes were found to settle to intermediate values. This stabilization at intermediate frequencies cannot be explained by a simple lethality of one or the other of the homozygotes, but it can be understood if heterozygous individuals have a greater genetic survival than homozygotes. This condition will result in populations evolving to a fixed, intermediate genetic structure. There are other possible explanations which are essentially variations on this model. Suppose that a population cage, even when it is kept at a constant temperature, has a variety of conditions from one part to another. Even a population cage can be considered as a collection of places and environments; some genotypes could have a high genetic survival in some parts and a low genetic survival in other parts. This can result in the whole population stabilizing at intermediate frequencies.

THE LIFE EXPECTANCY OF CHROMOSOMES

The advantage of inversion chromosomes resides in the constancy of their particular content of genes. Inversion chromosomes have a low rate of recombination when heterozygous, resulting in their having a greater life expectancy than normal chromosomes. The life expectancy of an individual is the probable duration of its existence, measured in intervals of time. The life expectancy of a chromosome is measured in generations; it is the duration of its unchanged transmission. Life expectancy is low for normal chromosomes because they recombine freely at each generation. Unless a chromosome is very short, it is unlikely to have a life expectancy of more than a few generations. An inversion chromosome has, conversely, a life expectancy of many generations because its rate of recombination with normal uninverted homologs is very low. If a particular inversion contains a set of genes that confer an advantage, this particular combination of genes can be transmitted unchanged for many generations, with the recipients gaining this advantage. A normal chromosome, with the same set of genes, would not have the same permanency in heredity.

The various inversion chromosomes in populations of Drosophila can each be considered to have a particular genetic content that is transmitted and inherited as a unit. Each particular genetic content confers advantages in particular conditions, and in particular combinations with other inversion chromosomes. A population can show genetic diversity involving several different inversion chromosomes because each of these has advantages in some seasons and in some regions, outweighing its disadvantages at other times and places.

The inversion chromosomes show that the genotype is not just an amorphous collection of genetic differences; the ways in which genes are combined is important. Mendel showed the value of restricting attention to a few genetic differences. This approach has been extraordinarily fruitful in elaborating the basic principles of genetic diversity. The next phase is to use these basic principles to gain an appreciation of how and why genes are organized into integrated systems.

Problems

1. Can an answer be given to the question: which is more efficient, selection for a dominant or for a recessive allele?

2. The Arrowhead and Chiricuhua inversions are introduced into a population cage at frequencies of 90% and 10% respectively. After 20 generations the frequencies are found to have changed to 70% and 30%. Further measurements in later generations show these to be stable values. What does this information allow you to deduce about these two chromosomes?

3. Suppose a particular genetic difference occurs at intermediate frequencies. What are the possible explanations?

4. The frequencies of a particular set of genotypes in a population are:

aa	aa^+	a^+a^+
30%	40%	30%

These frequencies do not agree with the Hardy-Weinberg expectation. What explanations can you give for the disagreement?

Chapter 18

SETS OF GENES

Genetics provides an objective way of classifying individuals, of separating a population into groups. A population of humans can be divided into classes on the basis of the M and N pair of blood group genes. There will be three classes: MM, MN, and NN. Similarly, if the Rh$^+$ and Rh$^-$ genes are considered, individuals can be separated into another set of three classes: Rh$^+$Rh$^+$, Rh$^+$Rh$^-$, and Rh$^-$Rh$^-$. If both pairs of genes are considered together, there will be nine classes:

MM; Rh$^+$Rh$^+$	MN; Rh$^+$Rh$^+$	NN; Rh$^+$Rh$^+$
MM; Rh$^+$Rh$^-$	MN; Rh$^+$Rh$^-$	NN; Rh$^+$Rh$^-$
MM; Rh$^-$Rh$^-$	MN; Rh$^-$Rh$^-$	NN; Rh$^-$Rh$^-$

If the genes for dark versus light eye colors are also included, there will be 27 classes. The Hb^A/Hb^S pair of genes will increase the number of classes to 81. For each pair of genes added, the number of classes is multiplied by three, a progression toward an absolute individuality. The number of classes is 243 for five pairs of genes; 729 classes for six pairs; 2,187 for seven pairs of genes.

The relationship of the number of different genetic types to the number of pairs of genes is given by the simple expression,

$$3^n = \text{number of genetic types}$$

where n is the number of pairs of genes. This number becomes very big for just a few pairs of genes. There are over two and a half billion different genetic combinations for 20 pairs of genes. This is not a large number of genetic differences—several hundred genes have been identified in Drosophila, and well over a hundred genes have been identified in man. The conclusion that the number of genetic classes is astronomically large is inescapable, and it is not unreasonable to consider that every individual has a unique combination of genes that probably has never occurred before and will never occur again. It would be possible, but not practical, to describe each individual by genetic content, with only an infinitesimally small probability that any description would be used twice. This can be a comforting conclusion for ardent individualists.

So far, we have only considered genetic differences with distinctive effects, but there are a great many characters in which several genes act together to determine the phenotypic effects. The genetic analysis of these systems is complicated because the individual genetic effects are all added together into one single effect. Single genetic differences cannot be identified in these systems.

EYE COLORS IN DROSOPHILA AND MAN

Drosophila normally have red eyes, but a very large number of genes have been identified that modify eye colors. Each of these genes is rare, and it was relatively easy to identify and analyze them because experiments could be easily restricted to one or two genetic differences at a time. However, suppose all of these genes did not occur as mutational oddities, but as a frequent cause of diversity. There would be no single eye-color characteristic of the species — they would range from white to red through every possible intermediate — and genetic analysis of such a melange would be extremely difficult. Eye color in man appears to be determined by such a system of genes; it varies from the lack of pigment in albinos to very dark shades of brown that can almost be called black. Consequently, genetic analysis of eye color in man has not been very successful. A few genes have been identified that affect eye color, but the main part of the variation of eye color cannot be attributed to specific differences.

Many characters have the same type of genetic basis as eye color in man. They have a pattern of segregation at a number of loci, with the alleles at intermediate frequencies. Eye color is a complex character, varying in several directions, but the same type of genetic complexity can occur for simpler characters in which only two extremes are possible. Height in man is such a character; number of eggs laid per year in chickens, and so on. These are the so-called *measurement characters*, in which no distinction can be made into classes, and description is by measurement. The normal methods of genetic analysis cannot be used for measurement characters; other methods had to be invented and tested.

MEASUREMENT CHARACTERS

A measurement characteristic is one in which all gradations can occur between extremes. The words "tall" and "short" are not very useful in describing height in man. "Dwarf" and "giant" are slightly more useful terms, but they are also inadequate for objective classification. How tall is a giant; how short is a dwarf? Adequate description of height involves a measurement in standard units.

The early days of genetics were marked by acrimonious controversies over the nature of the hereditary determination of measurement characters. The methods of Mendelian genetics obviously were not applicable to such characters; it was proposed that the inheritance of these characters did not follow Mendelian laws because they appeared to follow a pattern of blending inheritance. If two lines that differed in their expression of a measurement character were crossed, the F_1 was intermediate, and the parental levels of expression were not found in the F_2. A classical example of this type of inheritance is that of ear length in corn.

EAR LENGTH IN CORN

The ear length in corn is a continuously varying character in which it is not possible to distinguish distinct classes, but different strains do differ in their average length of ear and in the variation that occurs from one plant to the next. In two strains of corn, a short-eared popcorn and a long-eared sweet corn, the longest ear from popcorn was found to be shorter than the shortest ear of sweet corn. The cross between these lines had an intermediate length of ear, with an intermediate range of variation. The F_2 from these hybrids had a wider range of variation, but did not include plants with ears as short as the shortest popcorn—the potential to form short ears did not segregate. Clearly, these facts do not fit a simple pattern of inheritance of genetic alternatives, but it is possible to find an explanation in terms

FIGURE 18.1

Ear length in corn. A cross between long-eared sweet corn and short-eared popcorn produces hybrids whose ear length is intermediate. The second generation of this cross includes plants with a wide range of ear lengths, in which the parental ranges of length occur at low frequencies. There is no obvious Mendelian segregation.

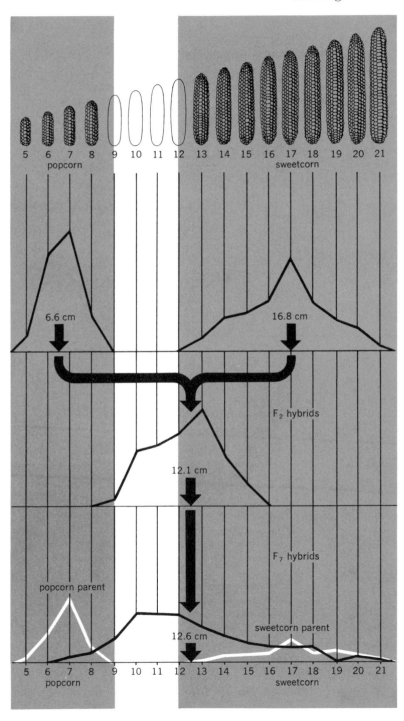

of a number of independently segregating but cooperatively acting genes.

Suppose the difference between the length of ears of popcorn and sweet-corn strains is determined by a single genetic difference. The F_2 should have a 1 : 2 : 1 ratio of long, medium, and short ears, with a clear discontinuity between the three lengths. This is not valid, so we can extend this to two genetic differences that are inherited in simple independence. Consider that these two pairs of genes act additively (a type of gene action where there are no complications of dominance, etc.). Suppose we say that each substitution of a "capital" for a "small-letter" gene adds 2.5 cm to the length of the ear.

$$1 \quad \frac{a\ b}{a\ b} \qquad\qquad = 6.5\ \text{cm}$$

$$4 \quad \frac{a\ b}{A\ b}, \frac{a\ b}{a\ B} \qquad = 9.0\ \text{cm}$$

$$6 \quad \frac{a\ b}{A\ B}, \frac{A\ b}{A\ b}, \frac{a\ B}{a\ B} = 11.5\ \text{cm}$$

$$4 \quad \frac{A\ b}{A\ B}, \frac{a\ B}{A\ B} \qquad = 14.0\ \text{cm}$$

$$1 \quad \frac{A\ B}{A\ B} \qquad\qquad = 16.5\ \text{cm}$$

This genetic model is getting closer to the actual results, but there will still be five distinct classes of length, and it cannot be accepted as a valid explanation of the data. We can go on, considering models of three, four, five, six pairs of genes, and each addition of another pair of genes will result in a model with expectations that are closer to the real data. It is clear that, if enough pairs of genes are included in the model, it is possible to account for the patterns of inheritance of measurement characters within the framework of genetic theory. The same kind of logic can be applied to any measurement character.

SKIN COLOR IN MAN

Crosses between Negroid and white populations produce mulatto progeny, who have brown skin intermediate between the extremes of the parents. This shows that the skin-color genes have no dominance; they are apparently simply additive in their actions. Crosses between mulattos produce progeny with a range of skin colors, in which the racial extremes occur infrequently. A model involving several genes is needed to explain this condition. A plausible model can be proposed on the basis of five or six genes.

A complication of measurement characters is that they are affected by environmental as well as by genetic variation. Skin color is not solely a genetic feature. Exposure to sunlight has a darkening effect, and any genetic analysis that did not take this into consideration could involve considerable inaccuracy. A "skin-color" racist would be likely to develop additional neuroses if asked to distinguish racial groups on the beaches of Australia where "white" individuals are often tanned by the sun to light shades of "black." A simple measure of amount of exposure to sunlight would not be sufficient to resolve this effect, since individuals who are equally "white" may differ markedly in their reactions to the sun.

Skin color illustrates several of the usual complexities of measurement characters: there are large numbers of genes involved; nongenetic environmental factors can modify the actions of the genes; and other genes with no obvious effects on skin color can affect reaction to the environment. There are effects of the inherited genotype, there are effects of the environment, and there are interactions between the genotype and the environment.

We have considered genetic models that *can* explain the features of quantitative inheritance, but it does not follow that they *are* the real explanation. It is necessary to show that factors located on the chromosomes are the primary determinants of measurement characters, and that these obey the same laws of transmission as genes.

EXPERIMENTAL PROOF

The first step in any proof of the genetic nature of the inheritance of measurement characters must be the demonstration that this type of inheritance is completely determined by the chromosomes. Ingenious proofs have been obtained in Drosophila, using the special inversion chromosomes such as the *ClB* chromosome. The important feature of these chromosomes is that the inversions they contain make crossing over a negligible quantity, and it is possible to manipulate normal chromosomes as fixed entities in crosses with the inversion chromosomes.

The use of these special "inversion" chromosomes can be illustrated from the analysis of the chromosomal location of the factors responsible for extra scutellar bristles in Drosophila. Normally, Drosophila have four scutellar bristles, with a few rare individuals having one or two extra bristles. Selection for these extra scutellar bristles has resulted in lines with an average of more than seven scutellar bristles. Crossing these lines to normal lines has shown that the occurrence of extra bristles is recessive, and that it does not segregate simply. It is presumably caused by the cooperative effects of a number of genes. Males of an extra-scutellar line with an average of 7.35 bristles were crossed to a stock with inversion chromosomes. This is illustrated in the figure for the "*ClB*," "*Cy*," and "*Ubx*" inversion chromosomes, which each have a distinctive dominant effect: "*ClB*" causes the carriers to have Bar eyes, "*Cy*" causes curled wings, and "*Ubx*" causes enlarged halteres. The presence of each of these chromosomes can be diagnosed from these effects. Crossing males of the extra-scutellar line to females of the inversion stock produced individuals that are heterozygous for each inversion chromosome against chromosomes from the extra-scutellar line. These triple heterozygotes had very few extra bristles, showing that the factors for extra-scutellars are recessive. Backcrossing these triple heterozygotes to the extra-scutellar line produced eight female genotypes that could be identified from the dominant marker effects of the inversion chromosomes. One of these genotypes does not contain any inversion chromosomes; it has the three main chromosomes of the extra-scutellar line recombined. The average number of bristles in this genotype was 7.42, which is not significantly different from the value characteristic of the parental line, demonstrating that the extra bristles characteristic of the parental line are caused by factors located on the chromosomes.

Such experiments allow the identification of the chromosomal location of the extra scutellar bristle genes. Comparisons between the various genotypes show which chromosomes carry the factors for extra bristles. They are located on the Ist and IIIrd chromosomes; extra bristles are only found when these chromosomes are homozygous. Such ingenious experiments have shown that the factors for measurement characters are located on the chromosomes; that they

FIGURE 18.2

Crossing a line of Drosophila characterized by extra scutellar bristles to a ClB, Cy, Ubx stock produced individuals that are heterozygous for the "selection" and "marker" chromosomes. These have no extra scutellars— the character has been lost. Back-crossing to the selection line produces individuals that do not contain any "marker" chromosomes; these have the same number of extra scutellars as the parent line. The character has segregated, showing that it is caused by recessive genes on the chromosomes. Consideration of the other genotypes show that these genes are located on the Ist and IIIrd chromosomes. Data from W. R. Scowcroft.

may be restricted to specific chromosomes; that they can be recessive; and that they may be nonadditive. In the above example, the Ist and IIIrd chromosomes together have a greater effect than would be expected from their separate effects.

The next step in demonstrating that inheritance of measurement

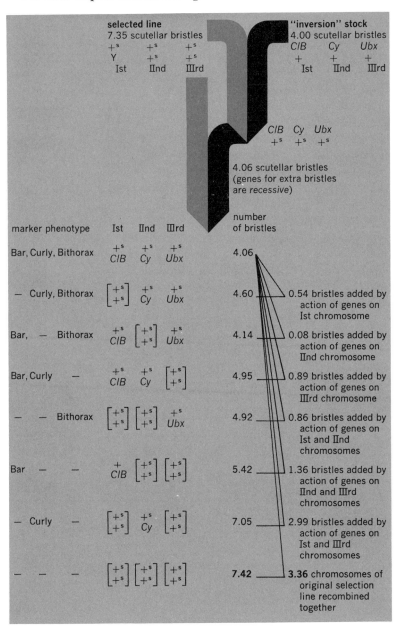

characters is controlled by genes on the chromosomes was to show that the factors determining measurement characters were located at specific fixed points on the chromosomes. This has not progressed to the same precision that has been achieved for genes having major effects, but particular segments of chromosomes have been shown to be the location of measurement factors. The techniques used depend on showing that all or some part of a difference between two lines in a measurement character are linked to a *marker gene.* (A marker gene is one with a major effect whose chromosomal location is known.) An example of this approach is the linkage of some of the factors responsible for extra scutellar bristles with the sex-linked white locus.

A red-eyed (w^+/w^+) extra-scutellar line of Drosophila with an average of 5.0 bristles was crossed to a white-eyed (w/w) unselected line. This cross produced female progeny that were heterozygous for both the sex-linked eye-color genes and for the genes determining the occurrence of extra scutellar bristles. If any of the extra-scutellar genes are located on the X chromosome near the location of w^+, they should show linkage with the eye-color genes. This was found: red-eyed male progeny had an average of 4.25 bristles compared to the white-eyed male progeny, in which extra bristles were rare. One or more of the genes that cause extra scutellar bristles are located near the *white* locus. More sophisticated variations of this theme have resulted in fairly precise statements of the location of "measurement" genes.

The demonstration that measurement characters are determined by genes located at fixed positions on the chromosomes shows that their inheritance follows the same rules as genes with major effects. The complexities of the inheritance of such characters lie in the number of genes involved, not in their having non-Mendelian modes of transmission.

It is not possible in most organisms to analyze the chromosomal nature of the inheritance of measurement characters, and even in organisms like Drosophila it is rarely possible to separately identify the various genes concerned. It is still possible, however, to obtain useful information by a variety of methods. The inheritance of intelligence in man is an interesting example of the application of many of these methods.

INTELLIGENCE

There is no single measure of intelligence that will take all of its subtleties into account, but tests have been devised that measure

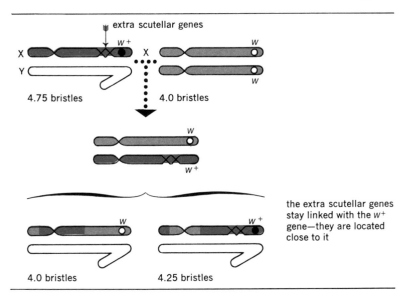

FIGURE 18.3

Crosses of a red-eyed (w⁺) selection line with a white-eyed (w) unselected line showed a linkage of a component of the difference of scutellar bristle number with the w⁺ allele.

various features of intelligence with reasonable accuracy. One of these, the Binet intelligence quotient test, gives a measure on a scale from 0 to 200: low values represent less-than-average intelligence, high values represent more-than-average intelligence. The I.Q. tests were originally designed to differentiate, among backward children, between the mentally inadequate and the mentally disadvantaged (the unteachable from the teachable). The use of these tests has been expanded to allow determination of this difference at all levels of education—they are to some degree a measure of ability to gain from education, although there is also an effect of previous education.

The first step in investigating the inheritance of a measurement character is to determine its reliability. How accurate is the measurement? Many versions of the I.Q. tests are available and, if the same individual is tested twice, an estimate can be gained of the reliability of the measure. The average difference of I.Q. is about five points; thus it appears to be a reliable measure.

Once the reliability of a measure has been established, the next step is to determine whether relatives are more similar than nonrelatives. Galton, as long ago as 1869, had shown that the relatives of brilliant people were more likely to be brilliant themselves if the relationship were close than if it were distant. This phenomenon could be due to heredity, but it could also be due to brilliant parents setting up environments that favor the development of brilliance in their offspring. Distinguishing between these alternatives can be accomplished by comparing identical with fraternal twins.

STUDIES OF TWINS

Twins may be "identical" or "fraternal." Fraternal twins are produced by the release of two eggs that are separately fertilized. They are genetically no more similar than brothers or sisters born separately, but they have developed in the same environment. If environment is a major force in determining I.Q., fraternal twins should have more similar ratings than ordinary sibs. Identical twins are produced by a single fertilized egg that divides to form two daughter cells which separate and develop into independent but genetically identical individuals. If heredity is a major factor in determining I.Q., identical twins should be more similar than fraternal twins in their intelligence ratings. Measurements have been made of I.Q. in twins; the condensed results are shown in Figure 18.4.

Another variant of this approach is to compare identical twins that were separated and raised in different environments. If heredity is preeminent in the determination of I.Q., separated twins should be no less similar than twins raised together. The results showed that separating twins into different environments increased the differences between them. The determination of I.Q. is partly genetic, partly environmental, and there is a strong suggestion that they are of equal importance.

There are other ways of measuring the relative importance of heredity and environment. These methods depend on comparing the I.Q. values for adopted children with those of "biological" children. The term "biological" is introduced in the absence of a better term to denote children who were not adopted. The assumption is that children who are adopted will have, on the average, a median I.Q. whereas biological children will have values related to the I.Q. of their parents. Since I.Q. values were not available for the parents, a separation was made on the basis of the father's occupation, which is correlated with I.Q. The results (in Figure 18.5) show that the adopted children do not differ as widely as biological children, by a factor of nearly two. The differences of upbringing are not more than halfway effective in modifying the performance of the adopted children to that of the biological children.

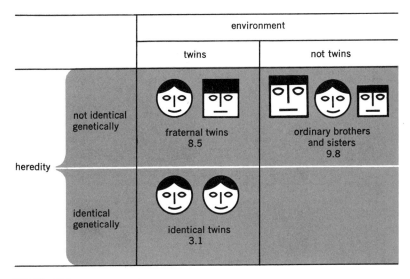

FIGURE 18.4

The measurements show that between fraternal twins and ordinary brothers and sisters there is no significant decrease of differences in I.Q. By contrast, the genetic similarity of identical twins greatly reduces the differences in I.Q. Thus heredity appears to be a major determinant of I.Q. An intriguing feature of the comparisons between the identical twins is that measurements by different individuals are more similar than different measurements on the same individual.

All these data add up to a picture of a genetic control of I.Q. involving a number of genes, each with a small effect, determining the actual value in conjunction with the effect of environment. This is a valid concept for the main range of I.Q., but does it hold for the rare extremes: for the very low values and the very high values, for the mentally defective and the mentally superior?

MENTAL EXTREMES

The genes determining I.Q. can be considered as having two types of alleles: positive alleles acting toward increased intelligence, and negative alleles acting toward decreased intelligence. On this model, inheritance of a high proportion of one or the other type of allele determines the potential toward one or the other extreme of intelligence, remembering that inferior and superior environments are also

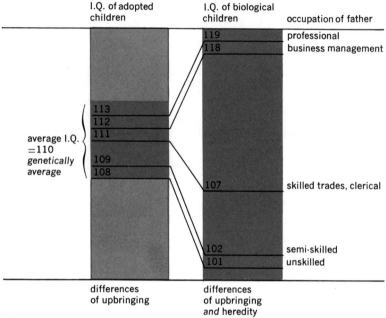

FIGURE 18.5

The comparison of the I.Q. of adopted with biological children in a range of different classes of families shows that the range of variation of I.Q. is much greater for the biological than for the adopted children.

concerned in determining I.Q. Some predictions can be made from this model. The occurrence of extreme individuals should be correlated with the general level of I.Q. of their relatives. The relatives of individuals with an extremely low I.Q. should, generally, have a lower-than-average I.Q. Similarly, the relatives of individuals with an extremely high I.Q. should, generally, have a higher-than-average I.Q.

Useful distinctions can be made between several classes of subnormal individuals:

Classification	Approximate average I.Q.
Normal	100
Dull	78
Feebleminded	56
Imbecile	34
Idiot	12

If the above model of the genetic basis of I.Q. is correct, the frequencies of these types of intelligence among relatives should increase in a progression from normality toward the extreme.

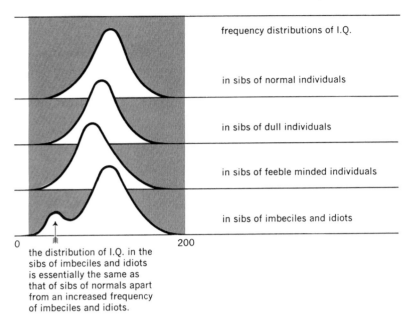

frequency distributions of I.Q.

in sibs of normal individuals

in sibs of dull individuals

in sibs of feeble minded individuals

in sibs of imbeciles and idiots

0   200

the distribution of I.Q. in the
sibs of imbeciles and idiots
is essentially the same as
that of sibs of normals apart
from an increased frequency
of imbeciles and idiots.

FIGURE 18.6

*The frequency distributions of I.Q., among the sibs of (1) normal, (2) dull,
(3) mentally defective, and (4) imbeciles and idiots, show a gradual decrease from the sibs of normals to the sibs of mental defectives, which is
not continued in the sibs of the most extreme type (imbeciles and idiots).
The sibs of imbeciles and idiots have, effectively, a normal distribution of
I.Q. apart from a much higher-than-normal frequency of imbeciles and
idiots. This shows that the genetic basis of the normal range of I.Q. is
different from that of the low extremes.*

Studies have been made of the sibs of individuals classified as
normal, dull, feebleminded, imbecile, or idiot. The results are shown
in a simplified form in Figure 18.6. The sibs of normals have the
same distribution of I.Q. as that characteristic of the whole population. The sibs of dull individuals have a distribution of I.Q. that
covers the full range, but has an average below normal. The sibs of
feebleminded individuals show an extension of this trend—they have
a lower-than-average distribution of I.Q. As far as normal, dull, and
feebleminded individuals are concerned, there is an agreement with
the prediction but, if the study is extended to imbeciles and idiots,
the distribution of I.Q. in their sibs is found to be essentially normal,
with a small group of sibs of imbeciles and idiots being in this class
themselves. This does not agree with prediction: if this low-level I.Q.
is caused by the inheritance of a high proportion of negative alleles,

the sibs should have similarly inherited a higher proportion of negative I.Q. genes. What seems to be the real explanation is that these individuals have a quantitatively different genetic causation, involving genes that have major effects. Such a gene is the recessive that causes phenylpyruvic idiocy. Another type of idiocy, Mongolian idiocy, is due to inheritance of an abnormal chromosomal constitution. On this basis the sibs of imbeciles and idiots would not be expected to be different from normal, unless they also inherit the same genetic abnormality. These data give a two-dimensional picture of the genetic causation of I.Q. One set of genes is responsible for normal-range I.Q., producing subtle variations of biochemistry which result in the modification but not the disruption of the development of intelligence. Another set of genes is responsible for extremely low values of I.Q., producing major changes of biochemistry which disrupt the development of intelligence. The names *switch* genes and *buffer* genes have been used for this type of genetic system. Genes like phenylpyruvic idiocy switch development into a completely abnormal path, whereas the normal I.Q. genes act to vary I.Q. within the normal path of development.

A question that has not been considered is the genetic causation of the opposite extreme of intelligence—namely, genius. Is this caused by the inheritance of major genes? There is no clear answer to this question, but there have been many family groupings of outstandingly intelligent individuals, which suggests that genius may have a strong hereditary component. It would appear unlikely that genius is due to rare major genes analogous to those that cause idiocy. A simple genetic effect may disrupt a delicately balanced process, but it is unlikely that similarly simple genetic effects can markedly increase the efficiency of such a process—it is more probable that genius is due to the rare combination of a number of genes.

This complicated model of the genetic causation of intelligence was arrived at by the application of fairly simple statistical methods to comparisons between relatives, between different types of twins, between adopted and biological children, and so on. The primary aim of such studies is to evaluate the relative roles of heredity and environment. A secondary aim is to subdivide the genetic system into its components: rare major genes versus common minor genes, genes affecting one component of the character versus other genes affecting other components, and so on.

Problems

1. Two lines of corn differ in eight genes affecting ear length, but they do not differ in their average ear length. How can you explain this?

2. Suppose I.Q. were determined by two genetic loci, with two alleles at each locus. How many classes of I.Q. would you expect?

3. The genes controlling the variation of a quantitative character cannot be identified individually. What do you consider is the *necessary* information to prove that such genes exist?

4. What steps would you take to determine that some particular human skill or defect was inherited?

5. I.Q. has a strongly inherited component, due to its determination by a multigenic system. What effect would you expect an increase of the mutation rate to have on the I.Q. of a population?

Chapter 19

SURVIVAL OF THE MEDIOCRE

The effects of selective breeding for a measurement character have always been spectacular, whenever such selection was applied consistently for enough time. An obvious example of this is size in dogs: selective breeding has produced extremes as far apart as the Great Dane and the Chihuahua. This is just one example of the success achieved by man in the genetic modification of many species of plants and animals. Wild species of sheep have coarse pelts that are mostly hair with a modicum of wool and weigh, at most, a pound or two. Selective breeding has resulted in breeds of sheep, such as the Merino, that consistently produce 5 to 10 times as much wool—fleece weights of 10 to 20 pounds are the norm. This raises the question of the origin of this potential to respond to long-continued selection. Did it exist in the original population, or did it occur by mutation during the period of selection? This question cannot be answered in retrospect, but data from similar selection in laboratory animals have shown that crossbred populations contain a considerable potential to respond to selection.

SELECTION FOR ABDOMINAL BRISTLES

Each segment of the abdomen in Drosophila has a group of abdominal bristles that vary in number from one individual to the next. The average number on two particular segments is 40 in unselected, crossbred populations, the variation ranging from a low of 30 to a high of 50. Individuals with more or less than this number are extremely rare. The character is affected by environmental factors, but there is a heritable component due to the variations of a set of genes, each having such a small effect that none can be identified individually.

Selection of parent flies with the greatest number of bristles results in a gradual increase of the number of bristles. In one such

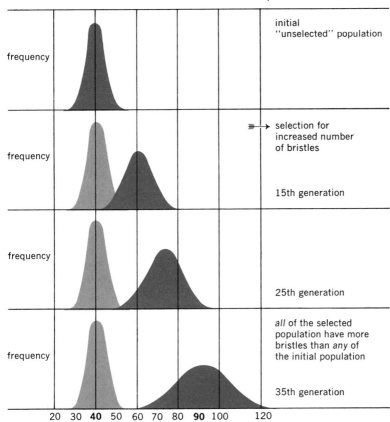

frequency — initial "unselected" population

frequency — selection for increased number of bristles / 15th generation

frequency — 25th generation

frequency — *all* of the selected population have more bristles than *any* of the initial population / 35th generation

20 30 **40** 50 60 70 80 **90** 100 120

number of abdominal bristles

FIGURE 19.1

The frequency distributions of number of abdominal bristles in Drosophila before, during, and after 35 generations of selection show that selection produced a population that was qualitatively different from that of the parent population. The simplest explanation of this is that the character is determined by a large number of genes, each with a very small effect. There are other explanations, such as linked sets of genes, epistatic interactions between genes, etc.

experiment, after 35 generations of selection, the selected population had an average of nearly 90 bristles, ranging from a low of 60 to a high of nearly 120. Selection had produced a population that was qualitatively distinct from the original population. Essentially the same differentiation was achieved by selection in the opposite direction.

The same kind of selection in inbred lines is ineffective, which shows that the effects of selection in crossbred lines cannot be explained as a consequence of mutations occurring during the progress of selection, unless inbred lines have a much lower mutation rate than crossbred lines. There is no reason to believe this, so we can conclude that crossbred lines have the genetic variability that allows them to respond to selection. This raises the question: if the genes that can affect the increased number of bristles are present in the original population, why are there no flies in unselected populations with as many or as few bristles as occur in the selected lines?

SELECTION FOR THE OPTIMUM

The answer to this question can probably be found in the nature of selection for number of bristles in the initial crossbred population. These are often called the "unselected" populations, but this is almost certainly a misnomer. Natural selection is probably acting in these populations—acting against extremes. Such selection may be very slight, but even small amounts of selection can produce marked effects over enough time.

An early example of how selection can favor the intermediate was found by Bumpus in 1898. A sudden, sharp storm stunned a number of sparrows, which he collected and cared for in his laboratory. Nearly half the birds died, and he found that the survivors had measurements closer to average than those of the dead birds. If we assume that these measurements were to some degree heritable, then the genetic survival of intermediates is greater than that of extremes.

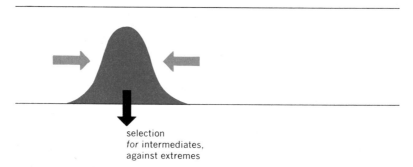

selection
for intermediates,
against extremes

FIGURE 19.2

Selection can favor intermediate phenotypes.

Other examples of the importance of being mediocre are a matter of casual observation. A shepherd going around his flock during lambing cannot help but notice that overly large and unduly small lambs have a lower survival rate than lambs of intermediate size. What will be the effect of such an increased genetic survival of intermediates? There are two ways to approach this question. One way is to select experimentally for intermediate phenotypes and see what effects result. The other way is to predict the consequences of such selection by examination of genetic models. A variation of this theme has already been mentioned (Chapter 14): the use of electronic computers which can be programmed to imitate the arithmetic essentials of genetic systems.

A SIX-GENE MODEL

Suppose a measurement character is determined by six loci, with two alleles at each locus. Letters are used to represent genes; small letters represent genes acting to reduce the measurement, and capital letters represent genes acting to increase the measurement. Assume the simplest situation, that all genes have the same degree of effect, and we can relate the genotype to its hypothetical measurement phenotype.

GENOTYPE			PHENOTYPE
All small-letter genes		*abcdef* *abcdef*	0
Eleven small-letter and *one* capital-letter gene	e.g.	*Abcdef* *abcdef*	1
Ten small-letter and *two* capital-letter genes	e.g.	*abCdef* *aBcdef*	2
Nine small-letter and *three* capital-letter genes	e.g.	*aBcdeF* *abcDef*	3
And so on:			
All capital-letter genes		*ABCDEF* *ABCDEF*	12

This model of a genetic system has been introduced into a computer, with all genes having the same frequencies; e.g., $p_a = 0.5$, $q_A = 0.5$; etc.

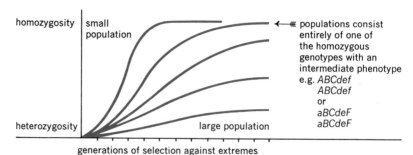

FIGURE 19.3

A diagramatic representation of the consequences of selection for the intermediate phenotype in computer experiments based on a six-locus genetic model. The graphs show the effectiveness of selection in causing a change from an initially heterozygous population to a population that contains only one intermediate homozygous genotype.

The computer then proceeded as ordered to imitate the genetic essentials in producing a generation of progeny whose phenotypes ranged from 0–12, with a peak at 6. An exaggerated scheme of selection was specified in which only individuals with a phenotype of 6 were selected as parents. This is very strong selection against extremes, and its effect was to eventually produce a population that was homozygous for some genetic combination with a phenotype of 6.

$$ABCdef \qquad aBcDEf \qquad AbcdEF$$
$$ABCdef \quad \text{or} \quad aBcDEf \quad \text{or} \quad AbcdEF$$

or any other genotype in which three loci are homozygous for small-letter genes and the other three loci are homozygous for capital-letter genes. This result occurred if the computer were allowed to continue for a sufficient number of generations, leading to the conclusion that selection against extremes will be expected to lead to the genetic uniformity of homozygosity, if it occurs for enough time. The phrase "enough time" conceals a considerable complexity. The time taken to reach a uniform homozygosity depends on the size of the population—it is shorter in small populations than in large populations. The reason for this can be understood by referring to Chapter 14, where it was shown that inbreeding is greater in small populations than in large populations. Inbreeding increases the frequency of homozygotes, and selection for intermediates will, therefore, increase the frequency of homozygous intermediates faster in small populations than in large populations.

The maximum size of population that has been imitated in a computer is 1,000 parents; this is large electronically, small biologically. Few organisms exist in such small populations. The time taken to reach genetic uniformity will be much longer in biologically large populations, so much longer that it is unlikely that selection in favor of intermediates has resulted in any significant increases in homozygosity. This conclusion is strengthened by considering more complicated genetic models.

It is unlikely that many measurement characters are controlled by as few as six loci. Consider a model of 30 loci with two alleles at each locus. Such a genetic system will result in 3^{30} genotypes, and the extreme combinations will be very rare. If the frequencies of all the alleles are nearly equal, then the frequency of the extreme combination will be $1/3^{30}$—an infinitesimally small number. The extreme combinations would be so rare that they would be effectively nonexistent. However, if selection is practiced toward one or the other extreme, the frequencies of these combinations would gradually increase until eventually they would be a frequent feature, resulting in a gradual shift of the distribution of the measurement character from its original value toward the extreme.

It would appear that, if measurement characters are controlled by a large number of separately located but similarly acting genes, many features of the effects of selection on such characters can be explained. It is plausible, but it can be considered a rather naive explanation, since we know that such genes are located on the chromosomes and that the ways in which genes act are frequently dependent on the occurrence of other genes. The effects of mechanical relationship due to linkage and biochemical relationship due to interaction need to be considered.

LINKED SYSTEMS OF GENES

So far we have considered the loci as being independent—this is unlikely. Genes are rarely, if ever, independent entities; they are physically related by linkage on the chromosomes, and physiologically related by the interplay of their actions. We will consider what effect linkage is expected to have on the characteristics of a genetic system.

A computer can be instructed to act as if the genetic system it is imitating consists of a set of linked genes. Synthetic selection experiments were performed with a model of six genes as before, except that the six genes were located on one chromosome. Selection against extremes was found to have different effects, depending on the degree of recombination that had been set to occur between the genes. The efficiency of selection in producing homozygosity decreased as the amount of recombination decreased. In experiments with recombination reduced to less than a few per cent, the trend to homozygosity was only slightly more than that occurring in unselected populations of the same size. These results confirm the conclusion that selection against extremes will be unlikely to result in the genetic uniformity of homozygosity if the population is large and if the genes are closely linked.

FIGURE 19.4

The effect of linkage when selection is for the intermediate phenotype in computer experiments based on a six-locus genetic model. The graphs show the effectiveness of selection in causing a change from an initially heterozygous population to a population containing only one intermediate homozygous genotype.

If selection against extremes cannot achieve uniformity by causing an increase of homozygosity, then the question can be asked: is it possible to achieve genetic uniformity by other means? An affirmative answer to this has already been given in Chapter 17, where "balanced lethals" were discussed. The Curly and Plum chromosomes can form a balanced lethal system in which a number of genes are held as heterozygotes because these two chromosomes are inverted relative to each other, and because each carries a different recessive lethal gene. Uniformity can be achieved by the means of balanced heterozygosity. The computer experiments show that an analogous balanced heterozygosity can evolve if the genes are located close enough to each other.

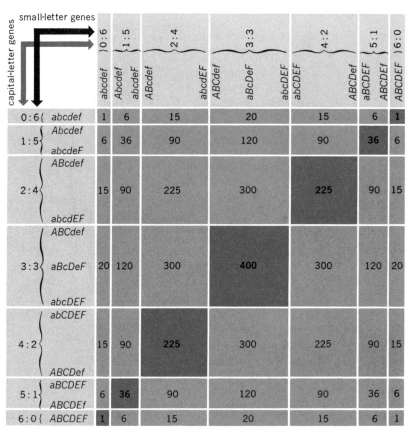

FIGURE 19.5

*The frequency square for the progeny of a population segregating at six
linked loci, in which all the possible chromosomes are equally frequent.
The resultant genotypes can be grouped in terms of their phenotype,
when all alleles are equally effective, and each capital allele adds a single
unit of measurement.*

BALANCED COMBINATIONS

Selection for intermediate phenotypes where the genes concerned
are closely linked has two effects.

First, there is a decrease in frequency of chromosomes whose
genetic constitution is such that they *rarely* form diploid combinations which produce the intermediate phenotype—and an increase
in frequency of chromosomes that *frequently* form diploid com-

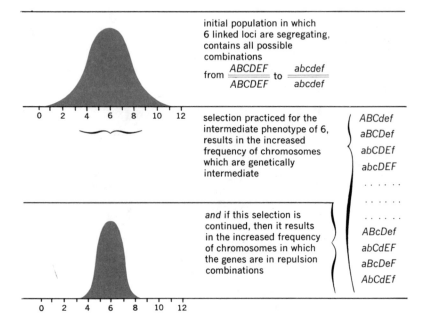

FIGURE 19.6

Selection for intermediate phenotypes favors chromosomes with balanced numbers of capital-letter and small-letter genes. Continued selection favors chromosomes with repulsion combinations, since these are less sensitive to the effects of recombination than chromosomes with coupling combinations.

binations which produce the intermediate phenotype. This can be understood by using the same six-gene model, in which selection for the intermediate phenotype was practiced. Initially, the computer was started with all possible types of chromosomes occurring equally often. There are 64 different types of chromosomes. Consider the *abcdef* type of chromosome; this will form an acceptable phenotype only in combination with the *ABCDEF* type of chromosome. All other combinations involving the *abcdef* chromosome will not have equal numbers of capital-letter and small-letter genes. The *abcdef* chromosome can be considered to have a genetic survival of $1/64$. Compare this with another type, the *ABCdef* type. This can form an acceptable phenotype in combination with any type of chromosome that has equal numbers of capital-letter and small-letter genes, e.g. *ABcDef* or *abcDEF* or *AbCdEf*. There are 20 such types of chromosomes; and the *ABCdef* type can be considered to have a genetic survival of 20/64. Clearly, the *ABCdef* chromosome will occur in more of the selected parents of the next generation than the *abcdef* chromosome, and we can conclude that selection will favor those chromosomes having the greatest probability of forming balanced combinations. In the absence of any recombination this would result in the population containing only those chromosomes with equal numbers of capital-letter and small-letter genes. Recombination does occur, even when linkage is very tight, and in each generation the parents will produce by recombination chromosomes that are not balanced—they do not have equal numbers of capital-letter and small-letter genes.

The *second* effect of selection for intermediates is to cause an increase in the frequencies of chromosomes whose *combinational advantage* is least affected by *recombination*. There are 20 types of chromosomes with equal numbers of capital-letter and small-letter genes, and although they have the same genetic survival as far as their combinational value is concerned, they differ widely in their recombinational value. This can be seen by considering two extreme examples.

	SINGLE CROSSOVERS	CAPITAL-LETTER GENES	SMALL-LETTER GENES
ABCdef	*abcdef*	0	6
$\overline{\textit{abcDEF}}$	*abCdef*	1	5
	abcDef	1	5
	abcDEf	2	4
	aBCdef	2	4
	AbcDEF	4	2
	ABCdeF	4	2
	ABcDEF	5	1
	ABCdEF	5	1
	ABCDEF	6	0

None of these chromosomes produced by a single crossover has a combinational value as high as the parent chromosomes; none has equal numbers of capital-letter and small-letter genes. This effect of recombination contrasts markedly with a genotype where the two types of genes are in repulsion (capital-letter and small-letter genes alternating along the chromosome).

		CAPITAL-LETTER GENES	SMALL-LETTER GENES
	SINGLE CROSSOVERS		
$\overline{\overline{AbCdEf}}$	abCdEf	2	4
$\overline{\overline{abCdeF}}$	abCdEf	2	4
	abCdef	2	4
	abCDEf	3	3
	abCdEf	3	3
	AbCdeF	3	3
	AbcDeF	3	3
	ABcDeF	4	2
	AbCDeF	4	2
	AbCdEF	4	2

Four of the ten chromosomes produced by single crossovers have the same combinational value as the parent chromosomes, and none of the single crossover chromosomes differ widely from the optimum of equal numbers of the two types of genes. This extreme comparison shows how chromosomes can differ in their recombinational value; those having a *repulsion* sequence are better than those with a *coupling* sequence (capital-letter genes more often alongside each other). Selection experiments on the computer show that chromosomes with a repulsion sequence *do* increase in frequency relative to those with a coupling sequence.

POLYGENES

The results from imitation genetics on computers have verified Mather's deduction that selection for intermediates would favor the formation of repulsion combinations of genes. He based this deduction on long-continued selection toward an extreme phenotype producing populations with phenotypes outside the range of variation of the parent population. He argued that this could be explained by the occurrence of repulsion combinations of linked genes, because these could only produce extreme combinations by crossing over occurring at several locations along the length of the linked complex. He gave the name *balanced polygene* to such a linked group of cooperatively acting genes.

Suppose selection was directed toward an extreme in a population that had previously been under selection against extremes until balanced polygenic combinations had become frequent; a possible sequence of events could be as shown in Figure 19.7.

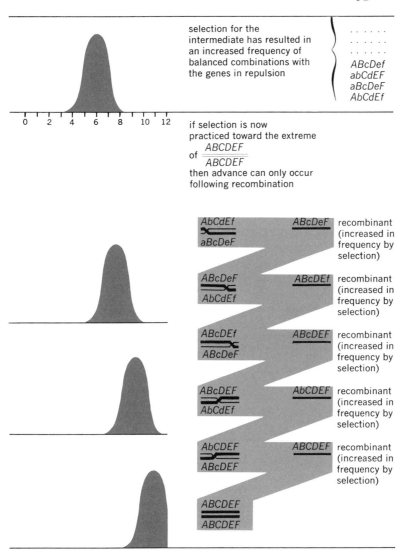

selection for the
intermediate has resulted in
an increased frequency of
balanced combinations with
the genes in repulsion

} ......
......
......
ABcDef
abcdEF
aBcDef
AbCdEf

if selection is now
practiced toward the extreme
of $\dfrac{ABCDEF}{ABCDEF}$
then advance can only occur
following recombination

AbCdEf
abcDef
→ *ABcDeF* recombinant
(increased in
frequency by
selection)

ABcDef
AbCdEf
→ *ABcDEf* recombinant
(increased in
frequency by
selection)

ABcDEf
ABcDeF
→ *ABcDEF* recombinant
(increased in
frequency by
selection)

ABcDEF
AbCdEf
→ *AbCDEF* recombinant
(increased in
frequency by
selection)

AbCDEF
ABcDEF
→ *ABCDEF* recombinant
(increased in
frequency by
selection)

ABCDEF
ABCDEF

FIGURE 19.7

Selection for intermediate phenotypes will result in populations having high frequencies of chromosomes with repulsion combinations of genes affecting a measurement character. If selection is now practiced for an extreme phenotype, one possible sequence of events is shown. Crossovers are needed to produce chromosomes with extreme combinations of capital-letter genes.

In the sequence shown in Figure 19.7, crossovers are needed to produce chromosomes with extreme combinations of capital-letter genes. If the linkage between the various genes is 1%, then such extreme individuals would only occur once in 10 billion gametes. Clearly, such extremes would not be a noticeable feature of the parent population, but they could be produced by continued selection toward an extreme, over a few thousand individuals, in relatively few generations.

The polygene concept has an attractive logic, but this is only a justification for its proposal, not for its acceptance. This must be based on real experiments, not algebraic and arithmetic models.

A number of selection experiments in Drosophila have been started from the progeny of single matings, each line derived solely from a single female and male. Many of these experiments have resulted in dramatic advances which are difficult to explain except by hypothesizing that the chromosomes of the parents contain balanced polygenic combinations.

Experiments determining the linkage of components of selection advances with marker genes have shown that at least some of the individual genes of a polygenic system do occur in balanced combinations. The evidence is fragmentary, and the polygene concept must be considered as plausible but unproven. There are other possible explanations of how an unselected population can contain genetic variability which is not manifested except as a consequence of long-continued selection toward an extreme.

DOMINANCE, INTERACTION, EPISTASIS

The effects of genes are not fixed, independent of the effects of other genes (see Chapter 2). The phenomenon of dominance is one illustration of this: a fully recessive gene has no effect in the presence of its normal allele. Interactions, similar to dominance, can occur between genes at different loci. The effects of genes determining coat color in mice are primarily dependent on the absence of the albino gene. When this gene is homozygous, the effects of other color genes are masked; in the absence of *any* pigment the effects of genes varying *type* of pigment are redundant. There are many examples of this type of dependency of the effect of one gene on the presence of other genes. Such interactions can be extremely specific; they can be between a specific allele of one locus and a specific allele of another locus. An example of this are the $su \cdot w^a$ and w^a eye-color genes in Drosophila. The w^a gene is an allele of the white locus which is suppressed in its effects by the $su\cdot w^a$ gene. This suppression is specific, acting only on the w^a gene; there is no suppression of any of the other alleles at the white locus.

Interactions may enhance as well as suppress; genes are known that act to enhance the effect of some other gene. The gene *Star* in Drosophila causes the eyes to be smaller and narrower, with a rough texture consequent from the irregular facets. These effects of the *Star* gene are considerably enhanced by a separate gene, *enhancer-Star*, which has no effects in the absence of Star.

Interactions can also occur between single genes and sets of genes. The effects of specific genetic differences can vary markedly from one strain to another. The *scute* gene in Drosophila causes a reduction of the number of scutellar bristles, which is not usually complete (scute flies usually have *one or two* bristles). In some stocks the effect of the gene is exaggerated, with the result that scute flies in these stocks do not have *any* scutellar bristles. The difference between the stocks in the expression of the scute gene is not due to any identifiable enhancer; it is a feature of the joint actions of several genes that cannot be separately identified.

Clearly, the genes affecting a character can involve a complex maze of interactions, and it is possible to explain many of the long-range effects of selection as consequences of such interactions.

NUMBER OF SCUTELLAR BRISTLES

In a population of *Drosophila simulans* the number of scutellar bristles was found to be normally four, with very few individuals having less than this number. Genetic tests showed that these rare flies were not due to single genetic differences, and selection for less than the normal number was successful when continued for several generations. The frequency of flies with only two or three scutellar bristles increased with selection. In later generations the response to selection increased markedly until flies with the norm of four bristles were rare in the selection line, and flies with no scutellar bristles were frequent. Crosses of the selection line back to the parent line showed that the loss of bristles was dominant, and that it now segregated as a dominant gene. The gene concerned was given the name *Bare*, because it caused not only a loss of scutellar bristles, but also caused the dorsum to have bare patches.

The occurrence of such a dominant gene was difficult to explain unless a mutation had occurred during the formation of the selection line. Further crosses were made of the Bare gene back to the parent population. These resulted in progressive changes of the characteristics of the gene. After two generations of such crosses the gene had become much less severe in its effects; a high proportion of heterozygotes had the norm of four bristles and none showed the bare patches on the dorsum. After three generations, the gene had become recessive, and with further generations of backcrossing the gene lost all its effects.

These results show that the Bare gene is normally an isoallele, which only has detectable effects in the genetic climate of missing bristles. The initial selection increased the frequency of genes that cause a decrease in the number of bristles; this resulted in a change of the effectiveness of the Bare gene, which was then selected, increasing its frequency and its expression.

This is but one variation on the theme of interactions and the effectiveness of selection. So far we have only considered interactions of genes with genes, but the effects of genes are also sensitive to variations of the environment, and we need to consider interactions between genes and environment.

BUFFERING AND HOMEOSTASIS

Selection against the extreme variants of a measurement character has, so far, been considered as if the occurrence of such extremes is solely the result of segregation and recombination of a polygenic system. This is an unlikely situation; most, if not all, measurement characters are to some degree sensitive to fluctuations of the environment. Selection against extreme variants can, therefore, act in two ways: to reduce the segregation and recombination of the genetic system, and to reduce the sensitivity to fluctuations of the environment. Selection against extremes will favor the increase of genotypes which are better buffered against the effects of environmental fluctuations. The word *homeostasis* refers to such buffering; an example is the maintenance of a constant body temperature in mammals. Humans have, normally, a body temperature of 98.6°, which is maintained at, or very near, this value over a very wide range of temperatures. Two aspects of how this constancy is maintained are the processes of shivering and perspiring: the muscular exertion of shivering increases the production of body heat, and the evaporation of perspiration cools the body. An individual who shivers in the cold and perspires in the heat is better adapted to maintaining a constant body temperature than someone else who shivers when it is hot and perspires when it is cold. Selection against extremes of body temperature will increase the frequency of genes that determine that shivering will occur in the cold and perspiring will occur in the heat.

Selection against extremes can lead to an increased buffering against the effects of the environmental fluctuation. This will involve the elaboration of biochemical and physiological processes which act to counter the variations caused by the environment. The same processes will also act to counter genetically caused variations; the evolution of buffering will act to reduce the expression of genetic variation.

Consider the example of body temperature: the genes responsible for perspiring in the heat will also act to counter a genetically determined increase of the production of body heat. Suppose an individual has genes for increased production of body heat; in the absence of the buffering action of perspiring, these genes would be manifested as an increase of body temperature. In the presence of this buffering action the body temperature would be kept constant, but the individual would perspire at a lower temperature. This is another way in which a population can contain more genetic variability than is usually manifested phenotypically.

The expression of genetic variability is reduced by processes of buffering. If selection toward an extreme is now initiated, this will act to reduce the buffering, allowing the expression of the buffered genes, which will then be selected, resulting in marked advances beyond the range of variability of the parent population.

PHENOCOPIES AND GENETIC ASSIMILATION

Buffering against fluctuations of the environment may not be complete. Exposure to sufficiently extreme environments can overcome buffering, resulting in extreme phenotypes. Many such extreme deviants were found that were similar to mutant individuals; they were given the name *phenocopies*. It was considered that the extreme environments interfered with development in the same ways that mutant genes interfere with development. The general view of such phenocopies was that they were in no way heritable. This was shown to be wrong when it was found that exposing different strains to the same extreme environments could have different effects; one strain might produce a greater percentage of more extreme phenocopies than another strain.

There are genetic differences of the resistance against the effects of extreme environmental stress. Waddington, in a very important experiment, showed that genetic variation of such resistance occurred in populations of Drosophila. Exposure of larvae to high temperature results in some of the adult flies having incomplete wing veins. Waddington studied the effect of temperature stress on a particular vein, the crossvein, which is only rarely incomplete in normally developed populations. He exposed a population to high temperatures and selected those individuals having incomplete crossveins. The progeny of those selected individuals were similarly exposed to high temperatures as larvae; the developed adults having incomplete crossveins were selected, and so on. The result of this continued selection was an increase of the percentage of affected individuals. Selection had decreased the resistance of the population to temperature stress during development. Waddington also allowed some cultures of the selection line to develop normally, without exposing them to a temperature stress. In the early generations these untreated cultures did include a small percentage of affected individuals, and this percentage increased in parallel with the increase in effectiveness of exposure to environmental stress. The selection for a decreased resistance to high temperatures had produced a response that was manifested in the absence of any abnormal temperatures. This can be understood if the development of the crossvein is determined by the actions of two sets of genes: a set of genes which is involved in the mechanisms of buffering, and another set of genes, which regulate aspects of development that are buffered. The mechanism is of buffering genes and buffered genes. High temperatures during development inactivate the buffering

FIGURE 19.8

At ordinary temperatures the buffering of wing development is sufficiently strong for none of the buffered genotypes to affect the development of the wing vein. Exposure to high temperatures during development inactivates the buffering genes to a degree that results in some of the buffered genotypes having an effect on the crossvein. Selection of these genotypes results in a shift of the buffered genotype until, eventually, it is frequently expressed in the absence of the high-temperature treatment. The buffered genotype has too extreme an effect to be inhibited by the buffering genotype.

not enough crossvein
substance to form
complete veins
(**crossveinless**)

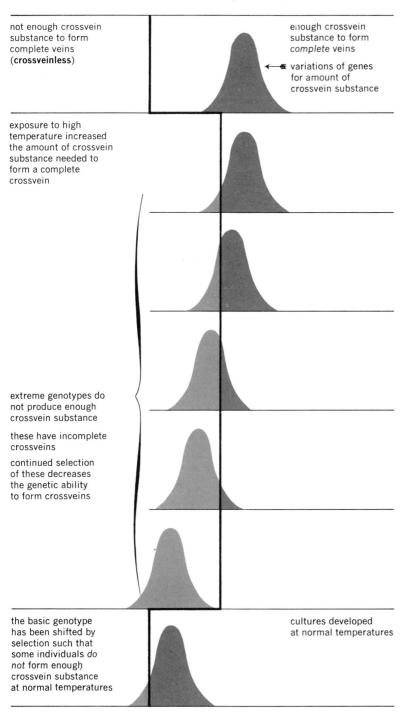

enough crossvein
substance to form
complete veins

◄─◄ variations of genes
for amount of
crossvein substance

exposure to high
temperature increased
the amount of crossvein
substance needed to
form a complete
crossvein

extreme genotypes do
not produce enough
crossvein substance

these have incomplete
crossveins

continued selection
of these decreases
the genetic ability
to form crossveins

the basic genotype
has been shifted by
selection such that
some individuals *do*
not form enough
crossvein substance
at normal temperatures

cultures developed
at normal temperatures

genes, which then cannot stop the buffered genes from having effects. Only those genotypes that are extreme will result in visible effects in the absence of buffering; these will be selected, and the continuation of this selection will effect an increase in the frequency of such extreme genotypes. Eventually the buffered genotype will be modified until its actions are too extreme to be contained by the buffering genes and they will be manifested even when the buffering genes are active. Waddington's experiments have shown that buffering can be potent in the restriction of the expression of genetic variability.

GENETIC SYSTEMS

The main conclusion derived from all these researches involving the long-range effects of selection is that genes may be organized into integrated systems on a variety of frameworks: physically in terms of their chromosomal location, and physiologically in terms of the interplay of their actions and effects. The gene is the basic unit of the genotype, which is organized into a coherent structure both at the level of the individual and at the level of the population.

Problems

1. Long-continued selection can produce responses that exceed the normal range of variability of the original population. What are the possible explanations of this?

2. In animal breeding, one concept has been to raise animals in the best possible conditions, under the thesis that this will result in the greatest possible expression of genetic differences. How does this thesis relate to Waddington's experiments on the use of environmental stress (genetic assimilation)?

3. All the individuals of a species have a number of characteristics in common. One explanation is that they are similarly homozygous for the genes concerned. Is this the only possible explanation?

Chapter 20

GENETIC INTEGRATION

The chromosomes are the carriers of the genes, and we can study one aspect of the integration of genes into a genotype by studying the variations of the chromosomes. An early illustration of the value of this approach was given by Bridge's studies of sex determination in Drosophila. We have already considered the role of the X and Y chromosomes (Chapter 4), but an extension of his work showed that the other chromosomes (the autosomes) are also concerned in the determination of sex.

AUTOSOMES VERSUS SEX CHROMOSOMES

In Drosophila, nondisjunction of the sex chromosomes results in individuals with abnormal numbers of sex chromosomes, but normal numbers of other chromosomes (chromosomes II, III and IV — the autosomes). The conclusion drawn from these abnormalities is that the sex difference is determined by the number of X chromosomes. Having one X chromosome determines maleness, whereas having two X chromosomes determines femaleness. Individuals with more than two X chromosomes are exaggeratedly female — they are *superfemales*. The Y chromosome does not have a major role in sex determination. These conclusions about the roles of the X and Y chromosomes derive from studies of individuals who are normal in the number of autosomes. Bridges extended his studies to individuals with abnormal numbers of autosomes (such individuals were produced by the simultaneous nondisjunction of the complete set of chromosomes). These individuals were *polyploid*; they had an extra set of chromosomes, being triploid instead of the normal diploid. A triploid female has three X chromosomes; in a diploid this would result in the

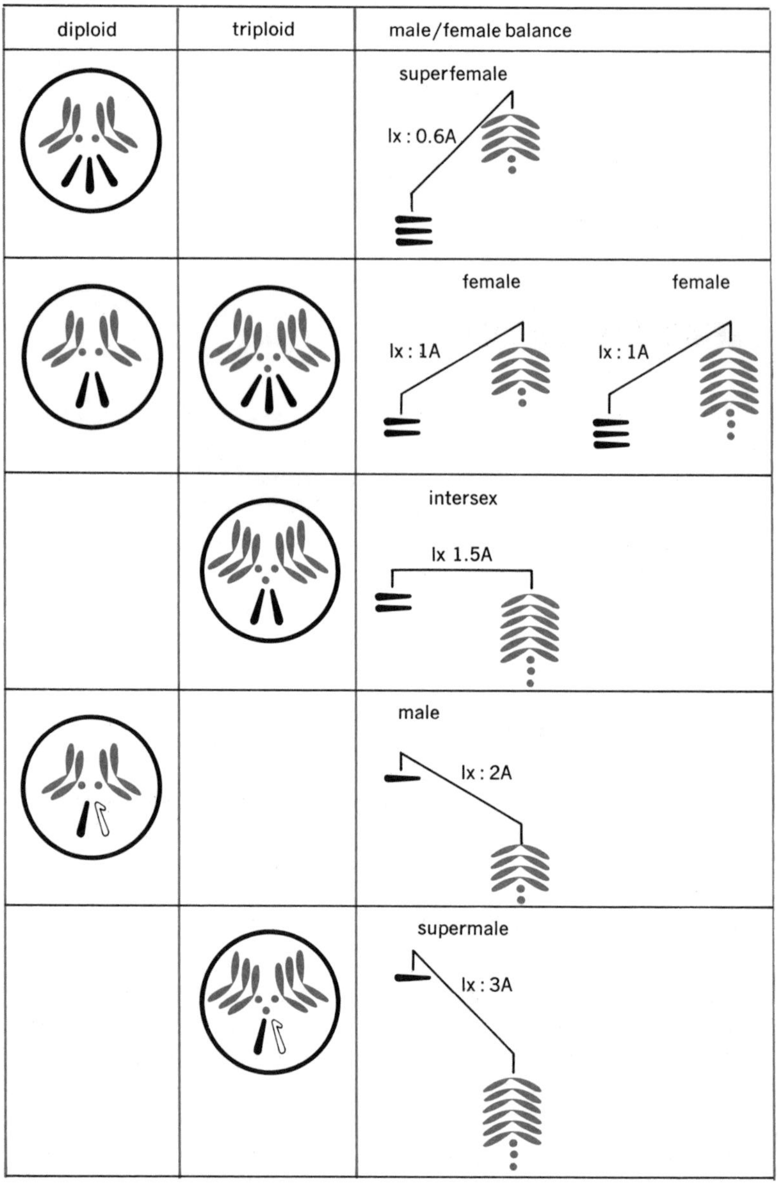

FIGURE 20.1

The relation of sex to chromosome constitution in Drosophila, showing
that this is determined by the balance between female-determining genes
on the X chromosomes, and male-determining genes on the autosomes
(chromosomes II, III and IV).

terility of superfemales, but this does not occur in triploids—
1ese females are fully fertile. If these triploid females are crossed
) normal males, several different types are produced. Correlating
1eir chromosomal constitution with their sexual type shows that,
lthough the number of X chromosomes is the primary determinant
f sex, this needs to be considered in relation to the number of
ets of autosomes. The autosomes carry male-directing genes; the
chromosomes carry female-directing genes. The balance between
1ese two sets of genes determines type of sex. Too many female-
irecting genes, i.e., an excess of X chromosomes relative to the
utosomes, results in a superfemale. Too few female-directing
enes, i.e., an excess of autosomes relative to the X chromosomes,
esults in a supermale. A balance at a genetic equality results in
n intersex. Normally the balance between X chromosomes and
itosomes is such that the difference between inheriting one or two
chromosomes determines the inheritance of normal male or female
ex. This balance has been achieved by the concentration of female-
irecting genes on the X chromosomes, and an equivalent concen-
ation of male-directing genes on the autosomes, followed by a
odification of the relative potencies of their actions. This balance
so positioned that the presence or absence of a single X chromo-
me neatly swings the sexual scale to one or other sex type. The
netic constitution, the genotype, has been adjusted as a whole;
though individual genes and alleles are the basic material, they
e important only in the context of their integration into the genetic
tality.

POLYPLOIDY AND ANEUPLOIDY

he phenomenon of *polyploidy* was introduced as an analog to
1euploidy. The latter is the inheritance of abnormal numbers of
dividual chromosomes, whereas the former is the inheritance of
onormal numbers of complete sets of chromosomes. Contrasting the
fects of polyploidy and aneuploidy demonstrates the dependence
' the normal phenotype on the occurrence of integrated genotypes.
he Jimson weed normally has a chromosome number of 24; there
e 12 pairs of chromosomes. Mutant types have been found with
ariants of this normal number, either in terms of individual chromo-
mes (aneuploidy) or in terms of complete sets of chromosomes
oolyploidy).

The addition of just one or two extra chromosomes has marke phenotypic effects. These are particularly evident in the form o the seed capsule; it is possible to identify the occurrence of a specifi chromosome from its morphological effects. Clearly, there are gene that act to determine the shape of the capsule on each of the twelv chromosomes; the addition of an extra chromosome adds a few c these genes to the genotype. This addition unbalances developmei in a particular direction, producing a marked phenotypic effect.

It would appear logical that, if the addition of single extra chrom somes produces marked phenotypic effects, the addition of more tha one type should produce a combination of the effects of each chrom some added separately. Addition of 12 extra chromosomes, one e each type, should result in the combination of their 12 separa effects. Just such an addition of complete sets of 12 chromosom occurs in polyloid variants—in triploids that have one extra set c chromosomes, and in tetraploids that have two extra sets of chrom somes. Such polyploid variants do have recognizably different see capsules, but the differences are minor compared to the effects c aneuploid variants; they are not the compound of all the separa effects of adding each chromosomes singly. This shows that tl genotype determining the form of the seed capsule is integrated its actions; the contributions of each of the 12 chromosomes a balanced. Addition of a single chromosome upsets this balanc whereas adding a complete set has little effect on the balance.

The effect of adding extra chromosomes decreases as the degre of polyploidy increases. This is understandable; adding one ext chromosome to a diploid with 24 chromosomes will disturb tl genetic balance more than adding the same chromosome to a tetr ploid of 48 chromosomes. A particular chromosome in Datura called the *Globe* chromosome because its addition causes the capsu to be flatter, rounder than normal. This effect is extremely evide in diploids, much less evident in tetraploids.

The addition of a complete set of chromosomes does not disru the genetic balance, if this balance is so organized that there is distinction between maternal and paternal chromosomes in the genetic role. Balance can be in terms of haploid sets of chrom somes, but the integration of the genotype can also involve the who diploid genotype, with the maternal and paternal genotypes int grated relative to each other. This is a feature of the Oenothera, tl Evening primroses, which have an exceedingly complicated set

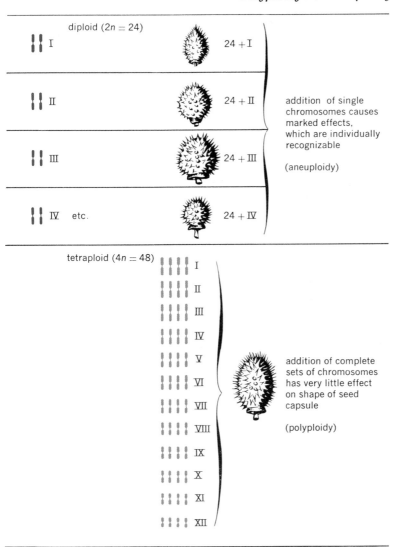

FIGURE 20.2

The Jimson Weed normally has 12 pairs of chromosomes. Addition of single chromosomes results in marked effects on the form of the seed capsule. Polyploid strains with additional sets of chromosomes do not have such abnormal seed capsules, and the addition of single chromosomes to polyploids does not have as marked effects as the addition of the same chromosomes to diploid strains.

chromosomes. The complications derive from the evolution of a genotype that is balanced both across each haploid set of chromosomes (as in Datura) and also between the maternal and paternal sets of chromosomes.

THE EVENING PRIMROSES

The Evening primrose has a chromosome number of 14, and this would, normally, result in the formation of seven pairs of chromosomes at meiosis. This does not occur; instead, the 14 chromosomes form one ring at meiosis, arranged in such a way that when the chromosomes separate to opposite poles, they separate regularly, seven chromosomes moving to each pole.

The key to understanding the complex pattern of meiosis in the Evening primrose is that the chromosomes do not pair off as units; instead they pair off by arms. In each chromosome the two arms pair separately, one arm pairing with an arm of one chromosome, the other arm pairing with an arm of a separate chromosome. This pairing of the chromosomes by arms has evolved until the chromosomes pair into one continuous loop. The evolution of this unusual pattern of pairing almost certainly began in a form with normal chromosome-to-chromosome pairing. A reciprocal translocation between two separate chromosomes would then result in two pairs of chromosomes associating at meiosis into a ring of four, in which pairing is part by part, rather than as entire chromosomes. This process can be envisaged as continuing with another reciprocal translocation adding another pair of chromosomes into the pattern. These will pair part by part, rather than as entire chromosomes, to form a ring of six chromosomes. The continuation of this process to include all 14 chromosomes will result in these pairing in a ring of 14 chromosomes. The separation of such a complex ring at meiosis would result in a wild mélange of unbalanced gametes unless this ring is orientated at meiosis in some regular way. This does happen; the ring *is* arranged so that alternate centromeres move to opposite poles, resulting in the formation of two types of gametes which are chromosomal complements. We will call these the A and B *genomes.* There is another feature of the Evening primrose that is important in maintaining its genetic system. The A and B genomes act as a balanced lethal system, analogous to the Curly/Plum balanced lethality discussed in Chapter 17. This lethality can follow two patterns; in some species the lethality is manifested in the gametes

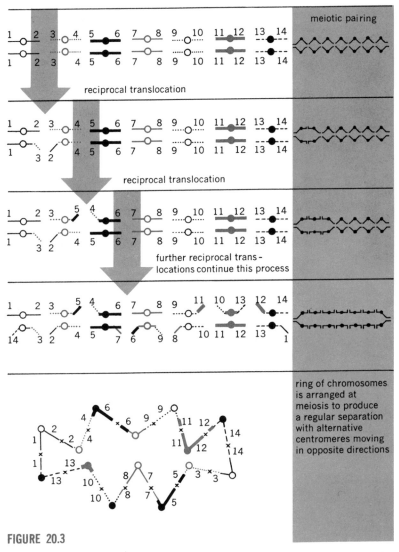

meiotic pairing

reciprocal translocation

reciprocal translocation

further reciprocal trans-
locations continue this process

ring of chromosomes
is arranged at
meiosis to produce
a regular separation
with alternative
centromeres moving
in opposite directions

FIGURE 20.3

Chromosome mutants and chromosome balance in Datura, as shown by differences in capsule form. Above, at left, the normal diploid type, from a plant with 12 pairs of chromosomes. Below (left), the mutant globe, in which one set of chromosomes has three members, thus upsetting the normal balance. The effect of this particular chromosome set is evidently to flatten the capsule, for the addition of an extra chromosome results in a flatter capsule than normal. The addition of two extra chromosomes (as shown to the right of this) has the effect of flattening the capsule still further.

Pollen carrying the A genome dies, and ovules carrying the B genome die, resulting in the maintenance of a permanent heterozygosity for the two genomes. In other species the lethality is manifested in zygotes; homozygotes for either the A or B genomes die.

The full detail of the cytology and genetics of Oenothera is even more complex than we have shown it to be, but enough of this intricate genetic system has been described to show that the chromosomes of a genome are balanced relative to each other, and that each genome is balanced relative to the other genome. The Evening primrose is a uniquely extreme example of how the genetic system can evolve to a balanced integration of its elements—the chromosomes and their genes.

The addition of complete sets of chromosomes is extremely common in plants, where the number of chromosomes in related species frequently forms a simple sequence of multiples of some common denominator. *Triticum monoccum, T. dicoccum,* and *T. aestivum* are three species of wheat that have haploid chromosome numbers of 7, 14, and 21 respectively—multiplies with a common denominator of 7. There are species of Solanum with numbers of 24, 36, 48, 60, 72, 96, 108, 120, and 144—all multiples of a common denominator of 12. This phenomenon suggests that although polyploidy does not disrupt the genetic balance, it does modify it in ways that are sufficiently beneficial to result in the frequent formation of new species.

ALLOPLOIDY AND AUTOPLOIDY

There are two distinct forms of polyploidy: a simple doubling termed *autoploidy;* and a more complex form, involving the formation of a hybrid between two species followed by a doubling of the chromosome number, termed *alloploidy.*

Both types of polyploids occur naturally. The formation of tetraploids in the tomato (*Solanum lycopersicum*) has been found to be associated with damage. If young plants are decapitated, some of the shoots that develop from the injured region are often tetraploid. There is a drug, *colcichine,* that has effects on cell division—treatment with this drug can inhibit the separation of chromosomes without affecting their replication. The result is the production of cells with double the normal complement of chromosomes. The technique of colcichine treatment has been refined to the point that the doubling of chromosomal complements is a major tool in plant breeding.

Autoploids do not usually differ in marked ways from their diploid ancestors, but they frequently are more vigorous. Their stems are thicker, with shorter, broader leaves and larger flowers and seeds. These differences appear to have been sufficiently advantageous in some species to result in the evolution of tetraploid races and species, which have occupied wider ranges than the diploid parental species. A major feature acting against the evolution of autoploid races and species is the occurrence of too many homologous chromosomes; this has disruptive effects at meiosis. In a tetraploid there are sets of four homologous chromosomes that can pair and crossover at meioses. This can result in chromosomes being associated in multiple groupings; three chromosomes of a set of four may have paired at points, resulting in a trivalent, with the fourth chromosome unpaired. Four chromosomes may pair at points to result in a quadrivalent. These deviations from the normal grouping in pairs result in the formation of aneuploid gametes. This disruption of the normal sequence leads to a lowered fertility, which can counterbalance any morphological or physiological advantages that result from the polyploidy.

The other form of polyploidy, *alloploidy*, does not involve quadruplication of one set of chromosomes; instead there is a duplication of two different sets of chromosomes. The first step in the formation of an alloploid is the crossing of two different species to form a hybrid, which will have received *one* set of chromosomes from each species. Such hybrids are often sterile because the chromosomes of the two sets are sufficiently different not to pair at meiosis. The absence of pairing results in a chaotic disruption of meiotic separation, producing gametes with unbalanced numbers of chromosomes. This defect of interspecies hybrids can be rectified by the doubling of the chromosomes to form an alloploid. There will now be *two* complete sets of *each* parental set of chromosomes, and meiosis will proceed normally by association and separation in pairs.

The genus Galeopsis contains two groups of species: one group has chromosome complements of 16, the other has complements of 32. It would appear that the species with 16 chromosomes are diploids and those with 32 chromosomes are tetraploids. Muntzing showed that one of the tetraploids, *Galeopsis tetrahit*, is almost certainly an allotetraploid resulting from the doubling of the chromosome complement of sterile hybrids between diploid Galeopsis species. He started with *Galeopsis pubescens* and *Galeopsis speciosa*, two diploid species. They each have a chromosome complement of 16, forming eight bivalents at meiosis. Crosses between these two species pro-

Galeopsis pubescens (2n = 16)	Galeopsis speciosa (2n = 16)
⌐⌐⌐⌐⌐⌐⌐⌐ ∟∟∟∟∟∟∟∟	⌐⌐⌐⌐⌐⌐⌐⌐ ∟∟∟∟∟∟∟∟

sterile because chromosomes have no homologous partners and meiosis is therefore highly abnormal	diploid hybrid (2n = 16) 	

doubling of the chromosomes

fertile because each chromosome has a homologous partner and meiosis is therefore normal	tetraploid (4n = 32)	

Galeopsis tetrahit (artificiales)

FIGURE 20.4

The formation of an allotetraploid from the cross of Galeopsis pubescens and Galeopsis speciosa. This allotetraploid is extremely similar to a natural species, Galeopsis tetrahit.

duce hybrids, with one set of eight chromosomes from pubescens, and another set from speciosa. These two sets are not homologous; meiosis in these hybrids is extremely irregular, with very few chromosomes paired. This results in a high degree of sterility, but doubling the chromosome number removes this defect—each chromosome now has a normal partner and meiosis proceeds regularly. An intriguing feature of this allotetraploid is its similarity with the natural species, *Galeopsis tetrahit*. Crossing the two diploid species and doubling the chromosome number experimentally has resulted in the artificial retracing of an evolutionary sequence.

Alloploidy is a means of combining two separately balanced sets of chromosomes, producing a new balance. The "cabbish" is an illustration of the experimental production of a new alloploid.

THE "CABBISH"

Crosses can be made between the cabbage (Brassica) and the radish (Raphanus). These are both diploids, each having 18 chromosomes.

The hybrids have one set of nine cabbage chromosomes, and another set of nine radish chromosomes, which are not homologous; and meiosis is irregular, leading to a marked sterility. Doubling the chromosome number of these hybrids produces fertile allotetraploids having 36 chromosomes—two sets of radish and two sets of cabbage chromosomes.

The fertile allotetraploid from the cross of the cabbage and radish is scientifically named *Raphanobrassica*, a polysyllable that hardly seems competition for the explicit simplicity of "cabbish." The cabbish combines features of both parents; it has the root system of the cabbage and the foliage of the radish. The fruit of the cabbish is like the cabbage at the bottom, like the radish at the top. This combination of characters is permanent and stable. It is an economic failure, but the research can be considered highly successful—it provided genetics with a major example of the combinative aspect of alloploidy.

Alloploidy has played a major role in plant evolution, but it cannot have been of more than minor importance in animal evolution because polyploidy disrupts the genetic basis of sex determination. An XX/XY system is converted into an XXXX, XXXY, XYXY, XYYY mix-up by polyploidy.

CHROMOSOMAL EVOLUTION IN ANIMALS

Although polyploidy has rarely occurred in animals, there is no doubt that animal evolution has involved changes of the number and structure of chromosomes. Inversions, deletions, duplications, and translocations have been the means by which this was achieved. There are many species of Drosophila, ranging from species so similar in appearance that it is almost impossible to tell them apart, to species that are clearly separate and distinct to a casual glance. There is a considerable range of variation of the number and shape of their chromosomes: some species have six pairs of chromosomes, others have five pairs; in yet others, such as *Drosophila melanogaster,* there are only four pairs, and in a few species there are only three pairs of chromosomes.

Hybrids can be produced between closely related species. In these hybrids it is possible to determine the pattern of the pairing of the chromosomes, particularly in the salivary-gland chromosomes. *Drosophila melanogaster* and *D. simulans* are very similar species that can be hybridized. Salivary-gland chromosomes show that these two species differ in a large inversion of the IIIrd chromosome. There

2n = 6

2n = 8

2n = 10

2n = 12

D. saltans   D. victoria   D. submacroptera   D. macroptera

FIGURE 20.5

The mitotic chromosome sets of four Drosophila species, illustrating the variations of type and number of chromosomes that have occurred.

are other smaller differences that can be seen from the sequence of bands' being different, involving small duplications and inversions. These small differences can result in the chromosomes' not being paired at those regions.

The number and extent of differences between chromosomes of Drosophila species become more and more extensive as species are compared that are more and more distinct taxonomically. It is clear that evolution can, and often does, involve the basic genetic system: changes of the number of sets of chromosomes, additions of parts of chromosomes, movements of parts of chromosomes to different locations. All have occurred in evolution. The genetic balance is plastic, and new patterns can evolve with different relationships; understanding these possibilities is basic to the full appreciation of the limitations and possibilities of organic evolution.

QUICK QUIZ *Chapters 15 through 20*

1. The effectiveness of selection against a recessive lethal gene decreases as the gene becomes rare. This is because:

   (*a*) the law of diminishing returns applies.

   (*b*) homozygotes are rare.

   (*c*) the frequency of homozygotes decreases with the square of the gene frequency.

2. Melanic forms of moths have increased in frequency because:

   (*a*) industrial pollution causes an increased rate of mutation to the melanic allele.

   (*b*) melanic moths are less sensitive to the pollution of the atmosphere.

   (*c*) melanic moths are less easily seen by predators in polluted areas.

3. Sickle-cell anemia is an example of:

   (*a*) transitional diversity.

   (*b*) heterozygous advantage.

   (*c*) the founder effect.

   (*d*) differential mutation rates.

4. The advantage of inversions in *Drosophila pseudo obscura* is based on:

   (*a*) the isolation of a linked set of genes from recombination.

   (*b*) the inversions including genes having a beneficial effect in some conditions, and a detrimental effect in other conditions.

   (*c*) both of the above.

5. The number of possible genotypes for five pairs of segregating genes is:

   (*a*) 243   (*b*) 729   (*c*) 500   (*d*) 32   (*e*) 11

6. Differences of I.Q. between twins are due to:

(*a*) environmental differences.

(*b*) hereditary differences.

(*c*) neither (*a*) nor (*b*).

(*d*) both (*a*) and (*b*).

7. Differences of I.Q. between identical twins (monozygotic twins) are due to:

(*a*) environmental differences.

(*b*) genetic differences.

(*c*) neither (*a*) nor (*b*).

(*d*) both (*a*) and (*b*).

8. The ability of selection to produce responses beyond the range of variation of the initial population can be explained by:

(*a*) the character being controlled by a very large number of genes.

(*b*) the genes being in linked combinations with opposite-acting alleles in repulsion.

(*c*) epistatic interactions between genes.

(*d*) homeostatic inhibition of the expression of variability.

9. Aneuploidy is:

(*a*) variation of the chromosome number.

(*b*) addition or loss of single chromosomes.

(*c*) addition or loss of whole sets of chromosomes.

(*d*) an exotic oriental disease.

10. Alloploidy differs from autoploidy in:

(*a*) involving the multiplication of one basic set of chromosomes.

(*b*) involving the multiplication of two different sets of chromosomes.

(*c*) occurring under experimental treatment with colcichine.

(*d*) resulting in even numbers of chromosomes.

Chapter 21

THE CYTOPLASM

The nuclei of cells range from being the most obvious single feature to being so insignificant that they can be identified only with
difficulty. A few special types of cells can even survive for considerable parts of their lives without nuclei (red blood cells have
no nuclei). Cells without nuclei can be produced experimentally.
An algal plant of the Mediterranean, called Acetabularia, is quite
large, but it consists of just one cell with a single nucleus. This
plant has a flat mushroom-like leaf connected by a long stalk to a
foot. The nucleus is usually located near the foot, and if cut off,
the plant will lack a nucleus. The parts without a nucleus can live
a long time. No cell division or reproduction can occur, which
shows that the nucleus has the primary role in this aspect; but the
long survival of the enucleated cell shows that the cytoplasm cannot be considered as just an amorphous cooking pot into which the
chemical catalysts of the nucleus are stirred. There is adequate
evidence that the cytoplasm has both dependent and independent
roles: the majority of its functions are initiated and directed from
the nucleus, but some of its functions are semi-independent, determined by the integration of the nuclear and cytoplasmic structures;
other functions are almost completely independent. Any complete
treatment of heredity needs to consider the relationship of the
nucleus to the cytoplasm.

The primary indication that inheritance in a particular case
does not follow a nuclear system is that inheritance is maternal,
with little contribution from the paternal side. In mice, large
females have more offspring per litter than do small females. The
size of the male parent is unimportant in this aspect. The inheritance of fecundity is complicated by this maternal effect of the size
of the female parent. The relationship of such maternal inheritance to the nucleus has been clearly established in many different
examples.

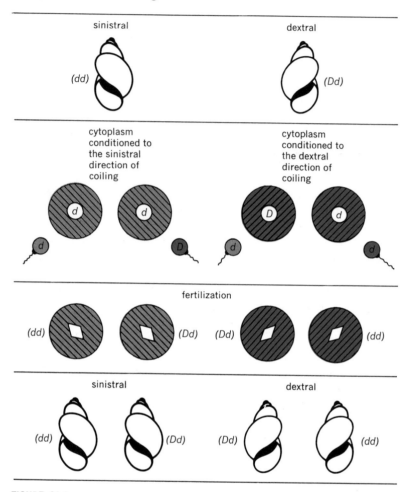

FIGURE 21.1

The direction of coiling in Limnea is determined by the genotype of the maternal parent, since it is this genotype that determines the left or right polarity of the first cell division of the eggs.

CYTOPLASMIC CONDITIONING

The shells of the snail, Limnea, may be coiled left-handed or right-handed (left-handed is called *sinistral* coiling, right-handed coiling is called *dextral* coiling). A gene *D* causes dextral coiling, and is dominant to a gene *d* for sinistral coiling. The genotype of the individual does not, however, determine the direction of coiling of its shell; this is determined by the genotype of the female parent.

The maternal inheritance of the direction of coiling can be understood if the angles of the first divisions of the egg are preset into the cytoplasm of the egg during its formation. Since the eggs are formed under the control of the female parent's genotype, the direction of coiling will be set according to that genotype. This is an example of the female parent's genotype conditioning the cytoplasm of the eggs. There is no indication that a separate system of cytoplasmic inheritance is involved; it is more a case of a temporary conditioning of the cytoplasm effective at an early crucial stage of development.

CYTOPLASMIC RESERVES

Larvae of the meal moth, Ephestia, normally have black eyes, but a mutant gene a blocks the synthesis of eye pigment at the kynurenine step. This gene is recessive; only homozygotes show the red eyes that are diagnostic of this biochemical inadequacy. A peculiarity is that a/a larvae initially have black eyes if they are progeny of a^+/a females. They manifest the characteristic red eyes late in development. This delayed effectiveness of the a/a genotype does not occur if the female parent is a/a.

	Black-eyed a^+/a a^+/a	$\times$	Red-eyed a/a a/a	Red-eyed a/a a^+/a	$\times$	Black-eyed a^+/a a/a
Young	All		Black-eyed	Black-eyed		Red-eyed
Mature	Black-eyed		Red-eyed	Black-eyed		Red-eyed

This peculiarity can be understood if a^+/a females store sufficient precursors of the black-eye pigment in the cytoplasm of their eggs to allow an a/a larvae that hatches from them to develop black eyes, until this inherited reserve of precursors is exhausted. When the reserve is exhausted, the genetic inadequacy becomes apparent.

These two examples show how the nuclear genes can act on the cytoplasm to impress a semi-permanent conditioning on it. The direction of coiling in snails has its basis in the genes of the female parent acting on the structure of the eggs to preset the direction of the first division of the eggs. Once this difference of direction has begun, it is self-maintaining. Here the maternal effect involves just a single cell division in its actions, but affects the complete structure of the adult as a consequence. The maternal modification of eye color in Ephestia is a similar but longer-lasting action. The formation of eggs by a biochemically adequate female results in these eggs having a reserve of kynurenine. As the eggs divide, this reserve of kynurenine will be used, until eventually the individual is thrown on its own resources; if these resources are not adequate, the effect of the inadequacy becomes apparent. There is no indication in either of these examples that a separate system of cytoplasmic inheritance is involved; it is more a case of passive effects of semipermanent imprints on the cytoplasm. There are, however, many examples of structures of the cytoplasm whose inheritance is, at least to a degree, independent of the nucleus.

CYTOPLASMIC ENTITIES

An obvious feature of the cytoplasm of plant cells are the *plastids*. These are usually green, from the chlorophyll they contain. There has been a question as to whether plastids can be synthesized under the control of the nuclear genes, or whether their existence is independent of the nuclear genes. This question was resolved by two types of observations.

A unicellular organism, Euglena, normally has plastids, but if it is treated with streptomycin the plastids are lost. This loss is permanent; Euglena of such a treated stock never form plastids. Removal of plastids experimentally results in a permanent inherited inability to produce plastids.

Another observation involved the algal plant, Spirogyra. A cell of this plant was found with two different types of plastids. Normally, the plastids of Spirogyra have pyrenoids surrounded by a dense sheath of starch granules. The abnormal type of plastid lacked pyrenoids, and the starch granules were scattered through the plastid. This difference was only inherited directly—cells with only one type of plastid did not produce cells with other than that type. The inheritance of plastid type was independent of the nucleus, each type of plastid being a self-contained unit of heredity.

Plastids are not, however, completely independent of the nucleus. Many genes are known that act on the form and function of the plastids. The green pigment *chlorophyll* is the end point of a biosynthetic sequence, and genes have been identified that act to block many different steps of this sequence. The gene xanth-10 in barley blocks the step to protochlorophyll, and this results in yellow instead of green plastids. There are other mutants that affect the structure of the plastids—the lutescens mutants are green in young seedlings, but the structure of the chloroplasts becomes disorganized in older plants.

The plastids are an example of how the genes of the nuclei and the structures of the cytoplasm interact. The cytoplasm has a structure and an inheritance of this structure; this can be considered as a frame-work determining the effectiveness of the actions of the genes of the nucleus.

The existence of independently replicating cytoplasmic entities conflicts with a major tenet of modern biology—the central role of DNA in the hereditary transfer of biological information. There have been unconfirmed reports that cytoplasmic entities do contain DNA, but in one case of cytoplasmic inheritance the role of DNA is undisputed.

KILLER PARAMECIUM

Paramecium is a minute, single-celled animal. Strains have been found that are genetically antisocial; these strains secrete a sub-stance, *paramecin,* which is poisonous to individuals not of that strain. These strains of paramecium are aptly called "killer" strains; genetic analysis has shown that the killer strains are characterized by a nuclear gene *K, and* by the occurrence of cytoplasmic particles called *kappa.* A strain must have the *K* gene to maintain kappa par-ticles in its cytoplasm, but the *K* gene is not responsible for the origin of these particles. This was shown in a series of elegant experiments.

A killer strain (*KK* with kappa) was treated with X rays, which killed the kappa, resulting in a nonkiller strain that was *KK* without kappa. This strain bred true; once the kappa particles had been lost it was not possible for the *K* gene to direct their formation. The same result occurred if a killer strain were grown under conditions in which growth and multiplication were very rapid. Eventually, after a number of cell divisions, strains were produced that were nonkiller (*KK* without kappa). Apparently the rate of replication of the kappa particles was too slow to keep up with the rate of division of the cells, and this resulted in a decrease and eventual loss of the kappa particles.

Another experiment involved growing nonkiller paramecia (*KK* without kappa) in suspensions of kappa particles formed by crushing killer paramecia. Some of the nonkillers were converted into killers by this treatment, and the conversion was inherited. Killer strains that were *KK* with kappa were produced by this treatment.

The same kind of experiment was performed with sensitive (*kk*) strains. Culturing these in suspensions of kappa particles resulted in their conversion into *kk* with kappa, *but* the introduced kappa par-ticles only survived for a few cell generations—kappa particles cannot replicate and be maintained in the absence of the *K* gene.

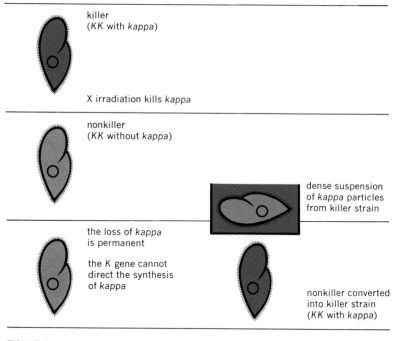

killer
(*KK* with *kappa*)

X irradiation kills *kappa*

nonkiller
(*KK* without *kappa*)

dense suspension
of *kappa* particles
from killer strain

the loss of *kappa*
is permanent

the *K* gene cannot
direct the synthesis
of *kappa*

nonkiller converted
into killer strain
(*KK* with *kappa*)

FIGURE 21.2

Killer strains of paramecium can be converted into nonkiller strains by treatment with X rays which kill the kappa particles. Nonkiller strains can be transformed into killer strains by transfer into dense suspensions of kappa particles. Some of these enter the nonkiller paramecia and multiply.

The kappa particles are extremely small, but they can be colored with the Feulgen stain, showing that they contain DNA. Other studies have shown that they also contain RNA and protein. Kappa is an example of cytoplasmic inheritance in which the role of DNA is indisputable.

The question has been raised as to whether kappa is a part of paramecium, or whether it is some other organism that has evolved to being dependent on paramecium for its existence. The kappa particles can be considered as a form of virus. The junction of two separate organisms into a single mutually advantageous unit is called *symbiosis,* and the kappa particles could be an example of such symbiosis.

There are many intriguingly complicated examples of extranuclear inheritance; as more attention is given to this possibility, it is certain that more examples will be found. Even so, cytoplasmic inheritance cannot be considered as more than a minor ancillary to nuclear inheritance; the pattern of inheritance from one generation to the next is primarily based on nuclear DNA.

Problems

1. How would you distinguish sex-linked inheritance, sex-modified inheritance, and cytoplasmic inheritance?

2. Heredity has its basis in the transmission of molecules of DNA. DNA is located in the nucleus. How can these statements be reconciled with the occurrence of cytoplasmic particles with self-determined heredity?

3. In cases of cytoplasmic inheritance, why is the mode of transmission completely, or mainly, from female parent to both male and female offspring?

Chapter 22

NEW PATHS OF GENETICS

J. B. S. Haldane produced a little book, *New Paths in Genetics*, in which he made a series of predictions of the fields of genetic research that would be most likely to lead to significant new lines of advance. Written nearly a quarter of a century ago, it was an exciting set of essays in prescience, which is marred today only by having missed the great breakthrough of the nucleic acids. Haldane can be excused for this error of omission—he was one of a good company of geneticists who made the same error.

Today genetics is advancing on so many fronts that the chances of making invalid predictions are very small, but some lines do seem more hopeful than others.

WHAT IS A GENE?

The accepted concept of the gene is that it is a DNA molecule, in which the long chain of nucleotides comprises a "message" sufficient to determine the synthesis of a polypeptide. The nucleotide message is almost certainly "read" as a series of triplets, with each triplet defining a specific amino acid of the polypeptide. This concept leaves many questions unanswered. Genes are not independent entities; they are located at fixed positions along chromosomes, and one key question is the relationship of the DNA genes to the chromosome. Is the chromosome just one long chain of DNA and, if it is, how are the different genes delimited? How does the process of "reading" know when it has "read" all of a gene and nothing but that gene?

One approach to this problem is to look at the chromosomes, using the full possible resolution of the electron microscope. It should be possible, if the technical difficulties can be overcome, to look into chromosomes and describe their molecular geometry.

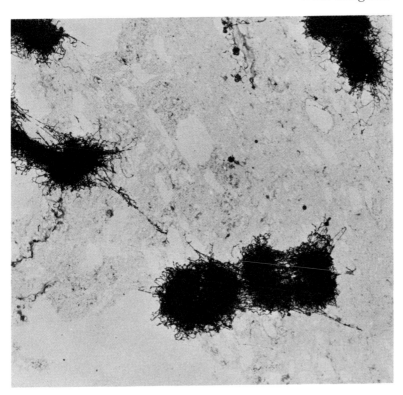

FIGURE 22.1

Chromosomes of mitotic metaphase from bovine tissue culture cells. These were processed by the "critical point" method: water in the specimen is replaced in sequence by alcohol and amyl acetate. The specimen, in amyl acetate, is then placed in a pressure vessel and the amyl acetate replaced by liquid carbon dioxide under pressure. This drying method takes advantage of the fact that carbon dioxide has a critical temperature of 31°C. Above this temperature, CO_2 does not exist as a liquid. The specimen vessel, containing liquid CO_2 at approximately 900 pounds per square inch, is heated from room temperature to 45°C; as the temperature passes the critical point at 31°C the liquid CO_2 in the vessel surrounding the specimen is converted almost instantaneously to a gas. This drying method, devised by T. F. Anderson, avoids the distorting forces created by a slowly receding interface encountered in ordinary drying. Magnification is 18,000X. (Electron-microscope photograph of grasshopper chromosomes, from the laboratory of Dr. S. Wolfe.)

A major technical difficulty is the simple phenomenon of surface tension. The surface tension of a liquid is a region of considerable force, sufficient to disrupt delicate living structures, yet it is necessary to dry any preparations that are to be examined in the vacuum of the electron microscope. As the material is dried, the surface of the liquid in which it is contained moves over and through the material, breaking it into senseless masses. A new technique neatly sidesteps this problem. The material is first transferred into alcohol, then amyl acetate is added until the alcohol has been replaced. Next the material is put under pressure, and liquid carbon dioxide is added until the amyl acetate has been replaced. If the preparation is kept under pressure, and the temperature is raised, the liquid carbon dioxide changes to a gas, without the material's being affected by surface tension. This technique and the others that will derive from it should allow the full detail of chromosomes to be examined. Already the view of chromosome structure gained by these techniques is very different from that gained by use of normal light microscopes.

THE GEOMETRY OF PROTEINS

The gene is a line of nucleotides that determines the synthesis of a particular line of amino acids into a polypeptide chain. This polypeptide may be a complete protein, or several different polypeptides may join together to form a protein. A major unsolved problem is how the linear sequence of nucleotides determines the tertiary structure of the polypeptide. Proteins are not just simple threads of amino acids; they are usually coiled and twisted into three-dimensional patterns.

The hemoglobin molecule is comprised of four separate polypeptide chains: two are called the α chains; the other two are called the β chains. The α chains are formed on the basis of the information contained in one gene, and the β chains are formed on the basis of the information contained in another gene. Somehow these separate chains are joined together and twisted into a convoluted three-dimensional structure. How is this joining achieved?

A line of research that may be leading toward solution of this problem is the study of *intragenic complementation*, which is where the combination of two different mutations of the same gene complement each other, resulting in the normal phenotype. Suppose we

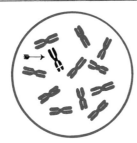

cell of line NCTC 2555(N₂)

notice the numerous
biarmed chromosomes

arrow indicates a
characteristic metacentric
marker

cell of line NCTC 2472(N₁)

arrows indicate the
two extra long chromosomes

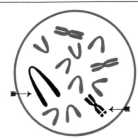

hybrid cell H–109t

arrows indicate the
two extra long
telocentric chromosomes,
markers of line N₁,
and the short metacentric
marker of line N₂

FIGURE 22.2

Mitotic chromosomes of three strains of cells maintained in tissue culture. The parent strains, N₁ and N₂, differ in that one has a few very long chromosomes and the other has a number of small chromosomes with median centromeres. The hybrid strain, N 1.2, contained both types of chromosomes. (Donald J. Marchant and James V. Neel, Editors, Approaches to the Genetic Analysis of Mammalian Cells. Michigan Conference on Genetics: pp. 84–85; Boris Ephrussi and Serge Sorieul, "Mating of Somatic Cells in Vitro.")

have a mutation in the *r*II gene of the T4 bacteriophage that causes the inability to multiply in the host bacteria; also suppose that we have a second mutation of the same gene that also causes the inability to multiply in the host bacterium. Recombination studies of these two mutations, m_1 and m_2, show that they are located at different points of the *r*II gene. Now consider a multiple infection of a bacterium with phage particles of both the m_1 and m_2 strains. These may in some way complement each other (multiplying), or they may not complement (no multiplication occurs). The exact chemistry of intragenic complementation is not fully understood, but it has been suggested that complementation relationships are a function of the complicated geometry of the proteins produced by the genes.

The first step in this kind of research is to map the internal structure of a gene by recombination studies that give a linear crossover map of the gene. Next, the mutations are compared in pairs to determine whether complementation occurs. This gives a second map—a complementation map—based on whether mutations do or do not complement each other. This map is usually not simple, but it can be related to the recombination map *if* the recombination map is twisted into some specific pattern—suggesting that the complementation map may measure the twisting of the polypeptide product into a three-dimensional protein. If this suggestion is verified, a major step forward will have been made toward the understanding of the spatial geometry of proteins in terms of the linear sequence of the nucleotides of the DNA gene.

The artificial synthesis of specific DNA and RNA molecules can be expected to evolve into a basic technique within a few years. This should allow the controlled synthesis of specific proteins, *if* the relationship of nucleotide order to three-dimensional structure is understood. The prospect of genes and proteins "made to order" is no longer a flight of poetic intuition; it is a legitimate long-term aim.

GENETIC SURGERY

The beginning of molecular genetics was Miescher's discovery of the nucleic acids, but this phase of genetics did not really begin to gather impetus until Avery, MacLeod, and McCarty discovered that bacterial transformation could be effected by DNA. Their experiment was not only the first major step in identifying the chemical basis of heredity; it was also the first proof that the direct modification of the structure of specific genes was possible.

Researches are under way in many laboratories, focused on the various ways of effecting genetic transformation and elaborating ways to reduce its improbability. These not only involve treatments with nucleic acid, they also are based on the phenomenon of transduction in which viruses act as carriers of DNA, picking it up from one cell and transferring it to other cells. Exciting advances can be expected in this field as more control of the genetic system is gained, allowing definition of which genes are to be transformed or transduced. This is only the beginning of genetic surgery; its culmination will be when ways are found to effect it in higher organisms. The first steps toward this are being made in the genetic analyses of tissue cultures.

TISSUE CULTURE

The genetic analysis of man has been hindered by the long interval between generations, the low rate of reproduction, and the inability to set up planned matings—humans take a long time to produce a few children and they have a marked aversion to any infringement of their right to choose their own mate. A way around these difficulties may be devised by the new work with tissue cultures; ways have been invented to culture cells on artificial media where they multiply to form particular strains. At first these techniques were considered to be aimed at the understanding of the processes of cellular differentiation, at understanding the basis for cartilage cells retaining their characteristic features, and for muscle fibroblast cells retaining their features even though repeated cell divisions occur. This kind of information is interesting enough, but there are hopes of much greater advances. If crosses could be made between different strains, genetic analyses would become feasible.

Ephrussi and his colleagues have reported that hybrid cells occurred in cultures started by mixing two different strains—the N_1 and N_2 strains. The cells of the N_1 strain had 55 chromosomes, most of which had their centromeres located near one end, and they contained 1 to 3 very long chromosomes. The cells of the N_2 strain had 57 chromosomes, in which a large number had their centromeres located centrally; there were no extra-long chromosomes. After several cell divisions of the mixed culture of N_1 and N_2 cells, a new type of cell was found having 114 chromosomes, in which 1 to 3 were very long, and a large number of chromosomes had midpositioned centromeres. These new cells had the chromosome constitution expected if the N_1 and N_2 had mated to produce a hybrid. This is an extremely hopeful beginning to what promises to be a new era in human genetics. Many questions are unanswered, particularly the key questions of how and why mating occurs. Answering these questions will be exciting and rewarding.

Genetic analyses in bacteria have shown that many genes with closely related functions occur side by side on the chromosomes. Jacob and Monod have introduced a new concept into genetics in which some genes act to determine whether linked genes act to determine whether linked sets of genes function. This is the regulator–repressor concept.

REGULATORS AND REPRESSORS

An intriguing phenomenon of the genetic control of biosynthesis in bacteria is that genetically identical strains may differ in their production of enzymes controlling a particular biosynthetic step. In *Escherischia coli*, the production of the different enzymes controlling the various steps of the synthesis of tryptophan is dependent on whether this substance is present or absent. If there is no tryptophan in the culture media, this bacteria produces all the requisite enzymes at full speed; if tryptophan is present, the enzymes are not produced. This is not a consequence of genetic differences; it occurs when there are no differences between the strains. The production of these enzymes is known to be under genetic control; the production of each enzyme is determined by a different gene, and mutations exist that cannot form the enzymes whether tryptophan is present or absent. The problem seems to involve the normal genes being switched on or off dependent on the presence or absence of some regulator substance. One of the major problems was how such a genetic switch could operate for a set of enzymes, each produced by a different gene. The answer came from linkage studies showing that many genes controlling different steps of a biosynthesis are located close to each other. This could be accidental, but it is much more likely that they have evolved into this closely linked relationship because it allows the whole set of genes to be switched on or off as a unit.

Jacob and Monod have put forward a very elegant scheme that relates all these facts. One variant of this scheme is that the "functional" genes—those producing the enzymes to activate the biosynthesis—are linked together as an *operon*, an operational unit. Located

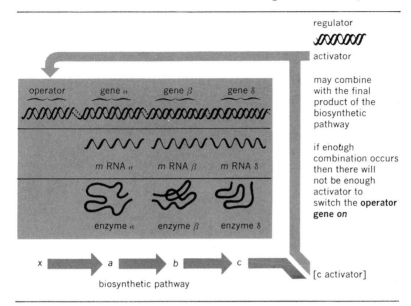

FIGURE 22.3

A scheme to explain how regulator and operator genes may interact to control the function of a set of genes controlling a biosynthetic pathway in which a substance X is changed to a, into b, and finally into c. The regulator gene is responsible for the synthesis of an activator substance that acts to switch the operator gene on. This activator gene may combine with the c product of a biosynthesis; if enough c combines with the activator substance, none is left to act on the operator, resulting in the functional genes being switched off.

at one end of this sequence of genes is another gene, the *operator* gene, which functions to switch the whole operon on or off. It can be considered as controlling whether RNA messages are read from the DNA of the operon. All this does is focus the problem to another aspect: what controls whether the operator switches on or off? Here another gene, not located near the operator, comes into the picture; this is the *regulator* gene. The relation of the regulator gene to the operator gene is one of repression. The regulator gene produces a substance that binds to the operator gene, switching it on. However, the repressor substance can also bind with the products of the biosynthesis actuated by the *functional* genes; so, if the synthesis is proceeding at full speed, there is a lot of the product of the biosynthesis around. This product binds to the repressor substance produced by the regulator gene, and this means that there is no repressor substance to bind to the operator gene which, consequently, is left in the off position. Eventually there will be a shortage of the product of the biosynthesis, so there will not be any binding to the repressor substance—this will be free to bind to the operator, switching it to the *on* position. There are literally dozens of variations of this theme, each more complicated than the last, but all giving valid ways to understand how the actions of genes are regulated. The key question now is whether such regulator-repressor-operator-operon systems occur in higher organisms, and whether there are master regulators. Are there genes that somehow control the functions of many different regulator genes? Also, how do these regulators and repressors work? This involves the full understanding of the functions of each and every aspect of the form of enzymes. Maybe enzymes are switched off or on by other molecules fitting into them, twisting them into new shapes. There is no dearth of ideas, and each one is rapidly being tested, resulting in an exciting stream of reports of new facts, new findings.

Understanding the patterns of interactions between genes is a necessary step toward the understanding of multigenic systems, where a number of genes control a single character. A major problem in this aspect of genetics is the overwhelming complexity. The number of possible genotypes is astronomical, and it has only been possible to consider such systems if almost all of the probable complexities are assumed not to occur. This need to oversimplify is removed by using electronic computers; the consequences of complex genetic systems can be examined with such computers. At present this field is only in the phase of gaining experience—finding out what is possible, probable, and economical. The next phase will be to use these machines for exceedingly complicated genetic systems in which the electronic models come much closer to biological reality.

Models, no matter how subtle and sophisticated, are only models until they are shown to be valid measures of reality. A major need, which has been realized, is to identify individual genes of a multigenic system. Several groups have begun this: among them Thoday and his colleagues, Milkman and his associates. These analyses are extremely laborious and much of the difficulty would be obviated if it were possible to identify the occurrence of individual genes directly, rather than from their final effect.

The genetic mode of thought has such a width that Haldane's warning of the danger of being a "jack of all trades and a master of none" is very real. The answer is not a retreat into specialty, but a stronger emphasis on the rewards of widened thought, especially to students facing the tribulations of producing evidence that they are competent in some particular specialty. This book is aimed at that widened viewpoint, but it is necessary to realize that this aim has been achieved by a ruthless rejection of details.

Problems

1. It is difficult in any textbook on genetics not to emphasize the role of heredity with a consequent underemphasis of the role of environment. The characteristics of an individual are to some degree determined by heredity, to some degree by environment, and by interaction between environment and heredity. List the places in this book where mention has been made of the modification of a character by environment.

2. The definition of the gene has become increasingly difficult. Initially this definition was based on the existence of genetic segregation. Why was this later regarded as an inadequate definition? Another definition was based on the existence of recombination with closely linked genes. Why was this later regarded as an inadequate definition? More recently the gene has been described as a unit of the chromosome responsible for the production of a specific enzyme. Why has this definition been discarded?

FURTHER READING

The aim of this book has been to introduce a way of thought, based on the simplest possible descriptions of the key experiments and analyses leading to this way of thought. There are many very good books that go beyond this introduction. A major text is:

E. W. Sinnott, L. C. Dunn, and T. Dobzhansky, "Principles of Genetics," 5th ed., McGraw-Hill Book Company, New York, 1958.

Another, having special emphasis on human genetics, is:

Stern, C., "Principles of Human Genetics," W. H. Freeman & Company, San Francisco, 1960.

The years since Stern's latest revision of his text have seen major advances in our understanding of the chemical nature of the hereditary mechanism. Treatments of these advances have been given in a wide range of texts. One of the best of these is:

Loewy, A. G., and P. Siekevitz, "Cell Structure and Function," Holt, Rinehart & Winston, New York, 1963.

The relationship of genetics to the modern concept of evolution is dealt with by:

Ehrlich, P. R., and R. W. Holm, "The Process of Evolution," McGraw-Hill Book Company, New York, 1963.

These books refer to others, in a multiplying sequence of greater depth and complexity.

Penrose, L. S., "Outline of Human Genetics," John Wiley and Sons, Inc., New York, 1958.

Ingram, V. M., "The Hemoglobins in Genetics and Evolution," Columbia University Press, New York, 1963.

Shields, J., "Monozygotic Twins," Oxford University Press, 1962.

Lerner, I. M., "The Genetic Basis of Selection," John Wiley and Sons, Inc., New York, 1958.

Wallace, B., and T. Dobzhansky, "Radiation, Genes and Man," Holt, Rinehart & Winston, New York, 1959.

Dobzhansky, T., "Genetics and the Origin of Species," Columbia University Press, New York, 1964.

ANSWERS

Chapter 1

1. (a) The colored gene is dominant.

   (b) 25%

   (c) All progeny will be albino.

   (d) No prediction can be made since colored mice may be homozygous or heterozygous for the colored genes.

2. (a) The albino and short-ear genes are recessive and, therefore, hybrids between albino, short-eared and pure-colored, normal-eared mice will be colored with normal ears.

$$cc \cdot sese \times +^c+^c \cdot +^{se}+^{se} \rightarrow +^c c \cdot +^{se} se$$

   (b) The backcross of colored, normal-eared heterozygotes to albino, short-eared mice produces four types at equal frequency (on an average):

Colored, normal ears

Colored, short ears

Albino, normal ears

Albino, short ears

$$+^c c \cdot +^{se} se \longrightarrow \left\{ \begin{array}{l} \textit{Gametes} \\ +^c \cdot +^{se} \\ +^c \cdot se \\ c \cdot +^{se} \\ c \cdot se \end{array} \right. \quad \begin{array}{l} \textit{Gametes} \\ c \cdot se \end{array} \left. \right\} \longleftarrow cc \cdot sese$$

$+^c c \cdot +^{se} se$	Colored, normal ears
$+^c c \cdot sese$	Colored, short ears
$cc \cdot +^{se} se$	Albino, normal ears
$cc \cdot sese$	Albino, short ears

293

(*c*) Since the colored and normal-ear genes are dominant, any progeny of a cross with a pure-colored, normal-eared strain will be colored with normal ears.

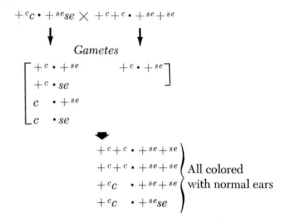

$$+^c c \cdot +^{se}se \times +^c +^c \cdot +^{se} +^{se}$$

Gametes

$$\begin{bmatrix} +^c \cdot +^{se} & +^c \cdot +^{se} \\ +^c \cdot se & \\ c \cdot +^{se} & \\ c \cdot se & \end{bmatrix}$$

$$\left. \begin{array}{l} +^c +^c \cdot +^{se} +^{se} \\ +^c +^c \cdot +^{se} +^{se} \\ +^c c \cdot +^{se} +^{se} \\ +^c c \cdot +^{se}se \end{array} \right\} \begin{array}{l} \text{All colored} \\ \text{with normal ears} \end{array}$$

3. The terms *homozygous* and *heterozygous* are more precise since they refer only to the genetic situation. Crosses between different races will produce hybrids, but some may be homozygous and others may be heterozygous.

4. (*a*) 50% MM and 50% MN

(*b*) All MN

(*c*) 25% MM, 50% MN, and 25% NN

5. Her husband must be MN since her children can only have received an N gene from her. One child was MN, showing that the husband must have the M gene. The other children were NN, showing that the husband must have the N gene.

If all her children were MN, her husband was most probably MM, but there is one chance in 1,024 that the husband could have been MN but not have transmitted the N gene. He could not have been NN.

6. MN

7. The wavy-coat character is caused by two different recessive genes: waved-1 (*wa-1*) and waved-2 (*wa-2*).

$$wa\text{-}1\ wa\text{-}1 \cdot +^{wa\text{-}2} +^{wa\text{-}2} \quad \times \quad +^{wa\text{-}1} +^{wa\text{-}1} \cdot wa\text{-}2\ wa\text{-}2$$

wavy   wavy

$$+^{wa\text{-}1}wa\text{-}1 \cdot +^{wa\text{-}2}wa\text{-}2$$

straight coats

	$+^{wa\text{-}1} \cdot +^{wa\text{-}2}$	$+^{wa\text{-}1} \cdot wa\text{-}2$	$wa\text{-}1 \cdot +^{wa\text{-}2}$	$wa\text{-}1 \cdot wa\text{-}2$
$+^{wa\text{-}1} \cdot +^{wa\text{-}2}$	$+^{wa\text{-}1}+^{wa\text{-}1} \cdot +^{wa\text{-}2}+^{wa\text{-}2}$	$+^{wa\text{-}1}+^{wa\text{-}1} \cdot +^{wa\text{-}2}wa\text{-}2$	$+^{wa\text{-}1}wa\text{-}1 \cdot +^{wa\text{-}2}+^{wa\text{-}2}$	$+^{wa\text{-}1}wa\text{-}1 \cdot +^{wa\text{-}2}wa\text{-}2$
$+^{wa\text{-}1} \cdot wa\text{-}2$	$+^{wa\text{-}1}+^{wa\text{-}1} \cdot +^{wa\text{-}2}wa\text{-}2$	$+^{wa\text{-}1}+^{wa\text{-}1} \cdot wa\text{-}2\,wa\text{-}2$ wavy	$+^{wa\text{-}1}wa\text{-}1 \cdot +^{wa\text{-}2}wa\text{-}2$	$+^{wa\text{-}1}wa\text{-}1 \cdot wa\text{-}2\,wa\text{-}2$ wavy
$wa\text{-}1 \cdot +^{wa\text{-}2}$	$+^{wa\text{-}1}wa\text{-}1 \cdot +^{wa\text{-}2}+^{wa\text{-}2}$	$+^{wa\text{-}1}wa\text{-}1 \cdot +^{wa\text{-}2}wa\text{-}2$	$wa\text{-}1\,wa\text{-}1 \cdot +^{wa\text{-}2}+^{wa\text{-}2}$ wavy	$wa\text{-}1\,wa\text{-}1 \cdot +^{wa\text{-}2}wa\text{-}2$ wavy
$wa\text{-}1 \cdot wa\text{-}2$	$+^{wa\text{-}1}wa\text{-}1 \cdot +^{wa\text{-}2}wa\text{-}2$	$+^{wa\text{-}1}wa\text{-}1 \cdot wa\text{-}2\,wa\text{-}2$ wavy	$wa\text{-}1\,wa\text{-}1 \cdot +^{wa\text{-}2}wa\text{-}2$ wavy	$wa\text{-}1\,wa\text{-}1 \cdot wa\text{-}2\,wa\text{-}2$ wavy

9 straight : 7 wavy

On an average, 7/16 of the progeny will have wavy coats.

Blue eye color is recessive to dark eye color.

(*a*) All the children should have blue eyes.

(*b*) On an average, half the children should have dark eyes, and half should have blue eyes.

Chapter 2

1. The yellow character in mice is caused by a gene (Y) that is lethal in homozygotes, which die early in development.

$$+^{Y}Y \qquad \times \qquad +^{Y}Y$$

$$\downarrow$$

1 ···· $+^{Y}+^{Y}$	Normal
2 ···· $+^{Y}Y$	Yellow
1 ···· YY	Die early in development

2. $Bb \cdot Cc$ Black

   $BB \cdot cc$ Albino

   $bb \cdot CC$ Brown

   $bb \cdot cc$ Albino

   $Bb \cdot Cc \times bb \cdot cc \longrightarrow$ 1 Black, 1 brown, 2 albino

   $Bb \cdot Cc \times Bb \cdot cc \longrightarrow$ 3 Black, 1 brown, 4 albino

   $Bb \cdot Cc \times Bb \cdot Cc \longrightarrow$ 9 Black, 3 brown, 4 albino

3. $cc \cdot BB \times CC \cdot bb \longrightarrow Cc \cdot Bb$

Chapter 3

1.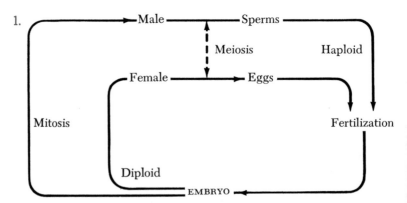

2.

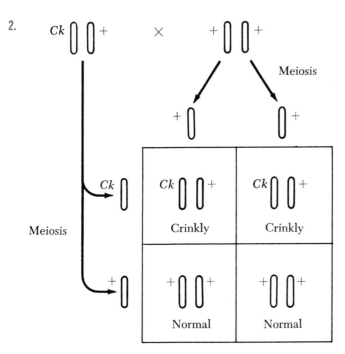

3. (a) If we assume that both the crinkly haired parent and the blue-sclerotic parent are heterozygous, then four types of progeny are expected:

Crinkly hair + blue sclerotics
Normal hair + blue sclerotics
Crinkly hair + normal eyes
Normal hair + normal eyes

(b) Equal frequencies

Chapter 4

1. No. It is possible that the female was homozygous for a dominant gene whose only effect was to suppress the effect of the Bar gene in males.

2. All females have red Bar eyes; all males have white normal-shaped eyes.

3. The correct answer to this question involves knowledge of the phenomenon of crossing over. If we assume, incorrectly, that no crossing over occurs, then

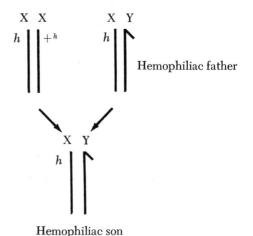

$$w \parallel w \quad \times \quad +^w \mid\mathbf{r}$$
$$+^B \parallel +^B \quad\quad B \parallel$$

$$w \parallel +^w \quad \times \quad w \mid\mathbf{r}$$
$$+^B \parallel B \quad\quad +^B \parallel$$

$$w \parallel w \quad:\quad w \parallel +^w \quad::\quad w \mid\mathbf{r} \quad:\quad +^w \mid\mathbf{r}$$
$$+^B \parallel +^B \quad\quad +^B \parallel B \quad\quad +^B \mathbf{r} \quad\quad B \parallel$$

White   Red, Bar   White   Red, Bar

Answer this question again after reading Chapter 5.

4. The hemophilia gene (h) is located on the X chromosome and a son cannot inherit his X chromosome from his father. The hemophiliac son of this family must have inherited this gene on the X chromosome from his mother. Since she is not hemophiliac, she must, therefore, be heterozygous for the gene.

X X   X Y
$h \parallel +^h$ $h \mid\mathbf{r}$ Hemophiliac father

X Y
$h \mid\mathbf{r}$

Hemophiliac son

5. 50% expectation

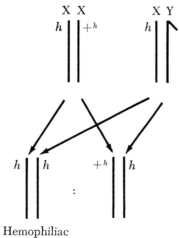

Hemophiliac

Chapter 5

1. (*a*)

$$\delta \; \delta \; Progeny$$

$$\frac{y^+ \quad sn^+ \quad lz^+}{y \quad sn \quad lz} \rightarrow$$

$\overset{\leftrightarrow}{a} \quad \overset{\leftrightarrow}{b}$

$$\left. \begin{array}{l} \dfrac{y^+ \qquad sn^+ \qquad lz^+}{\text{wild type}} \\[1em] \dfrac{y \qquad sn \qquad lz}{\text{yellow, singed, lozenge}} \end{array} \right\} \text{Noncrossover}$$

$$\left. \begin{array}{l} \dfrac{y \qquad sn^+ \qquad lz^+}{\text{yellow}} \\[1em] \dfrac{y^+ \qquad sn \qquad lz}{\text{singed, lozenge}} \end{array} \right\} \begin{array}{l} \text{Single} \\ \text{crossover} \\ \text{(a)} \end{array}$$

$$\left. \begin{array}{l} \dfrac{y \qquad sn \qquad lz^+}{\text{yellow, singed}} \\[1em] \dfrac{y^+ \qquad sn^+ \qquad lz}{\text{lozenge}} \end{array} \right\} \begin{array}{l} \text{Single} \\ \text{crossover} \\ \text{(b)} \end{array}$$

$$\left. \begin{array}{l} \dfrac{y \qquad sn^+ \qquad lz}{\text{yellow} \qquad \text{lozenge}} \\[1em] \dfrac{y^+ \qquad sn \qquad lz}{\text{singed}} \end{array} \right\} \begin{array}{l} \text{Double} \\ \text{crossover} \\ \text{(a. b)} \end{array}$$

(b)

$$\frac{y \quad sn^+ \quad lz}{y^+ \quad sn \quad lz^+}$$

$$\underset{a}{\leftrightarrow} \quad \underset{b}{\leftrightarrow}$$

♂ ♂ Progeny

$$\left.\frac{\underset{\text{yellow}}{y} \quad sn^+ \quad \underset{\text{lozenge}}{lz}}{\underset{\text{singed}}{y^+ \quad sn \quad lz^+}}\right\} \text{Noncrossover}$$

$$\left.\frac{\underset{\text{yellow, singed}}{y \quad sn \quad lz^+}}{\underset{\text{lozenge}}{y^+ \quad sn^+ \quad lz}}\right\} \begin{array}{l}\text{Single}\\\text{crossover}\\\text{(a)}\end{array}$$

$$\left.\frac{\underset{\text{yellow}}{y \quad sn^+ \quad lz^+}}{\underset{\text{singed, lozenge}}{y^+ \quad sn \quad lz}}\right\} \begin{array}{l}\text{Single}\\\text{crossover}\\\text{(b)}\end{array}$$

$$\left.\frac{\underset{\text{yellow, singed, lozenge}}{y \quad sn \quad lz}}{\underset{\text{wild type}}{y^+ \quad sn^+ \quad lz^+}}\right\} \begin{array}{l}\text{Double}\\\text{crossover}\\\text{(a, b)}\end{array}$$

2. $$\frac{y \quad w^a \quad w^{e+} \quad sn^+}{y^+ \quad w^{a+} \quad w^e \quad sn}$$

$$\underset{a}{\leftrightarrow} \quad \underset{b}{\leftrightarrow} \quad \underset{c}{\leftrightarrow}$$

♂ ♂ Progeny

$$\left.\frac{y \quad w^a \quad w^{e+} \quad sn^+}{y^+ \quad w^{a+} \quad w^e \quad sn}\right\} \text{Noncrossover}$$

$$\left.\frac{y \quad w^{a+} \quad w^e \quad sn}{y^+ \quad w^a \quad w^{e+} \quad sn^+}\right\} \begin{array}{l}\text{Single}\\\text{crossover}\\\text{(a)}\end{array}$$

$$\left.\frac{y \quad w^a \quad w^e \quad sn}{y^+ \quad w^{a+} \quad w^{e+} \quad sn^+}\right\} \begin{array}{l}\text{Single}\\\text{crossover}\\\text{(b)}\end{array}$$

$$\left.\frac{y \quad w^a \quad w^{e+} \quad sn}{y^+ \quad w^{a+} \quad w^e \quad sn^+}\right\} \begin{array}{l}\text{Single}\\\text{crossover}\\\text{(c)}\end{array}$$

$$\left.\frac{y \quad w^{a+} \quad w^{e+} \quad sn^+}{y^+ \quad w^a \quad w^e \quad sn}\right\} \begin{array}{l}\text{Double}\\\text{crossover}\\\text{(a, b)}\end{array}$$

y	w^{a+}	w^e	sn^+
y^+	w^a	w^{e+}	sn

} Double crossover (a, c)

y	w^a	w^e	sn^+
y^+	w^{a+}	w^{e+}	sn

} Double crossover (b, c)

y	w^{a+}	w^{e+}	sn
y^+	w^a	w^e	sn^+

} Triple crossover (a, b, c)

3.

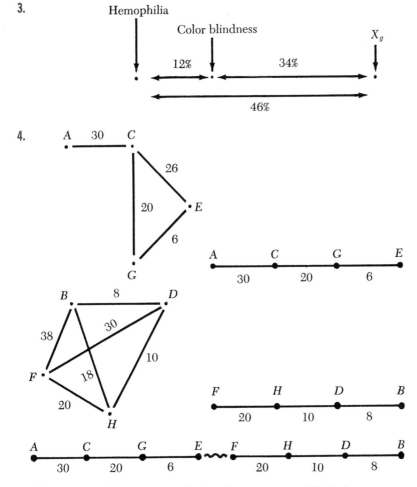

4.

There is no evidence as to whether these two sets of linked genes are located on the same or different chromosomes.

Chapter 6

1.

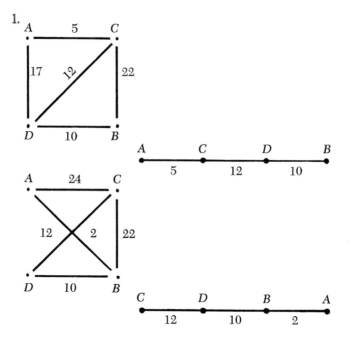

The position of *A* relative to *CDB* has been changed. This could be due to an inversion of the section containing *CDB*.

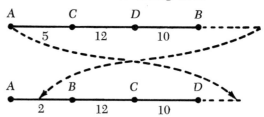

2. The two strains differ (i) in a large inversion, (ii) a small deletion, and (iii) a small duplication.

1. T A G C G T A A T

2. A + G = C + T

3. Nothing

Chapter 8

1. Although the *o* gene has a series of effects, these can be shown to be due to one initial action causing the inability to synthesize ornithine. The other effects are secondary to this.
2. The biosynthesis proceeds in the sequence:

$$D \rightarrow C \rightarrow E \rightarrow A \rightarrow F \rightarrow B$$

Chapter 10

1. The parents transmit the hereditary information in the form of DNA molecules contained in the sperms and eggs and located in the nuclei of the developing offspring. Specific parts of the complete set of DNA molecules are translated into messenger-RNA molecules which move out from the nucleus into the cytoplasm where they form a complex with the ribosomes. Amino acids are then positioned along the messenger-RNA by the mediation of transfer-RNA molecules. These sequences of amino acids are then joined, forming proteins that act as enzymes to direct the biochemical activity of the cell.
2. The differences between DNA and messenger-RNA are: (i) thymidine in place of uridine, (ii) double-strand structure in contrast to single-strand structure. The sequence of nucleotides that form messenger-RNA is derived from the sequence of nucleotides of the DNA which was translated into messenger-RNA.

    The function of DNA is the maintenance and replication of hereditary information, whereas that of messenger-RNA is the movement of this information from the nucleus into the cytoplasm, and its translation into physiologically functional entities (enzymes).
3. Messenger-RNA, ribosomal-RNA, and transfer-RNA

Chapter 11

1. The only conclusive proof would be the demonstration that there had been a change of the nucleotide sequence, which had not been effected by deletions, duplications, inversions, or translocations.
2. There is no way to prove this conclusively. If, however, the parents were of populations in which no albinism had been recorded over very large numbers of individuals, the possibility of mutation would seem feasible. However, albinism is recessive, and two mutational events would be needed to explain the occurrence of such an individual—if the mutation rate is 1:100,000, such an origin by mutation would only be expected in 1:10,000,000,000 births.

3.

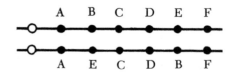

Pairing of inverted sequences occurs in loops.

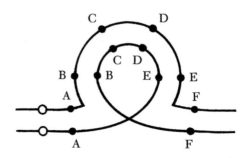

Crossing over within the loop can lead to deletions and duplications.

Chapter 12

1. (*a*) Neither; they involve equal amounts of irradiation.
   (*b*) Neither; they involve equal amounts of irradiation. However, the actual results show that exposure to large amounts of irradiation produces slightly less mutations per roentgen than exposure to small amounts.

2. (*a*) 0.1%
   (*b*) 0.01%

Chapter 13

1. $q_a^2 = 1{:}20{,}000$ then $q_a = 1{:}142$

2. $q_b^2 = 0.16$ then $q_b = 4{:}10 = 0.40$, and $2pq$, the frequency of hetero-zygotes $= 0.48$, and the frequency of marriages in which both parents were heterozygotes would be $0.48^2 = 0.23$, i.e., 23%.

Chapter 14

1. (a) 500
   (b) 250
   (c) 1:1,024
   (d) Effectively zero
2. (a) 0.0198 (1.98%)
   (b) 1% × 1% = 0.01%
3. There is no absolute way to distinguish between large and small populations, except to say that random fluctuations of gene frequencies are of no relevance in an infinitely large population.

Chapter 15

1.

	Dark	Light	
Generation 0	1,000	100	Immigrants
	910	90	Parents
	Mating and reproduction		
Generation 1	992	8	
After a very long period of this immigration		100% Light	

2. 1/1,500
3. A steady directional migrational stream will result, eventually, in the replacement of the genetic structure of the host population by that of the donor population. The establishment of new populations by the emigration of small groups into uninhabited areas will result in chance variations of genetic structure from that of the donor population. The general movement in all directions between genetically distinct populations will result in the formation of a single, genetically homogenous group.
4. This question has no objective answer. One could say that such a demonstration would need to establish that the genetic structure of the nation was distinct and separate from that of other nations, but this would only require definition of "distinct and separate."
5. Not to any useful degree since an Rh^+Rh^+ individual could be a member of most racial groups. Single genetic differences are not of much use in identifying individuals as being of one race or another. However, if a specific population of a few thousand individuals were found to lack the Rh^- gene, this would be indicative that the population was racially connected with the American Indians.

Chapter 16

1.

	AA	Aa	aa
	p^2	$2pq$	q^2
Survival	1	1	0
	p^2	$2pq$	0

$$q = \frac{pq}{1 - q^2}$$

$$q - q = \frac{pq}{1 - q^2} - q \qquad [p^2 + 2pq = 1 - q^2]$$

$$= \frac{pq - q(1 - q^2)}{1 - q^2}$$

$$= \frac{q(p - 1 + q^2)}{1 - q^2}$$

$$= \frac{q(-q + q^2)}{1 - q^2}$$

$$= \frac{-q^2(1 - q)}{1 - q^2} \qquad [1 - q = p]$$

$$= \frac{-pq^2}{1 - q^2}$$

2. (a) $\dfrac{s \times 0.1 \times 0.9^2}{1 - (s \times 0.9^2)} = \dfrac{s \times 0.081}{1 - (s \times 0.81)}$

(b) $\dfrac{s \times 0.5 \times 0.5^2}{1 - (s \times 0.5^2)} = \dfrac{s \times 0.125}{1 - (s \times 0.25)}$

(c) $\dfrac{s \times 0.9 \times 0.1^2}{1 - (s \times 0.1^2)} = \dfrac{s \times 0.009}{1 - (s \times 0.01)}$

3.

$$q^2 = \mu s$$

$$q = \sqrt{\mu s}$$

$$= \sqrt{0.000005 \times 0.8}$$

$$= \sqrt{0.000004}$$

$$= \sqrt{\frac{4}{1,000,000}}$$

$$= \frac{2}{1,000} = \frac{1}{500}$$

4. Selection is a directive force whereas mutation is not directive.

5. The very slow increase of the frequency of these diseases until mutation from the normal alleles is counterbalanced by mutation from the defective alleles. This increase will only be noticeable over periods of hundreds of generations.

6. This equation represents the balance between selection against a recessive detrimental gene and mutation of the normal allele to the detrimental recessive.

Chapter 17

1. There is no answer to this question since the efficiency of selection is dependent on the frequency of the gene. Selection for a dominant allele will be more effective than for a recessive allele when they are at low frequencies, but the reverse is true when they are at high frequencies.

2. That a dynamic equilibrium has been established in which the genetic survivals are such that selection against both homomorphic types is balanced.

Arrowhead (A) Chiricahua (C)
0.7   0.3   *Gametic frequencies*

AA AC CC
0.49   0.42   0.09   *Zygotic frequencies*

$1 - s_1$ 1 $1 - s_2$

where s_1 and s_2 have values such that

$$0.7 = \frac{0.49\,(1 - s_1) + 0.21}{1 - 0.49s_1 - 0.09s_2} \qquad 0.3 = \frac{0.09\,(1 - s_2) + 0.21}{1 - 0.49s_1 - 0.09s_2}$$

3. (i) Equilibrium between mutation pressures where little if any differences of genetic survival occur can result in intermediate gene frequencies.

(ii) Migration between genetically distinct populations can result in intermediate gene frequencies.

(iii) Selection operating against one of the genes may be occurring and the population is in a transitional state.

(iv) A dynamic equilibrium involving the heterozygotes having a greater genetic survival than either homozygote will result in intermediate gene frequencies.

4. (a) The occurence of inbreeding would explain the excess of homozygotes above that expected from the Hardy-Weinberg law.

(b) If the population is small, the deviation could be a chance fluctuation.

Chapter 18

1. If the different loci have approximately equal effects, then the two strains could differ in eight genes and yet these genes could act to

produce the same phenotype.

Strain 1:
$$\frac{A \ B \ C \ D \ e \ f \ g \ h}{A \ B \ C \ D \ e \ f \ g \ h}$$

Strain 2:
$$\frac{a \ b \ c \ d \ E \ F \ G \ H}{a \ b \ c \ d \ E \ F \ G \ H}$$

2. Nine:

$$\frac{A \ B}{A \ B}; \quad \frac{A \ b}{A \ B}; \quad \frac{a \ B}{A \ B}; \quad \frac{a \ B}{a \ B}; \quad \frac{A \ b}{A \ b}; \quad \frac{A \ B}{a \ b}; \quad \frac{a \ B}{a \ b}; \quad \frac{A \ b}{a \ b}; \quad \frac{a \ b}{a \ b}$$

3. That the inheritance of the character can be explained by the inheritance of the chromosomes, involving demonstrations of segregation and linkage.

4. (a) Find a way of measurement of the skill or defect.

   (b) Determine the variations of this measurement which occur from time to time in the same individual.

   (c) Measure a set of parents and progeny and determine whether there is any degree of relationship.

   (d) Compare identical and fraternal twins for the measurement. If there is a degree of relationship between parents and progeny, and if identical twins are less different than fraternal twins, then we can conclude that the character is to some degree inherited.

5. If the determination of I.Q. is due only to a multigenic system, then an increase of mutation rate will have very little effect unless the frequencies of the various alleles deviate markedly from equality. Even if this is the case, mutation will have only a small effect over normal periods of time.

Chapter 19

1. (a) The character is controlled by a large number of genes.

   (b) The character is controlled by a smaller number of genes, linked in combinations of alleles acting in opposite directions. Recombination then allows the formation of extreme combinations.

   (c) The character is controlled by a number of genes with complicated interactions.

2. The correct concept for a plan of animal breeding is to raise the animals under conditions that maximize the hereditary differences between individuals. For some characters these conditions will be those that are "best" in the sense of being beneficial to growth and development, whereas for other characters the necessary conditions will be detrimental to the animal's wellbeing. Waddington's discovery that exposure to heat shock results in the expressions of genes for incomplete wing veins is an example.

3. No. (i) Constancy can be due to homeostasis – produced by the buffering of developmental processes which are genetically variable. (ii) Constancy can be due to mechanisms that enforce heterozygosis as in the complex chromosomal systems of Oenothera.

Chapter 21

1. Sex-linked inheritance follows the inheritance of specific chromosomes involved in the determination of the sex difference, and the pattern of inheritance will differ according to the direction of the cross, e.g., the inheritance of Bar eye in Drosophila—a dominant gene located on the X chromosome.

	Parents				Offspring	
	♂		♀		♂	♀
	$B \cdot y$	×	$+ +$	=	$+ \cdot y$	$B \cdot +$
	$+ \cdot y$	×	BB	=	$B \cdot y$	$B \cdot +$

Sex-modified inheritance does not follow the inheritance of the X and Y chromosomes, but the expression of the sex-modified genes is determined by the sex of the individual, e.g., baldness in humans, which is probably due to a gene that is dominant in males, recessive in females.

Parents		Offspring			
♂	♀	♂		♀	
$B \cdot +$ ×	$+ \cdot +$ =	$B \cdot +$:	$+ \cdot +$	$B \cdot +$	$+ \cdot +$
(Bald)	(Normal)	(Bald)	(Normal)	(Normal)	(Normal)
$+ \cdot +$ ×	$B \cdot B$ =	$B \cdot +$		$B \cdot +$	
(Normal)	(Bald)	(Bald)		(Normal)	

Cytoplasmic inheritance due to self-replicating particles in the cytoplasm will mainly, or entirely, be transmitted via the cytoplasm of the egg. Inheritance will be essentially maternal.

Parents			Offspring	
♂		♀	♂	♀
Plastids	×	no plastids	=	no plastids
No plastids	×	plastids	=	plastids

2. Both these statements have been shown to be oversimplifications. Heredity can involve the transmission of molecules other than DNA, e.g., the RNA viruses, and DNA is not solely located in the nucleus—particles of DNA have been found to occur in the cytoplasm. It is, therefore, plausible to consider cytoplasmic inheritance as being based on nucleic acid in the form of either RNA or DNA. The latter appears to be the most likely basis for such non-nuclear inheritance.

3. Both male and female offspring similarly inherit the cytoplasmic content of the female gamete.

Chapter 22

1. See pages 21, 22, 27, 228, 232–235, 240, 254–258.

2. Genetic segregation is a chromosomal phenomenon and the occurrence of segregation is not diagnostic of any phenomenon other than the segregated transmission of homologous chromosomes.

Recombination between closely linked genes appeared at first to have minimum values such that recombination could be postulated to occur only between genes. More extensive and detailed studies have shown that recombination, although very rare, can occur along the length of a gene.

The production of a specific enzyme can involve more than one gene, each producing parts of the final molecule.

There is no satisfactorily final definition of a gene, but the present state of the science indicates that a gene can be envisaged as that unit of heredity responsible for the transcription of a specific messenger-RNA molecule.

Quick Quiz: Chapters 1 through 4

1. *b*

2. *a*

3. *c*

4. *d* [There is no more precise answer than that albinos may be produced from many different kinds of matings: $a/a \times a/a$; $a/a \times a/+$; $a/+ \times a/+$]

5. *c*

6. *c* [The only way to determine whether independent occurrences of the wavy character are genetically independent is to make crosses and determine whether independent segregation occurs.]

7. *b*

8. *c*

9. *b*

10. *e*

11. *b*, *c*, and *d* are all correct.

12. *a*

13. *b* is most generally accepted, but there are concepts of the sequence of meiosis which consider that crossing over occurs before replication.

14. *b*
15. *b*
16. *c*

Quick Quiz: *Chapters 5 through 9*

1. *d*
2. *c*
3. *b*
4. *d*
5. *d*

6. *a* and *b*
7. *c*
8. *d*
9. *d*
10. *c*

Quick Quiz: *Chapters 10 through 14*

1. *d*
2. *a, b, c, d* are all correct.
3. *b*
4. *c*
5. *c*
6. *d*
7. *b, c*
8. *b*
9. *a* is the best answer, but *c* is to some degree correct.

Quick Quiz: *Chapters 15 through 20*

1. *c*
2. *c*
3. *b*
4. *c*
5. *a*
6. *d*
7. *a*
8. *a, b, c, d* are all valid explanations.
9. *b*
10. *b*

GLOSSARY AND INDEX

Adenine   91, 135

A purine base found in nucleic acid.

Albinism   16, 18, 28, 61

The absence of pigmentation in the eyes, skin, and hair of animals, and the absence of pigmentation in the chloroplasts of plants.

Alcaptonuria   117

An inherited metabolic defect in man, characterized by the excretion in the urine of excessive amounts of homogentisic acid.

Allele   26

One of the genetic variants that can occur at a specific locus, e.g., the albino allele.

Allopolyploid   266, 267

A polyploid that originated by the combination of separate chromosome sets that are genetically distinct.

Amino acid

A chemical compound characterized by an amino (NH_2) group and by a carboxyl (COOH) group. Proteins are formed by the junction of the amino acids.

Anaphase

The stage of cell division when the chromatids or homologous chromosomes separate to opposite poles of the dividing cell.

Anderson   281

Aneuploid   261

Having a chromosome number that is not an exact multiple of the basic set, e.g., XXY individuals are aneuploid in having an extra sex chromosome.

Antibody

Introduction of a foreign substance (an antigen) into the blood or body fluids leads to the formation of antibodies which can combine specifically with that antigen.

Antigen

See Antibody. Antigens are usually proteins.

Asynapsis

The failure of pairing of homologous chromosomes during meiosis. See also Nondisjunction.

A polyploid that originates by the multiplication of one basic set of chromosomes.

Autosome

A chromosome other than the sex chromosomes.

The cross of a hybrid (heterozygote) with one or other of the pure bred (homozygous) parent types.

A virus whose host is bacteria.

Bivalent

The association of a pair of homologous chromosomes during meiosis.

Blending inheritance

Inheritance in which the characters of the parents appear to blend at an intermediate level in the hybrid with no apparent segregation in later generations.

The classification of types of blood based initially on the occurrence of clumping (agglutination) of the red blood cells when blood of incompatible groups is mixed.

Centromere 35

The special structure of a chromosome at which it is attached to the spindle during cell division.

Chiasma 35

The points of junction of homologous chromosomes in meiotic bivalents—resulting from the occurrence of crossing over.

Chromatid 30, 33, 35

Chromosomes split along their length, except at the centromere, into chromatids.

Chromomeres 79

The small bodies located along the strand of the chromosome which differ in their characteristic size and linear arrangement.

Chromosomes 30, 33, 35

The threadlike structures that become visible during cell division. They can be stained with basic dyes. The genes are arranged along the chromosomes in linear sequence.

Cistron

A section of the chromosome or of the DNA that specifies the formation of a particular polypeptide chain.

Codon

A section of DNA that specifies one amino acid. See also Triplet code.

Complementation 282

The interaction of two genes to result in an action that cannot be determined by their separate actions.

Copy-choice 96

An explanation of genetic recombination based on the replication of DNA alternating between "paternal and maternal" strands of DNA.

Eugenics

The science of control of the genetic structure of the human race. Positive eugenics—favoring the reproduction of superior types. Negative eugenics—inhibiting the reproduction of inferior types.

F₁ 7

The progeny of the cross between pure (homozygous) lines.

F₂ 7

The progeny produced by intercrossing or self-fertilization of F_1 individuals.

Gamete

A special cell, produced by meiotic cell division, which contains a single, haploid set of chromosomes. The fusion of gametes in pairs restores the normal, diploid number of chromosomes.

A unit of the mechanism of heredity, located at a specific region of a chromosome, concerned with a special biochemical function.

The frequency of an allele in the individuals of a group or population.

See also Triplet code.

Genotype

The genetic constitution of an individual.

Guanine   91, 135

A purine base found in nucleic acids.

Gyandromorph   103

Individuals that are a mosaic of male and female tissues.

Haldane   1, 280

Haploid   43

Having a single set of chromosomes, as in gametic cells. Contrast with diploid and polyploid.

Hardy-Weinberg   172, 190

Helix   91

A spiral shape; the complementary strands of DNA are arranged in a double helix.

Hemizygote   81

The state of being heterozygous for a deficiency.

Hemophilia   56

An inherited defect in humans which results in a decrease of the clotting function of the blood. Caused by a sex-linked recessive gene.

Henking   44

Hershey and Chase   87

Heteromorphic

Homologous chromosomes that differ to a degree that is visible microscopically, as in the XY pair of sex chromosomes.

Heterosis   214

The greater vigor in growth and survival of hybrids, usually between highly inbred pure lines.

Heterozygote   23

An individual that has inherited two different alleles at one or more loci.

Hippocrates   24

Homeostasis   254

The regulation of physiology to maintain a constant state, as in the regulation of body temperature in mammals.

Homologs   35, 38

Chromosomes that are sufficiently similar to pair during meiosis.

The paired cell divisions that result in the reduction of the diploid to the haploid number of chromosomes.

Ribonucleic acid involved in the transfer of information from the DNA of the nucleus to the ribosomes of the cytoplasm where it acts as a template for the production of proteins.

Cell division that results in the two daughter cells having a complement of chromosomes identical to that in the parent cell.

A particular type of congenital idiocy, caused by chromosomal non-disjunction, characterized by a facial expression reminiscent of the Mongoloid race.

Comprised of two genetically distinct types of tissue.

The property of a substance or agent which causes an increased rate of mutation.

A sudden heritable change of the genotype. This can be either of quantity, quality, or arrangement of the genetic material.

The smallest unit of DNA whose change can result in a mutation—probably a single nucleotide.

Myxomatosis 197

Neurospora 111

Nirenberg 133, 138

Nondisjunction 48, 74, 145

The failure of separation of homologous chromosomes at meiosis, resulting in some daughter cells receiving both homologs and others receiving none.

Nucleic acid 84, 87, 155

A class of chemical compounds formed by the combination of purine and pyrimidine bases with a sugar and phosphoric acid.

Nucleotide 89

The basic unit of nucleic acid, consisting of a sugar molecule (either deoxyribose, or ribose), a phosphate, and an organic base (cytosine, thymine, guanine, adenine, or uracil).

Nucleus 29

A small body that contains the complement of chromosomes.

Operon 287

Overdominance 214

The phenomenon of heterozygotes having a more extreme phenotype than either homozygote.

Painter 79

Paramecium 277

Parthenogenesis

The development of an individual from an egg without fertilization.

Pauling 120

Penetrance 23

The proportion of individuals of a certain genotype that shows its effect.

Phenocopy 255

The alteration of the phenotype, by exposure to environmental stress during development, to a form imitating that characteristic of a genetic effect.

Phenotype

The expression of the effects of the genotype and environment on the growth and differentiation of an individual.

Pure line   4

A strain of an organism that is homozygous because of long-continued inbreeding.

Purine   89, 91

Pyrimidine   89, 91

Race

An interbreeding division of a species characterized by heritable differences from other races of the same species.

Recessive   14, 16, 26

An allele that does not exhibit its effect when heterozygous with the dominant allele.

Recombination   60, 136, 150

The occurrence of progeny with combinations of characters other than those that occurred in the parents.

Recon

The smallest unit of DNA capable of recombination.

Regulator   287

Repulsion   62

Ribonucleic acid (RNA)   84, 128, 139, 284

A nucleic acid characterized by a ribose sugar, and the base, uracil.

Ribosome   128, 130

A unit of the cytoplasm at which proteins are synthesized.

Roentgen   160

A unit of ionizing radiation.

rII factor   136

Salivary-gland chromosomes

See Polytene chromosomes.

Scowcroft   231

Segregation   20

The separation of alleles at meiosis.

Sex chromosomes   74

Chromosomes that are particularly concerned with the determination of sex, e.g., the XY chromosomes in man.